KU-240-778

IODINE AND PLANT LIFE

ANNOTATED BIBLIOGRAPHY
1813 - 1949

IODINE AND PLANT LIFE

ANNOTATED BIBLIOGRAPHY 1813-1949

With Review of the Literature

1950

CHILEAN IODINE EDUCATIONAL BUREAU

STONE HOUSE BISHOPSGATE LONDON EC2

Printed in Great Britain by
THE SHENVAL PRESS
London and Hertford

PREFACE

SCIENTIFIC literature of the world includes more than 30,000 papers which contain facts about the role of iodine in biology and medicine. For several years the Chilean Iodine Educational Bureau in London has been gathering and correlating this vast corpus of information, and intends to publish from time to time annotated bibliographies of the collected knowledge in classified and orderly sequence.

Iodine and Plant Life is the first of the series. The book includes all references the Bureau has been able to discover relating to fundamental and applied knowledge of iodine and vegetable life—marine flora, land plants, bacteria, fungi. This field has so many links and alliances with other branches of biological science that the line of distinction between what is included and what is withheld has of necessity been rather severely drawn.

Excluded and reserved for treatment in forthcoming bibliographies are all papers dealing with the iodine chemistry of soils; all papers concerning plant substances used as natural or processed foods in which the iodine content has been determined purely from the standpoint of human and animal nutrition and not in reference to plant physiology or biochemistry; and all papers which present bactericidal and fungicidal knowledge of iodine from a strictly medical angle.

The bibliography consists of 794 separate papers, 24 of which are listed twice—in different sections—thus making the total number of entries 818. The duplicate listing of these comparatively few items makes each section of the work a self-contained information unit. All the 794 papers cited have been checked and annotated from the originals except three which could not be located and for which the annotations are borrowed from *Chemical Abstracts* (107, 564) and *Biedermanns Zentralblatt* (226). Copies of most of this literature, especially of the rarer and less readily obtainable items, are filed in the library of the Chilean Iodine Educational Bureau, London and are available to accredited workers who may wish to consult them.

As may be seen from the table of contents on page ix, the material of the bibliography is arranged in five main sections and twenty-three subsections by a classification of subject-matter considered to be of the most practical help and convenience to the user. Within each section or subsection the order in which the entries are given is chronological by year of publication and then alphabetical according to authors' names where there is more than one entry for any particular year. By this means the reader may follow with ease and understanding the development of knowledge in any particular field which interests him. Annual reports are entered under the year to which they refer, not under year of publication. Reports covering more than one year are entered under the latest of the years to which they refer.

The compilers have sought not only to observe established rules of bibliography but to formulate certain standards of spelling, abbreviation, terminology and typography that should help to preserve uniformity of usage and presentation throughout the projected series of bibliographies as a whole. Some of these procedures may be mentioned.

Authors' names and designations are given exactly as in the original publication except in the case of one or two important historical figures whose initials are extended to full Christian names. Surnames with prefixes are dealt with according to Rule 26 in *Cataloguing Rules* (London: Library Association, 1945). The names of Russian authors are printed both in Russian characters and in a transliterated form.

Academic credentials and designations, places of origin of work, and other particulars following authors' names are also transcribed directly from the original accounts; but where necessary, and always consistent with factual accuracy, these have been abbreviated or expanded to conform to a uniform style of presentation throughout the whole work. Where an author has more than one publication listed in the same year, his credentials are recorded only in the first entry for that year.

The names of Russian authors and the titles of Russian periodicals are transliterated according to a system based on that of the Council of the Royal Geographical Society of London. This system involves the principle that vowels are pronounced as in Italian and consonants as in English. *The Statesman's Year-Book* (London: Macmillan and Co., Ltd., 1949) has been used as a guide to the spelling of foreign place names. In setting down the names of Universities and other academic institutions, the editors have generally followed the practice of *The World of Learning* (London: Europa Publications Ltd., 2nd edition, 1948). The abbreviations used to denote the titles of scientific periodicals are those of the *World List of Scientific Periodicals* (London: Oxford University Press, 2nd edition, 1934) modified in some instances for the sake of greater clarity. The given title of a journal is that by which the journal was known at the time of reference, not necessarily its modern title.

The provenance of all papers in the bibliography, and the rate of their appearance in scientific literature grouped in 25-year periods, are tabulated below. Eighty per cent of papers are the outcome of work in the last 25 years (1925-1949) one-third of which was done in the United States of America; thirteen per cent fall in the first quarter of this century, and the remaining seven per cent are mainly the pioneer investigations of France, England, Germany and Chile between 1800 and 1899.

OUTPUT OF PAPERS IN 25-YEAR PERIODS CLASSIFIED ACCORDING TO THE COUNTRIES IN WHICH THE PUBLISHED WORK WAS CARRIED OUT

	1800* 1824	1825 1849	1850 1874	1875 1899	1900 1924	1925 1949	Total
United States of America				1	19	208	228
British Commonwealth	2	2	3	3	21	105	136
Germany		4	5	4	9	99	121
France	2	2	9	7	16	65	101
Russia				1	3	39	43
Japan					10	15	25
Sweden					5	15	20
Czechoslovakia					2	16	18
Italy		2	1		5	9	17
Netherlands				1	1	11	13
Switzerland					3	8	11
Austria					3	7	10
Chile				6		1	7
China						7	7
Denmark						5	5
Norway					1	4	5
Belgium				1		3	4
Hungary					1	3	4
Rumania					1	3	4
Spain		1				2	3
Cuba			2				2
Costa Rica						2	2
Estonia						2	2
Finland						2	2
Egypt						1	1
Poland						1	1
Portugal					1		1
Sudan						1	1
Total	4	11	20	24	101	634	794

* Iodine was discovered in the year 1811. Published announcement of the discovery was not made until 1813.

CONTENTS

Preface vii—viii

Introductory Review 1—24

ANNOTATED BIBLIOGRAPHY

Page

REVIEWS AND GENERAL PAPERS 27

MARINE PLANTS

Iodine Content of Seaweeds

Qualitative and Quantitative Data 29

Seasonal Variation 35

Form: Liberation: Distribution 36

LAND PLANTS

Iodine Content of Land Plants

Iodine Occurring Naturally 40

Influence of Iodine Application 44

Effect of Iodine on Growth

Iodine: Iodides: Iodates 47

Iodine in Chilean Nitrate of Soda 60

Thyroxine: Thyroid Preparations 64

Growth Regulating Substances 66

Other Biochemical Aspects

Absorption of Iodine by Seeds 69

Enzyme Action: Photosynthesis, etc. 69

Hydroponics 70

MICRO-ORGANISMS

Effect of Iodine on Bacteria and Fungi

Soil Microflora: Nitrogen Cycle 71

Bacteria 72

Yeasts

Inorganic Iodine 74

Iodoacetic Acid 75

Fungi Imperfecti 78

PLANT PROTECTION

General 79

Soil and Plant Treatments 80

Seed Disinfection 83

Fruit Preservation 85

Weed Killers 86

Iodine Insecticides 87

INDEXES AND KEY TO ABBREVIATED TITLES OF PERIODICALS

REVIEW OF THE LITERATURE OF IODINE AND PLANT LIFE

REVIEW OF THE LITERATURE OF IODINE AND PLANT LIFE

KNOWLEDGE of iodine in plants begins—like all iodine knowledge—with the discovery of iodine in seaweed ash by Bernard Courtois towards the end of 1811. From then until the end of 1949 more than eight hundred iodine studies with a direct bearing on plant life have been published in the authoritative scientific literature of the world. This total takes no account of the very large number of papers relating to iodine in soils and the iodine content of vegetable materials used as human and animal food; nor does it include the voluminous data on commercial procedures for extracting iodine from seaweed, and chemical methods for estimating the quantities of iodine in plant sources. These allied fields of study are the subjects of separate bibliographies.

MARINE PLANTS

IODINE CONTENT OF SEAWEEDS

QUALITATIVE AND QUANTITATIVE DATA (21-107). Investigators in the first half of the nineteenth century were mainly interested to confirm Courtois' discovery and to find out whether or not iodine existed in marine plant species other than those in which he had found the element. Their data are purely qualitative and today have only academic interest. Nevertheless, they materially contributed to knowledge in two ways: they have helped us to reach the general conclusion that all marine algae contain iodine and, secondly, through these early chemical studies, the technical methods for the quantitative determination of iodine were gradually refined and improved for the benefit of later workers.

As the economic significance of iodine in medicine and industry became increasingly apparent, exact determinations of the amount of iodine in marine algae assumed a special importance and between 1850 and 1920 a mass of quantitative data accumulated with reference to many different kinds of seaweed from many widely separated parts of the world.

These studies were made less from an academic standpoint than from commercial motives. At one time or another almost every industrial sea-girt country has taken stock of its seaweed resources in terms of actual or potential iodine supply. For instance, quantitative data from France and Scotland—the principal producers of commercial iodine in the second half of the nineteenth century—and to a lesser extent from Germany, Spain and Holland, figure largely in the literature prior to 1900. Somewhat later, Norway, the United States of America, and Australia began to take an interest in seaweed iodine, and contributions by their chemists form part of the story to 1914.

Then came the 1914-1918 war and with it a flood of papers by analysts in many countries anxious not only to protect themselves against possible blockade of supplies from Chile whose nitrate ores had become by that time the chief source of iodine, but also to share in the expanding world market for this valuable chemical commodity. In 1915 the economic value of Pacific coast kelp was determined in California. The importance of seaweeds as raw material for chemical industry was re-investigated in Scotland in 1916. In the same year the iodine in Japanese algae was evaluated for the first time. And, in 1917 "seaweeds of the seas of the Russian realm" were examined as sources of iodine for military needs. Sweden, Australia, Germany and Italy also joined in the quantitative iodine researches of this era.

This interest in the iodine constitution of seaweeds

TABLE 1

Genus	Percentage in Fresh Weed of			Percentage of Iodine in			100 Tons of Fresh Weed Contains
	Moisture	Dry matter	Ash	Fresh weed	Dry matter	Ash	
Fucus	80	20	5	0·012	0·06	0·24	27 lb. iodine
Ecklonia	85	15	3·75	0·060	0·40	1·60	134 lb. ,,
Phyllophora	80	20	5	0·100	0·50	2·00	224 lb. ,,
Laminaria	80	20	5	0·120	0·60	2·40	270 lb. ,,

has in fact never ceased. It developed again to some extent during the war of 1939-1945, particularly in Denmark, Russia, China and Japan, and modern data on the seasonal variation in the iodine content of littoral and sub-littoral species common to Scotland were published in a series of five papers by the Scottish Seaweed Research Association as lately as 1948-49.

The accompanying annotations show that the amount of iodine in seaweed is subject to wide regional, seasonal and specific variations. Perhaps most analytical attention has been paid to the genera *Laminaria*, *Fucus*, *Phyllophora* and *Ecklonia* because they are fairly common and give the richest yields of iodine. As a yardstick by which to compare other analytical figures, the foregoing tabulation of the average amount of iodine found in each of these four genera may be helpful (Table 1).

Fresh weed as collected contains about 80 per cent of water and under the best conditions of drying would therefore yield 20 per cent of its weight of dry matter. Most of the analytical data quoted in our bibliography are for completely dry material of this kind. Some determinations, however, have been made on air-dried weeds which still contain varying proportions of moisture while others have been made on "ash" with no clear indication about its quality or the percentage amount obtainable from the original fresh material. Hence, it is impossible to correlate or compare all the available data. Nevertheless, it may be said that it takes about 100 tons of fresh seaweed to produce 20 tons of dry matter which on incineration yields 5 tons of pure kelp ash. Assuming an average iodine content of 0.5 per cent in the dry material one would expect to obtain 224 lb. of iodine from 5 tons of ash, if yields were perfect and there was no loss on burning. In actual practice, however, methods of burning seaweed to kelp are crude and wasteful, and as much as 50 per cent of iodine may be dissipated in the process.

SEASONAL VARIATION (108-121). Fourteen papers which specifically mention seasonal variation in the iodine content of seaweeds are grouped separately from the main body of quantitative analytical data. Eleven studies are devoted to *Laminaria*, but they do not report the consistent results which might have been expected. According to Lapicque (109), the mineral content of *Laminaria flexicaulis* decreases from spring to September. This is in harmony with Black's observations that the iodine in Scottish sub-littoral *Laminaria* is at a maximum in the early spring and that the richest months for *Ascophyllum nodosum* are January to March. On the other hand, Freundler and his colleagues, who have done more work on this question than anyone else (110-116), conclude that maximum iodine coincides with maximum sun and that samples collected in July have a higher content than those collected in March. And, going full cycle, there is the finding of the Russian investigator Vedrinski (118) that seaweeds of the White Sea collected in late autumn have an iodine content four times greater than those collected in summer.

There appears to be no certainty that the iodine content of seaweeds will always be higher or lower at particular seasons. It varies from spring to summer and from autumn to winter, but the direction of these changes is inconstant and differs in different localities.

Interesting also in this series of papers are Freundler's observation (110) that iodine content decreases with advancing age, Black's finding that there is in general more iodine in frond than in stipe (119), and Scurti's belief (108) that iodine excites reproductive development of the plant.

FORM: LIBERATION: DISTRIBUTION (122-182). While analytical chemists were gradually accumulating practical facts about iodine contents, other investigators were engaged on deeper academic questions of the form in which iodine exists in seaweed, its distribution in different parts of the plant, and whether or not the element is liberated from the living organism by natural agencies. Contributions to these branches of knowledge came from botanists and biochemists of high repute and are distinguished by their consistently high quality.

In 1894, the Russian botanist Golenkin noted that iodine was liberated in the free state from special cells in *Bonnemaisonia asparagoides*. This observation was confirmed by Harald Kylin in 1915 when he found that *Bonnemaisonia* contained labile iodine compounds from which free iodine is easily split off. Nothing more appears to have been said on this point until 1925 when Camille Sauvageau of the University of Bordeaux affirmed that iodine actually exists in the *free* state in special vacuoles inside the young cells of *Bonnemaisonia* and other marine algae. This opinion aroused a spirited controversy which lasted for a further eight years and evoked forty papers between 1925 and 1933. Conspicuous among those who joined in the discussion with Sauvageau were Chemin of the marine biological laboratory at Dinard, Dangeard and Freundler at the University of Paris, and Kylin of the botanical laboratory, University of Lund.

From studies on the *Florideae*, especially *Falkenbergia*, Chemin concluded that iodine is not present in the free state but in unstable combination from which it is liberated by weak or strong acids depending on species. This coincides with Kylin's results in 1915. Dangeard, after many careful experiments on various kinds of *Laminaria* and *Fucus*, reached the conclusion that they liberate appreciable quantities of free iodine in their natural habitat and that this is brought about by certain iodogenic cells situated in the periphery of the plant, available oxygen being necessary for the process. Two Norwegian investigators, Lunde and Closs, contend that the iodine in *Laminaria* is released by an "iodine liberator" which may also be detected in an extract of the weed and acts only in acid solution. In 1928, Kylin repeated his earlier work and reaffirmed his opinion that living seaweed cells contain no free iodine but may contain combined iodine which, in the presence of certain acids, is liberated in the free state. He could find no evidence of an iodine liberator in extracts of *Laminaria*, but demonstrated the presence of an iodide-oxidase in the surface cells of the living plant, a view in harmony with that of Dangeard.

There is general agreement that iodine in seaweeds is combined in both organic and inorganic forms. Regarding the organic forms, Masuda (170 and 177) alone approaches precision. By oxidizing the organic iodine compounds in *Ecklonia cava*, he obtained five decomposition products one of which was triiodoacetaldehyde.

LAND PLANTS

IODINE CONTENT OF LAND PLANTS

NATURAL IODINE CONTENT (183-230). Following the discovery of iodine in marine vegetation, chemists and botanists next turned their attention to land plants and, not unnaturally, first looked for the element in aquatic terrestrial species and in plants growing near the sea.

When Andrew Fyfe wrote in 1819 that he could not find iodine in *Salsola kali*, the saltwort or prickly glasswort of the seashore, he did not say what was not true. His chemical description of *Salsola* was limited by the analytical techniques at his disposal. At that time iodine had only recently been discovered and nobody had yet devised a method sufficiently delicate to detect the minute quantities present in land plants, let alone measure them. Knowledge of iodine has depended for its advances on the perfection of methods and instruments for revealing and determining it in ever finer degrees of accuracy. Throughout the nineteenth century qualitative methods in the hands of experienced chemists were dependable enough; but it was not until well into the twentieth century that reasonably accurate methods for the quantitative estimation of traces of iodine became available. Even then heated controversy raged round the reliability of various techniques and, with a few prior exceptions, it is only results published since about 1930 that may be considered sufficiently accurate and reliable upon which to base firm and definite conclusions.

So it comes about that the very early workers could easily find iodine in seaweeds, because the amounts are comparatively large and simple to detect, but not in land plants which contain traces too small to answer the only known tests of those times. However, it was not long before the characteristic blue coloration which iodine gives with starch—incidentally, a reaction discovered within four months of the announcement of the discovery of iodine itself—came to be employed in developing increasingly delicate methods of detection, and by 1842 Dr. George Dickie (185) was able to say with certainty that iodine was present in land plants gathered near the sea at Aberdeen. This was confirmed seven years later by Dr. Augustus Voelcker (189) who, on examining seapinks from three different localities, found iodine only in those specimens grown near the seashore.

The first systematic chemical inquiry into the distribution of iodine in the terrestrial mass, including plants, was begun in 1850 by the French botanist and chemist, Gaspard Adolphe Chatin (1813-1901), to whom belongs the credit of showing for the first time that deficiency of iodine in man's environment —air, water, soil, and food—is associated with the occurrence of goitre. Although today his conclusions stand completely justified, they did not convince his contemporaries owing to certain anomalous analytical results. Chatin found iodine in watercress and in all plants growing in fresh running water (190). He could not at first detect any in land crops, but later (201) he reports its presence in plants of the Antilles and of the Mediterranean coast, and also in French and Havana tobaccos.

Between this time and 1900 qualitative methods gained further in refinement and a great deal of miscellaneous qualitative data found its way into the literature. In 1850 Fehling detected traces of iodine in sugar beet. In the same year Marchand reported its presence in the ash of most forest trees, an observation in line with that of Righini five years previously who found it in dead and rotting leaves and woodland ferns. Meyrac noted that species of *Anabaina* and *Oscillaria* growing in thermal waters were rich in iodine; and Personne confirmed Marck's observation of 1847 that liverworts contain it. Watercress was repeatedly examined. Müller's positive finding of 1843 was supported by Chatin in 1850 and by Vyvere in 1851 but negatived by Casaseca in 1853 and again by Nadler in 1866, and had to await final confirmation by the Kentucky Agricultural Experiment Station in 1931, and by Schwarz in 1934 who found 448 microgrammes of iodine in a kilogramme of watercress from south Germany. Sarsaparilla, bananas, maize, tobacco, and pondweed were other species which came under qualitative investigation in the pre-1900 era.

Not until 1899 did references to quantitative data appear. In that year Paul Bourcet published the results of his analysis of twenty-eight different plant species in which the amounts of iodine varied from zero in potatoes to 0.94 milligramme per kilogramme in garlic. And Armand Gautier, also in 1899, recorded that certain freshwater algae contained from 0.25 to 2.40 milligrammes of iodine per 100 grammes of dried material.

As knowledge unfolded, botanists and biochemists began to look at the iodine content of land plants from two quite distinct points of view. On the one hand, plant physiologists were interested to know whether iodine performs some special function indispensable to the life of the plants in which it had been found, or whether it is there merely as a functionless incidental unavoidably absorbed into the plant system from the nutrient medium in which plants live. Accordingly, they analysed and tested as many species as possible to determine if all have iodine in them. If a species could be found healthy and physiologically complete and yet containing absolutely no iodine then it would be a fair inference that iodine is *not* essential to all plant life. No such plant species has ever been found. It seems that all land plants contain iodine, however small the amount. Cameron (211), Winterstein (212), and Fellenberg (213), the great pioneers of the quantitative era which opened just prior to the 1914-1918 war, found iodine in the majority of the plants they examined. Failure to detect it in others was solely due to the still imperfect methods at their disposal. Justus (209) went so far as to say that iodine is always present in the nucelus of plant and animal cells.

The second broad outlook on the iodine content of plants belongs almost entirely to the twentieth century and arose with the new and developing science of human and animal nutrition. When it became known in 1895 that iodine is a normal constituent of the thyroid gland and an element essential to higher animal life, new impetus was given to iodine research and an enormous number of quantitative data accumulated from all parts of the world on the nutritional value of different food plants as sources of iodine for man and animals. As the bulk of these data are purely nutritional and have no botanical significance they are not listed or reviewed here but in a subsequent bibliography of the iodine content of human and animal foods.

Against the expanding but more or less uniform background of qualitative and quantitative effort of the nineteenth and early twentieth centuries, very little information stands out significantly in regard to the *purpose* of iodine in plants. Analysts were not concerned with this problem. Other experimentalists approached it in other ways and consideration to their findings is given in a later section. However, when Fischer (226) was studying changes in the proportions of mineral substances in vegetables he noted that iodine occurs principally in organic combination and he gained the impression that it bears relation to the chlorophyll, carotene or vitamin A content of the plant. This suggestion gives point to Remington's finding (222) that iodine is most concentrated in those parts of the plant which contain most chlorophyll, and to Gautier's much earlier belief (207) that all plants which contain chlorophyll contain iodine.

Several workers, not content merely to state that iodine exists in plants, go further and tell us something about its distribution. Glimm and Halasa (219) found that in cereals iodine is distributed generally throughout the whole plant but the percentage concentration is lowest in the ear and highest in the root, a fact easy to believe but which could not be taken for granted without factual evidence. Blom (225) records that the iodine content of South African pastures is at a minimum during the dry season and increases markedly during active growth following rains.

It is impossible in this brief review even to summarize all the mass of data on the natural iodine content of land plants. The figures in Table 2, however, give an indication of their general order of magnitude. These are taken from the accompanying annotations and, bearing in mind the factors which influence the iodine content of individual plant species—season, locality, soil-type, age—are in broad agreement with what will be found for other land plants on consulting original papers.

TABLE 2

	Iodine in Dry Matter	
	μg. per 100 g.	per cent
Wheat straw (224)	7	0·000007
Orchard grass hay (224)	12	0·000012
Grass, *Cyanodon* (229)	15	0·000015
Red clover (221)	31	0·000031
Watercress (227)	45	0·000045
Grass, *Setaria* (229)	118	0·000118
Feijoa sellowiana (223)	894	0·000894

Broadly, the run of values lies between 10 and 100 microgrammes of iodine in 100 grammes of dry matter. This is ten-thousand times less than the amounts present in the richest seaweeds. The above table contains one value distinctly out of line with the others, namely 894 μg. per 100 grammes for *Feijoa sellowiana*. The remarkable finding of the Russian chemist, Sergeev (223), that the dried fruit of this species contains between 7·69 and 10·2 milligrammes of iodine (average 8·94) per kilogramme is quite exceptional. *Feijoa* must be one of the richest iodine-containing fruits known.

Of the forty-eight papers reviewed in this section two express opinions contrary to accepted experience. Heymann (214) thinks it very probable that plants absorb more iodine from the air than from the soil. The same view was put forward in 1930 by M. von Wrangell (218) who considered that plants obtain their principal supply of iodine from the atmosphere by absorption through the leaves. There does not appear to be any foundation for these conclusions which are entirely at variance with all other work on the subject.

IODINE CONTENT INFLUENCED BY IODINE APPLICATION (231-270). All who have studied the iodine content of plants agree that the amount of iodine a plant absorbs is directly proportional to the amount of available iodine contained in the soil or other medium in which the plant is grown. Species differences, stage of growth, soil type, acidity or alkalinity of the nutritive medium, the form in which iodine is presented to the plant, and other similar factors undoubtedly influence the precise degree of absorption which will take place; but the broad fact remains that the more iodine there is available the more a plant will absorb, until toxic levels are ultimately reached.

This is amply proved by many laboratory and field experiments in which iodine has been added artificially to soils, sands and culture solutions, and the plants therefrom chemically examined and compared with those from untreated media. Iodine has been applied as iodide, iodate, biniodate, periodate; it has been applied in its naturally occurring form in Chilean nitrate of soda; it has been added to synthetic sodium nitrate and to special "complete" fertilizers; it has been mixed in powder form with soil;

TABLE 3

Vegetable	Microgrammes (μg.) of Iodine in 1000 Grammes of Fresh Substance		Iodine Content Increased
	Before Application of Iodine	After Application of Iodine	
Beans	8	10	25%
Sugar peas	12	62	5 times
Kohlrabi	14	106	7·5 times
Head lettuce	13	210	16 times
Yellow beets	20	291	14·5 times
Savoy cabbage	4	320	80 times
Mangold	16	841	52·5 times
Spinach	330	4750	14 times

dissolved in liquid culture media; sprayed in solution on soil prior to sowing; and sprayed on the growing plant. In fact, there has been no standard technique and, in consequence, results are exceedingly variable and difficult to correlate.

Nevertheless, by one method or another, all experiments reach the same conclusion, namely, that the iodine content of plants can be artificially increased by simple additions of iodine to the nutritive medium. Table 4 correlates a selection of the available data and shows the order of magnitude of the increases in iodine content obtained by different investigators when potassium iodide is added to soil in amounts varying from 0.6 to 12 kilogrammes per hectare, or when iodized fertilizers are used. Equivalents in grammes per square yard and pounds per acre are included in the table for ease of reference.

Practically all experiments in this field of inquiry have fallen within the range of iodine application shown in Table 4. Representative of the actual amount of iodine in plants before and after iodine treatment are the data (Table 3) of Maurer, Schropp and Ducrue (240) who applied potassium iodide at the rate of 2·5 kilogrammes per hectare to various garden vegetables and were able thereby to raise the iodine content from an average of 12 microgrammes (excluding value for spinach) per kilogramme of fresh material to anything from 5 to 70 times that figure.

The relatively high proportion of iodine contained as a natural constituent in Chilean nitrate of soda has brought this fertilizer into great prominence in connection with the role of iodine in plants. Consideration of the iodine effect of Chilean nitrate properly belongs to a later section, but one aspect falls to be dealt with here.

Many experiments have been made to determine whether the amount of iodine present in Chilean nitrate is sufficient to raise the iodine content of crops grown on soils to which the fertilizer has been applied in the usual manurial quantities. The answer is not in doubt. Data from three different sources set out in Table 5 clearly show that Chilean nitrate

TABLE 4

INFLUENCE OF ARTIFICIALLY APPLIED IODINE ON IODINE CONTENT OF PLANTS

	Amount of Potassium Iodide Artificially Applied			Plant Species	Iodine Content Increased
	Grammes per Hectare	Grammes per Sq. Yd.	Pounds(lb.) per Acre		
Hiltner & Bergold (231)	600	0·05	0·53	Pasture	5 times
Fellenberg (310)	2000	0·17	1·8	Fodderbeet (root)	Doubled
Fellenberg (310)	2000	0·17	1·8	Fodderbeet (leaves)	9 times
Hercus & Roberts (233)	2400	0·20	2·1	Lettuce & Turnips	25% to 8 times
Maurer *et al.* (240)	2500	0·21	2·2	Vegetables	25% to 80 times
Teske (261)	3270	0·27	2·9	Valerian	43 per cent
Mack & Brasher (263)	5820	0·49	5·2	Beans & Turnips	3 to 120 times
Hercus & Roberts (233)	12000	1·00	10·6	Lettuce & Turnips	4 to 13 times
Pfeiffer & Courth (245)	0·5 gramme iodine per pot			Carrots & Radishes	500 to 700 times
Simpson (256)	Dilute potassium biniodate soln.			Various species	17 times
Scharrer & Schwaibold (235)	Synthetic $NaNO_3$ plus iodine			Sugarbeet (leaves)	15% to 16 times
McHargue *et al.* (439)	Chilean nitrate of soda (0·022% I)			Red clover	16 times
Ødelien (270)	Complete fertilizer (0·005–0·0625% I)			Potatoes (leaves)	Great increase

of soda containing the usual average of 0.02 per cent of iodine and applied at the rate of 400 kilogrammes per hectare doubles or trebles the iodine content of meadow hay, lucerne, potatoes, grapes, tomatoes, lettuce, and of maize, rye, oats, wheat and barley straw. The grain of these cereal crops is not affected.

Incidentally, the table brings out a feature commonly met with in the literature of iodine contents, namely, the discrepancy between the determinations of different authors for the same type of crop. Rietsema's value for tomatoes is more than ten times that of Sirot. And Sirot's values for meadow hay and lucerne are five times less than those for cereal straws as determined by Schmalfuss. These variations are much greater than can be accounted for by differences in manurial treatment, soil type, and other environmental factors. They are due to differences in sampling, drying, and analytical technique. However, within the individual groups of data themselves the values are of the same order and distinctly show the relative change in iodine content which takes place on manurial treatment with Chilean nitrate of soda.

TABLE 5

INFLUENCE OF CHILEAN NITRATE OF SODA ON IODINE CONTENT OF PLANTS

PLANT SPECIES	CONTROL WITHOUT FERTILIZER	SYNTHETIC NITRATE OF SODA	CHILEAN NITRATE OF SODA	Percentage of Iodine in Chilean Nitrate	Rate of Application per Hectare	Grammes of Iodine Applied per Hectare
SIROT'S EXPERIMENTS REPORTED BY DERAMOND (451)						
Meadow hay	0·96	1·10	2·25	0·02	400 kg.	80
Lucerne	0·81	1·30	2·05	0·02	400 kg.	80
Potatoes (tuber)	0·09	0·09	0·36	0·029	400 kg.	116
Grapes (fruit)	0·05	0·06	0·19	0·029	400 kg.	116
Tomatoes (fruit)	0·77	0·90	1·50	0·02	400 kg.	80
THE EXPERIMENTS OF RIETSEMA (456)						
Tomatoes (fruit)	—	13·0	44·0	Not stated	Not stated	Not stated
Lettuce	—	13·0	37·0	Not stated	Not stated	Not stated
THE EXPERIMENTS OF SCHMALFUSS (460)						
Maize (straw)	—	5·1	11·8	0·019	750 kg.	142
Rye (straw)	—	9·5	18·0	0·019	437 kg.	83
Oats (straw)	—	8·5	19·2	0·019	437 kg.	83
Wheat (straw)	—	5·1	13·7	0·019	437 kg.	83
Barley (straw)	—	5·5	16·8	0·019	437 kg.	83
Maize (grain)	—	3·1	5·3	0·019	750 kg.	142
Rye (grain)	—	5·1	4·8	0·019	437 kg.	83
Oats (grain)	—	5·7	6·5	0·019	437 kg.	83
Wheat (grain)	—	3·7	2·9	0·019	437 kg.	83
Barley (grain)	—	2·5	3·9	0·019	437 kg.	83

Notes.—The iodine contents (columns 2, 3 and 4) are all expressed as microgrammes (μg.) per 100 grammes of dry matter.

The Schmalfuss data are an average of the results of experiments carried out in two consecutive years.

EFFECT OF IODINE ON GROWTH AND DEVELOPMENT

At the root of all plant research with iodine lies the fundamental question whether the element is indispensable to plant life or whether its presence in plants is merely incidental.

The only certain method of establishing the essentiality of an element is to exclude it absolutely from the media in which plants grow and then observe the effect. Owing to immense technical difficulties, no one has yet succeeded in creating an artificial environment entirely deprived of every trace of iodine but providing all other nutrients in adequate amounts. Consequently, the question of essentiality has not been answered. We do not yet know with certainty whether iodine is a necessity for any phase of plant growth, development or metabolism.

The impossibility of setting up these rigid experimental conditions has led research workers to approach the problem in other ways. Observation of the stimulating or depressing effect on plant growth following the application of minute quantities of certain trace elements is a method which has been widely adopted in recent years. If stimulation occurs with a particular element it is legitimate to infer that a deficiency of that element may be involved and may be a limiting factor to crop growth and health. Accordingly, small amounts of iodine in different forms have been added to soil and other growth media with the object of measuring their effects and of determining, if possible, the critical level of requirement.

Admittedly this is an inconclusive method by which to settle the question of essentiality since it does not follow that an element which will stimulate growth is necessarily essential for growth. Nevertheless a great many experiments have been made along these lines and much useful information has been gathered.

Special significance attaches to this aspect of research on account of the desire to know whether synthetic fertilizers which contain no minor elements are fully adequate for plant growth. By the same token, the producers of naturally occurring fertilizers—particularly Chilean nitrate of soda which has a relatively high content of iodine and other unusual elements—have been active investigators in this field in order to establish claims to superiority for these over synthetic products. For this reason the objective of iodine experiments on plants has been less to determine the essentiality of the element in the academic sense than to answer the practical question whether iodine will under any circumstances increase the yield or improve the quality of economic crops, vegetables and fruit.

Two sections of our bibliography classify this province of research. The first, containing 148 entries numbered 271 to 418, lists all references to the effect of direct applications of iodine, iodides, iodates and other iodine compounds. The second, containing 42 entries numbered 419 to 460, refers exclusively to experiments designed to determine the effect of iodine naturally present in Chilean nitrate of soda.

IODINE: IODIDES: IODATES (271-418). Systematic study of all the available data shows that, according to type, experiments involving the simple application of iodine and its soluble compounds belong to one or other of the following six groups:

- Seed treatments with iodine prior to sowing.
- Water culture experiments with solutions of known iodine concentration.
- Pot culture experiments with sands and soils containing known amounts of added iodine.
- Watering or spraying experiments with solutions of known iodine strength.
- Manurial experiments in open fields.
- Applications of iodine vapour, injections of iodine compounds and other miscellaneous methods.

The very first iodine stimulation experiments in the world of plants were undertaken to find out whether the soaking of seeds in iodine solutions prior to sowing has any improving action on germination. In 1834 the German botanist, Goeppert, stated that iodine solutions and hydriodic acid cause seeds to germinate more quickly. The same conclusion was reached by Heckel in 1875, and again early this century by J. A. Voelcker who found that soaking the grain of wheat and barley in a 1 per cent solution of sodium iodide for ten minutes before sowing stimulated growth and increased crop yield. Seeds soaked in a 1 per cent solution of manganese iodide also derived considerable benefit, according to Voelcker; but higher iodide concentrations were harmful.

Nothing more seems to have been done on this particular question until 1925 when Nadson and Žolkevič showed that mustard seed previously treated with solutions of potassium iodide grew much better on exposure to radium than untreated seeds. Also giving positive effects are the comparatively recent experiments of Malhotra (347) and of Vlasyuk (359). Malhotra placed maize seeds in 0·05 per cent iodine solution and incubated them at temperatures varying between 25° and 60°C. Iodine appeared to stimulate germination at 25°–30°C, but retarded it at higher temperatures. Vlasyuk obtained markedly increased crop yields of vegetable marrows, carrots, sugarbeet and mangolds by soaking the seeds before sowing in an aqueous solution (1 : 10,000) of potassium iodide.

The only negative results from experiments of this kind are those of Amadori (324) who found no stimulating effect on the germination of seeds treated with a solution containing 0·3 milligramme of iodine per millilitre of water, and of Rabuteau (275) who tried the effect of ethyl iodide on garden cress seeds and found it harmful.

Regarding the next four types of experimentation in the foregoing classification, namely, greenhouse experiments with precise nutrient solutions, controlled experiments with soils in standard pots, the less exact indoor or outdoor spraying experiments, and large-scale outdoor field trials, we have reduced a mass of hitherto uncorrelated data to a series of simple tables. In these the strengths of iodine applied, expressed in comparable terms, are arranged in decreasing order of magnitude with an indication opposite each experiment of the nature of the effect observed and the name of the responsible author.

Without such a methodical analysis it is impossible to gain any clear appreciation of the status of knowledge and experience in this field. Indeed, the orderly examination and correlation of all available data in this way ensures that facts fall in to their proper place, and much that at first sight may appear unrelated and even conflicting is capable of reasonable interpretation when viewed in its proper setting.

Water Culture Experiments (Table 6). Wheat, maize, oats, buckwheat, flax, hyacinths, tomatoes, peas, mustard, cress, and other vegetables have been grown in aqueous culture solutions with iodide concentrations ranging from 1 part in 300 parts of solution to 1 part in 10 million parts of solution—a difference from the weakest to the strongest of 33,000 times. Potassium iodide, sodium iodide, calcium iodide, magnesium iodide, ammonium iodide, and free elemental iodine are the forms in which iodine has been added.

The table clearly shows that no species withstands a concentration greater than 1 part of iodide in 1 million parts of solution. Indeed, at this strength the growth of peas and mustard is retarded, and any

TABLE 6

WATER CULTURE EXPERIMENTS

Ref.	Author	Iodide Concentration in Culture Solution		Result	
277	Coupin	NH_4I	1 : 300	Toxic to young wheat plants	—
277	Coupin	KI	1 : 2000	Toxic to young wheat plants	—
277	Coupin	NaI	1 : 2000	Toxic to young wheat plants	—
273	Knop	KI	1 : 4000	Toxic to maize, cress, oats, buckwheat	—
276	Demoussy	KI	1 : 5000	Toxic to colza	—
279	Coupin	MgI_2	1 : 10,000	Toxic to young wheat plants	—
279	Coupin	CaI_2	1 : 10,000	Toxic to young wheat plants	—
345	Cotton	KI	1 : 19,200	Toxic to buckwheat plants	—
297	Mazé	KI	1 : 50,000	Harmful to maize	—
367	Wynd	KI	1 : 50,000	Depressed growth of tomatoes	—
297	Mazé	KI	1 : 100,000	Harmful to maize	—
241	Orr, Kelly & Stuart	KI	1 : 100,000	Harmful to hyacinth, peas, mustard	—
297	Mazé	KI	1 : 250,000	Harmful to maize	—
401	Lewis & Powers	KI	1 : 500,000	Toxic to maize	—
345	Cotton	KI	1 : 600,000	Depressed growth of buckwheat	—
367	Wynd	KI	1 : 1,000,000	Depressed growth of tomatoes	—
241	Orr, Kelly & Stuart	KI	1 : 1,000,000	Retarded growth of peas and mustard	—
358	Shkolnik	KI	1 : 4,000,000	Flax seedlings grew normally	o
356	Khalizev & Remizov	Iodine	1 : 8,000,000	Improved growth of vegetables	+
241	Orr, Kelly & Stuart	KI	1 : 10,000,000	Stimulation of pea seedlings	+

— =harmful   o=no effect   + =stimulation

higher concentration is definitely harmful. Only when the concentration is reduced to 1 part of iodide in 5 or 10 million parts of solution has any favourable stimulatory effect been observed. Unfortunately, very few experiments have been carried out at these high dilutions and it is therefore desirable that further research should be devoted to concentrations of this order.

Pot Experiments (Tables 7 and 8). Sands and soils to which iodine has been added in known quantities per unit of weight have been used in many well-controlled pot experiments to determine the effect of iodine on different crops. The essential findings are set out in Tables 7 and 8. The first of these compares all findings except those of the Bavarian workers, Scharrer and Schropp (350 and 351), whose 260 experiments at the Institute of Agricultural Chemistry, Weihenstephan, are too numerous for convenient inclusion with the others and are therefore summarized separately in Table 8.

Potassium and sodium iodide have been the compounds of choice in the majority of pot trials; but Scharrer and Schropp also tested iodates and periodates, and in a few experiments they used elemental iodine. Among the plants selected for study are pasture grass, wheat, rye, barley, oats, flax, sugar and fodder beet, peas, beans, tomatoes, carrots, radishes, chicory, lettuce and mustard. They have been grown in pure quartz sands, sandy loams, peat, gravel, clay and other soils.

As in the water culture experiments, the range of concentration used in pot trials is exceedingly wide. In the experiments listed in Table 7 it varies from 1 part of iodide in 2000 parts of soil to 1 part of iodide in 48 million parts of soil—a difference in

TABLE 7

POT CULTURE EXPERIMENTS

Sands and soils to which iodine has been added in known quantity

Ref.	Author	Parts of Iodide added to Parts of Soil		Result
375	Young	KI	1 : 2000	Harmful to timothy in coarse sandy loam
303	Brenchley	NaI	1 : 8470	Very harmful to mustard and barley
372	Schmidt	KI	1 : 10,000	Harmful to leaves and roots of beet seedlings
375	Young	KI	1 : 10,000	Harmful to timothy in coarse sandy loam
372	Schmidt	KI	1 : 25,000	Harmful to leaves and roots of beet seedlings
303	Brenchley	NaI	1 : 42,370	Harmful to mustard and barley
375	Young	KI	1 : 100,000	Stimulated timothy in coarse sandy loam
394	Leroux	NaI	1 : 170,000	Increased yield of stems, leaves and seeds of peas
405	Hageman *et al.*	KI	1 : 190,000	No effect on growth of tomatoes
303	Brenchley	NaI	1 : 211,860	Mustard retarded at first but later surpassed controls
303	Brenchley	NaI	1 : 211,860	No stimulating effect on barley
384	Kasparova	KI	1 : 333,000	No effect on chicory yield; but disease resistance increased
281	Suzuki	KI	1 : 380,000	Significantly increased yield of peas
327	Fellenberg	KI	1 : 384,600	No significant effect on yield of carrots
379	McHargue *et al.*		1 : 400,000	Marked benefit to yield and quality of tomatoes
394	Leroux	NaI	1 : 424,000	Increased yield of stems, leaves and seeds of peas
371	Khalizev *et al.*	KI	1 : 500,000	Significantly increased yield of flax, mustard and oats
309	Stoklasa	KI	1 : 600,000	Markedly increased yield of leaves and roots of beet
384	Kasparova	KI	1 : 1,000,000	No effect on chicory yield; but disease resistance increased
303	Brenchley	NaI	1 : 1,059,320	No significant effect on mustard and barley
283	Suzuki & Aso	KI	1 : 3.5 million	Improved yield of oats and radishes
388	Shcherbakov	KI	1 : 6.1 million	Improved yield, and N & P assimilation of buckwheat
378	Muckenhirn	NaI	1 : 6.5 million	No effect on growth of lettuce
301	Söderbaum	KI	1 : 10 million	No effect on growth of oats and beans
373	Shcherbakov		1 : 40 million	Increased growth and yield of flax
348	Meyer	KI	1 : 48 million	Improved growth and yield of buckwheat

— =harmful   ○=no effect   + =stimulation

TABLE 8

POT EXPERIMENTS BY SCHARRER AND SCHROPP (350 & 351)

Parts of Iodide added to Parts of Soil	No. of Expts.	Harm-ful	No effect	Stimu-lation
1 : 11,000–1 : 66,600	52	47	5	0
1 : 110,000–1 : 166,000	52	23	18	11
1 : 1,100,000–1 : 1,660,000	52	6	27	19
1 : 11,000,000–1 : 16,600,000	52	1	26	25
1 : 110,000,000–1 : 166,000,000	52	4	21	27

strength of 24,000 times between the two extremes. Scharrer and Schropp (Table 8) worked in the range 1 in 11,000 to 1 in 166 million, a difference of 15,000 times.

With all these many and varying factors—form of iodine applied, species of plant, kind of soil, and concentration of the added iodine—it is not surprising that few generalizations can be made from the results. However, there is one conclusion that stands out clearly. Concentrations of *added* iodine greater than 1 part in 100,000 parts of soil are definitely harmful in every case. Indeed, it seems that we are not out of the danger zone until concentrations are reduced to below 1 part of added iodine in 200,000 parts of soil, that is, to below 5 milligrammes of added iodine per kilogramme of soil. From this level down to concentrations of 1 part of iodine in 1, 5 and 10 million parts of soil, and below, the results are either beneficial or without significance. Out of 20 separate experiments (Table 7) in iodine concentrations decreasing from 1 part in 100,000 of soil to 1 part in 48 million of soil, 14 showed some positive benefit; six were without significant effect either way; and none showed any toxic symptoms.

We come now to an essential point which in our opinion has not been given sufficient attention by the planners of pot experiments. Soils themselves have a natural iodine content which at its highest is very much less than, and at its lowest is very much greater than, many of the amounts of iodine added to soils in experimental work.

The average iodine content of heavy-textured fertile clays and loams and of highly acid peats rich in organic matter is 10,000 μg. per kilogramme or 1 part in 100,000. In clays and loams this rarely falls below 1 part in 200,000 and at the other end of the scale may reach 1 part in 50,000 or even higher. Sandy and other light-textured soils, on the other hand, seldom contain more than 1 part of iodine per million, and as often as not have but half this amount or even less, say, 1 part in 2 to 10 million.

As may be seen from Tables 7 and 8, the range of added iodine in experimental work (from 1 : 2000 to 1 : 166 million) extends well above and well below the range of the natural iodine content of soils (from 1 : 50,000 to 1 : 10 million) and, in consequence, almost every conceivable kind of result can be obtained depending on the type of original soil used. A high concentration of added iodine can throw an already iodine-rich soil into the toxic class and bring about harmful results; a small amount added to an iodine-poor soil may make all the difference between deficiency and adequacy—between crop failure and good growth; a small amount, say, 1 part in 1 million, added to a good soil having a natural iodine content of, say, 1 part in 100,000, raises this only to 1 in 91,000, a change which can make but little difference to plant growth if the natural iodine contained in the soil is in freely available form.

Many apparently irreconcilable results can assuredly be explained on these grounds, and unless experimentalists have taken care, as is clearly not always the case, to use iodine-poor soils or pure quartz sands their experiments have no validity as tests of the effect of iodine on plants.

One other extraneous factor which can affect the action of added iodine must be taken into account. For chemical reasons about which very little is known the iodine originally present in soils may be unavailable to the plant. Soil types and conditions may conceivably exist in which appreciable chemical quantities of iodine are locked-up in insoluble form thus giving a soil the effect of iodine deficiency so far as plant needs are concerned.

Only if one or other of these factors is operative, namely, absolute impoverishment or unavailability, is it possible to account for the positive stimulating effect which follows the addition of soluble iodine in the minute quantities used, for example, by Scharrer and Schropp. Apart from these considerations, however, the fact that stimulation does actually occur at all is capable of only one interpretation. Iodine added under the particular conditions of these experiments must have supplied some definite metabolic need. The many instances of stimulation cannot be ignored and the fact that they occur with increasing frequency as the concentration of added iodine is lowered justifies the conclusion that iodine is a true "trace" element exercising its effect in soluble form in the most minute concentrations.

TABLE 9

WATERING OR SPRAYING EXPERIMENTS

with solutions of known iodine strength

Ref.	Author	Iodide Concentration of Solution Applied		Result	
341	Gum	KI	1 : 1000	Harmful to rape, cress, mustard	–
341	Gum	CaI_2	1 : 1000	Harmful to rape, cress, mustard	–
318	Amadori		1 : 1666	Harmful to beans, tomatoes, nasturtiums	–
299	Free	KI	1 : 2000	Caused yellowing of geraniums	–
290	Hollrung	KI	1 : 10,000	No effect on beet	o
354	Schmidt	KI	1 : 10,000	Necrotic symptoms on leaves of beet	–
364	Sukhov *et al.*	KI	1 : 10,000	Intracellular inclusions in tips of beet seedlings	–
349	Picado	KI	1 : 20,000	Increased the carbohydrate reserves of	+
349	Picado	KI	1 : 100,000	cabbage, radish, beet and sugarcane	+
354	Schmidt	KI	1 : 100,000	Necrotic symptoms on leaves of sand-grown beet	–
343	Stoklasa	KI	1 : 200,000	Improved growth and vigour of beet seedlings	+
343	Stoklasa	KIO_3	1 : 200,000	Improved growth and vigour of beet seedlings	+
348	Meyer	KI	1 : 4,000,000	Improved growth and yield of buckwheat	+

– =harmful   o=no effect   + =stimulation

Watering or Spraying Experiments. Table 9 groups the results of various experiments in which iodides have been applied in solution from a watering-can to plants and edible vegetables grown either on open plots or in greenhouses. This method of application is to a large extent uncontrolled and inexact. Nevertheless, when arranged in descending order of concentration used, these experiments again demonstrate that only the most dilute solutions improve the growth and vigour of the plants to which they are applied.

Open Field Experiments (Table 10). Of all the different methods which have been used to elucidate the influence of iodine on plant growth, broad-scale manurial experiments on open plots or fields are the most numerous. They are, too, the most indecisive and because of their crude practical nature and lack of scientific refinement, contribute least to answering the fundamental questions under study. Notwithstanding these drawbacks there emerges from them some helpful information regarding effective quantities which in a broad general way confirms the findings of more exact experiments.

The summary of Table 10 in the next column shows that stimulation is more likely with lighter than with heavier applications of iodine. It would appear to be wasteful, and possibly harmful, to apply amounts higher than 2 kilogrammes per hectare. Indeed, the most favourable zone of application seems to lie below half a kilogramme per hectare. Of nine separate trials with dressings of half a kilogramme of iodide or less, six showed stimulatory effects, two were indecisive, and in only one—that by Gum on dwarf beans—was any injury observed.

SUMMARY OF TABLE 10

No. of Expts.	Grams Iodide per Hectare	Harmful	No effect	Stimulation
11	over 5,000	6	1	4
11	3,200–5,000	4	2	5
12	1,300–3,120	1	6	5
12	25–1,237	2	2	8
46		13	11	22

Miscellaneous Methods of Application. Besides the simple and straightforward applications of soluble iodides, living plants have been subjected to all sorts of unusual iodine treatments by inquiring minds. These are perhaps the more botanically interesting because they are not founded on any practical or economic pattern. They lie outside the realm of "applied research" conducted with perhaps

TABLE 10

OPEN FIELD EXPERIMENTS

Ref.	Author	Form	Grams Iodide per Hectare	Result	
287	Voelcker	KI etc.	251,060	Harmful to barley	—
287	Voelcker	KI etc.	125,530	Harmful to wheat	—
295	Albano	KI	100,000	Accelerated growth of jute plants	+
278	Voelcker	NaI	62,765	Harmful to wheat and barley	—
295	Albano	KI	50,000	Accelerated growth of jute plants	+
361	Beaumont *et al.*	KI	16,000	Increased yield of turnips	+
361	Beaumont *et al.*	KI	16,000	No increased yield of spinach	o
380	Vegesack	Iodine	8,000	Toxic to lupins, sugarbeet and mangolds	—
378	Muckenhirn	KI	7,285	Increased yield of onions on one peat soil	+
378	Muckenhirn	KI	7,285	Decreased yield of onions on another peat soil	—
336	Doerell	KI	5,400	Decreased yield of hops	—
295	Albano	KI	5,000	Accelerated growth of jute plants	+
304	Costa	KI	5,000	No effect on yield of sugarbeet	o
309	Stoklasa	KI	5,000	Reduced sugar content of beet	—
341	Gum	KI & CaI_2	5,000	Harmful to dwarf beans	—
341	Gum	KI & CaI_2	5,000	Not injurious to carrots and cress	o
341	Gum	KI & CaI_2	5,000	Increased yield of celery	+
360	Vlasyuk	KI	5,000	Slightly decreased yield of sugarbeet	—
360	Vlasyuk	KI	5,000	Markedly increased yield of mangolds, carrots and marrows	+
36	Doerell	KI	4,300	Increased yield of hops	+
09	Stoklasa	KI	4,000	Reduced sugar content of beet	—
36	Doerell	KI	3,200	Increased yield of hops	+
37/8	Münter	$NaIO_3$	3,120	No effect on growth, dry matter or sugar of beet	o
37/8	Münter	KI	2,616	No effect on growth, dry matter or sugar of beet	o
17	Werba	KI	2,616	Increased yield of roots and leaves of beet	+
16	Ungerer	KI	2,000	Decreased yield and sugar content of beet	—
13	Lafon *et al.*	KI	2,000	Increased yield of sugarbeet	+
10	Fellenberg	KI	2,000	No effect on yield of beet	o
80	Vegesack	Iodine	1,920	Increased yield of lupins, sugarbeet and mangolds	+
98	Moore	KI	1,853	Unquestionable stimulation of growth of radishes	+
09	Stoklasa	KI	1,720	Markedly increased yield of beet leaves, roots and seed	+
12	Iterson *et al.*	KI	1,720	No effect on yield of sugarbeet	o
7/8	Münter	$NaIO_3$	1,560	No effect on growth, dry matter or sugar of beet	o
7/8	Münter	KI	1,308	No effect on growth, dry matter or sugar of beet	o
88	Uchiyama	KI	1,237	Increased yield of sesame	+
88	Uchiyama	KI	1,200	Increased yield of spinach	+
16	Ungerer	KI	1,000	Decreased yield and sugar content of beet	—
41	Gum	KI & CaI_2	500	Harmful to dwarf beans	—
41	Gum	KI & CaI_2	500	Not injurious to carrots and cress	o
41	Gum	KI & CaI_2	500	Increased yield of celery	+
89	Uchiyama	KI	500	Increased yield of barley	+
89	Uchiyama	KI	376	Increased yield of millet	+
85	Aso & Suzuki	KI	250	Indecisive results with rice	o
88	Uchiyama	KI	120	Increased yield of spinach	+
85	Aso & Suzuki	KI	25	Stimulated seed production in rice	+
88	Uchiyama	KI	25	Increased yield of sesame	+

—=harmful   o=no effect   +=stimulation

an ulterior motive, and hence in result are all the more unbiassed and acceptable.

Ethyl iodide is a compound which has been accorded more than passing attention, and here we find the beginnings of research into growth regulators or "plant hormones" as they are sometimes called—a subject dealt with in a later section. In 1910, Stuart of the Vermont Agricultural Experiment Station found that when ethyl iodide was applied in vapour form to dormant lily-of-the-valley, growth was speeded-up. At the Boyce Thompson Institute for Plant Research, New York, F. E. Denny (319) had an analogous experience with potatoes. Exposure of the cut tubers to low concentrations of ethyl iodide vapour for 24 hours accelerated sprouting. He also proved (334) that twigs of dormant lilac plants started to grow following exposure to ethyl iodide vapour while untreated controls remained quiescent. And, in later experiments (391) Denny found that of seventy-seven volatile compounds tested only three, including ethyl iodide, induced stronger growth on the upper than on the under side of potato leaves.

The effect of injecting potassium iodide into living plant tissue has been investigated by one or two botanists, but, as might be expected, harm is done unless the solution is exceedingly dilute. In his studies of heredity and environic forces in plants, MacDougal (291 and 296) produced permanent modification of the germ plasm by injecting the embryo-sacs of seed-plants with 1 in 40,000 solution of potassium iodide. Lipman and Gordon (314) injured the leaves and branches of pear and apricot trees by trunk injections of solutions of 1 to 5 grammes of potassium iodide in 2·5 litres of distilled water. The only beneficial result of injection treatment is that of Verner (397) who found that a 1 in 300,000 potassium iodide solution injected into the stems of sunflowers at the time of flowering stimulated oil formation in the seeds.

Iodine vapour (362), iodine chloride (389) and iodoform (392) are other carriers of iodine which have been applied in various experiments. In the concentrations employed all were toxic. Particulars will be found in the respective annotations cited within brackets.

IODINE IN CHILEAN NITRATE OF SODA (419-460). The fact that Chilean nitrate of soda naturally contains an appreciable proportion of iodine which thereby reaches the soil in the course of ordinary fertilizer practice has been responsible for more applied research into the function of iodine in plant nutrition than any other single factor.

Probably the first to recognize the agricultural value of the "impurities" in Chilean nitrate was De Grazia of the faculty of agriculture, University of Naples, who in 1906 put forward his view that the observed superiority of Chilean nitrate could be attributed to the presence of ingredients other than nitrogen; but he was unable to identify iodine with any particular effect.

In 1924 the famous Czechoslovakian botanist, Julius Stoklasa, director of the State Experiment Station in Prague, stated categorically that Chilean nitrate of soda owed its efficacy in part to the iodine which it naturally contains. Immediately, plant physiologists near and far turned their attention to this question—stimulated in part by commercial interests alive to the possibility of a new selling point and by others in the synthetic fertilizer industry anxious to prove the contrary. So it came about that the era 1924 to 1939 saw an extraordinary outpouring of papers, mostly from Germany, some to deny and some to support Stoklasa's contentions.

In the forty-two papers annotated in this section, sixteen authors draw the conclusion that, on account of its iodine content, Chilean nitrate of soda is superior to synthetic sodium nitrate; fourteen consider that this claim is groundless and that the amount of iodine in the Chilean product does not enhance growth or yield and therefore has no economic significance in fertilizing; seven authors regard their results as inconclusive and that more experiments are necessary before a definite decision is reached; and five who deal exclusively with the up-take of iodine by plants all agree that Chilean nitrate of soda contains enough iodine to influence the iodine content of forage crops and vegetables, a fact already discussed fully on pages 6 and 7.

Considering the number of investigators who have tested the iodine potency of Chilean nitrate of soda it is strange that very few have taken the trouble to calculate the actual amount of iodine which is applied per hectare or per acre when this fertilizer is used, and to compare the amount with that applied in manurial experiments employing pure soluble iodides alone.

On average, Chilean nitrate contains 0·02 per cent of iodine. Applications of 250 kilos per hectare—a rate equivalent to 100 kilos or approximately two hundredweights per acre—will therefore spread 50 grammes of iodine over one hectare. Some investigators have employed 400 kilos and others 800 kilos of nitrate per hectare, corresponding respectively to 80 and 160 grammes of iodine per hectare.

Now, these amounts are precisely of the same order as those which give the most consistently stimulating effects in open field experiments with pure iodides, (*see* Table 10). They lie in what appears to be the most favourable zone of application in experimental work namely, below half a kilogramme of iodine per hectare. Some have expressed the opinion that an amount of iodine so small as 50 grammes spread over one hectare could not conceivably exercise any effect on plants whatever. This is a dangerous assumption. We have already pointed out that on an iodine impoverished soil an application even of this low order might make all the difference between the survival of a plant and its extinction. We know with certainty that dressings of Chilean nitrate provide sufficient iodine to increase the iodine content of plant tissues and hence improve their nutritive value for animals and man.* Since this increase is quantitatively demonstrable by crude man-made chemical means, obviously it must be sufficient to affect the intricate biochemical and cellular activities of the plant.

And, if further argument be needed to emphasize the influence of the merest chemical traces in plant physiology we have only to recall the incredible activity of plant growth-hormones. A total of 0·3 gramme is all that is required for an acre of land—that is to say, one ounce is sufficient for a hundred acres.

Here we naturally reach two further considerations which are of especial interest and significance in relation to the iodine content of Chilean nitrate of soda. First, there are definite indications that iodine does not work alone but exercises optimum action only in conjunction with other trace elements. Secondly, there is the problem of the influence of iodine on the assimilation and utilization of nitrogen by plants and the part which it seems to play in the process of nitrogen fixation and breakdown by the bacterial flora of the soil.

When A. H. Meyer (348) at the Louisiana Agricultural Experiment Station added small quantities of boron, zinc, aluminium, manganese and copper to a basal nutrient solution he did not get optimum growth and yield until a trace of iodine was also included. Mazé (297) noticed the same phenomenon in 1915. Although the concentrations of iodine with which he worked were not optimal for growth, he clearly saw the cumulative benefit to be derived from adding trace elements in succession and came to the conclusion that iodine was one of those necessary to bring about the total effect. Noteworthy in this connection, also, are the results of McHargue and Calfee (379) who obtained very marked beneficial effects on yield and quality of tomatoes by adding iodine jointly with other minor elements to soil cultures containing adequate amounts of the major plant nutrients.

In short, it is not improbable that the absolute content of any single trace element may be of less importance than the relative amounts of two or more acting together. Thatcher (8) believes there is sufficient evidence to justify the opinion that manganese and iron on the one hand and copper and zinc on the other are pairs of mutually co-ordinating catalysts for oxidation-reduction reactions. The same may very likely be true of the associations of iodine in plant metabolism, and the observation referred to in Deramond's report (451) that iron added with iodine enhances the iodine effect would seem to confirm this idea.

The combined or synergistic effect of minor elements has also been studied by the Russian scientist, Shcherbakov (373, 374, 388), who found that a mixture of trace chemicals, including iodine, increased the growth of flax and buckwheat. He elicited the further important fact that the plants assimilated more nitrogen and phosphorus from the basal nutrient solution after the trace-element salts including iodine had been added to it.

Increased nitrogen assimilation following the iodine treatment of plants has also been observed by Brenchley (303), Stoklasa (330 and 550), Leroux (399), Audidier (441) and Brioux (445). Further research is certainly needed to answer outstanding questions, but the indications are already more than sufficient to support the assumption that iodine does in fact assist nitrogen metabolism. It is not improbable that this effect is linked with the observation made by several workers independently, that iodine promotes growth of nitrifying bacteria in the soil—a subject covered in entries 549 to 562 and discussed more fully on pages 18 to 20.

Nitrate accumulation due to ineffective nitrate utilization is known to occur in plants in cases of deficiencies of either molybdenum or of sulphur, and it may well be that iodine also is associated in some way with this phenomenon. Whatever the truth, we commend the problem of iodine-nitrogen relationships and of iodine-trace-element relationships to serious and intensive investigation because the evidence here surveyed suggests that only through biochemical studies of this intricate nature shall we be in a position to integrate and interpret the many isolated facts known to us, and eventually be able to define with precision the exact role of iodine in plant physiology. That it has a positive role and is not merely a passive element in plant life, we have not the slightest doubt.

THYROXINE AND THYROID PREPARATIONS (461-492). The suggestion that thyroid substances are as essential to plants as to animals has been put to experimental test by a number of botanists, zoologists and medical scientists interested in biochemical parallelisms in plant and animal life.

* Sommerfeld has estimated that in Germany during the 1914-1918 war the scarcity of Chilean nitrate of soda meant an annual loss to the soil of 65 tons of iodine and that as a result goitre became much more prevalent (see *Iodine Facts* No. 314).

Since thyroxine and thyroid extracts contain iodine as an essential constituent, our bibliography necessarily takes account of these studies. In virtue of their relationship both to plant and animal physiology they are to be found not only in botanical literature but in *Gynécologie*, the *Lancet* and other purely medical journals.

The effects of thyroid hormone have been tested in four main directions, namely, on the root system of bulbs—particularly hyacinth bulbs and bulbs of the onion class; on budding and leaf formation in tree twigs such as lilac and poplar; on the germination of seeds; and on the development of various garden flowers and vegetable crops, including soya beans, tomatoes and cress.

As may be seen from the annotations, no very clear-cut conclusions can be drawn from the results of these experiments. Some authors have observed stimulating effects, others the exact opposite. On the whole, however, the majority found evidence of stimulation if not of growth at least of development and differentiation. For example, Scaglia (468) accelerated the development of hyacinth flowers by adding thyroid preparations to the culture solution. Davis (473) got a similar result in onions by injecting thyroxine into the bulb. Hykes (471) provoked the precocious development of leaves in dormant tree twigs by using thyroxine solution and Dunn (485) stimulated the growth of buds on poplar twigs by the same means.

One of the earliest workers on this aspect of plant metabolism was Niethammer of Prague (464 and 465). She found that injection of dilute aqueous solutions of thyroid extract into dormant lilac buds promoted cell division and also that germination of various seeds is stimulated by thyroid hormone. Others who have similarly excited germination by applying solutions of thyroid material to seeds are Sellei (474), who experimented with wheat grains, and Meyer (481) who used cottonwool soaked in thyroxine solution on which to stimulate the germination of garden cress seed and lentils.

As might be expected, these effects have for the most part been obtained with dilute solutions of thyroxine and thyroid substance. Strong solutions have generally proved harmful (480, 482, 483). Helpful reviews of literature in this field are those of Havas and Caldwell (479), Brain (484), Nicol (486) and Zollikofer (489).

GROWTH REGULATING SUBSTANCES (493-523). Iodine compounds figure to some extent in the comparatively new and rapidly developing science of plant growth regulators. These substances are of two origins.

First, there are those occurring naturally in the plant—various indole and phenyl compounds—which are essential for organized growth and normal development. No evidence exists that iodine has any connection with these, either as part of their chemical constitution or as influencing their innate character or effects.

Secondly, there are the artificially prepared growth substances—naphthalene compounds, substituted benzoic acids and phenoxy compounds, now numbering more than one hundred—which are being applied with remarkable practical consequences in horticulture. It is in this class that an iodine interest particularly lies.

Depending on type and concentration, synthetic growth regulators are capable either of initiating and accelerating cellular activities or of arresting and inhibiting them. Thus, certain compounds promote the growth of roots and are on this account recommended for the successful propagation of plant cuttings; others stimulate the development of unfertilized ovaries and thus induce both the setting of fruit and the production of seedless varieties of fruit. Among inhibitory effects, on the other hand, are prevention of the development of abscission cells between fruit and stalk, a fact turned to practical account in the use of plant growth regulators for preventing pre-harvest fruit drop. Another useful application of the inhibitory effect is the retardation of bud development to avoid frost damage. Similarly, the sprouting of potatoes can be inhibited, thus allowing them to be stored well into summer without risk of deterioration. Many growth regulators are highly selective, acting only on one or two species. This property has been applied in the formulation of selective weed killers by means of which root-tip growth is arrested but radial growth becomes so excessive that the stem literally bursts and exposes the inner tissues to damage by parasites, fungi and other noxious influences.

The part which the halogens, including iodine, can play in these manifestations is well exemplified in their power to intensify the effect of phenoxyacetic acid and its derivatives. This compound, relatively inert as a root growth promoter, becomes highly active when chlorine, bromine or iodine is introduced into the ring. Used in concentrations designed to give excessive root-stimulating effects, 2 : 4-dichlorophenoxyacetic acid is one of the best selective weed killers known. Entries 508 and 513 refer especially to the preparation and properties of several iodo-phenoxyacetic acid derivatives, including 2-iodo-4-chloro-, 2-chloro-4-iodo- and 2 : 4 diiodo-phenoxyacetic acids.

The effects of these compounds are paralleled by

2 : 3 : 5-triiodobenzoic acid which, according to some investigators, offers promise of being even more effective as a weed killer than the halogenated phenoxyacetic acids. When vaporized in the presence of young tomato plants, triiodobenzoic acid has the further interesting property of causing the shoots which arise in the leaf axils to become flower shoots instead of leafy shoots. In fact, triiodobenzoic acid is the first substance shown to be specific for flower forming in tomatoes. Incidentally, this compound originally attracted attention because of the abnormal colour of leaves which it induced. Another substituted benzoic acid compound which has received research attention as a plant growth regulator is 2-iodo-3-nitrobenzoic acid (see entries 512 and 515).

Growth regulators apparently exercise their effects through the oxidation-reduction systems of the living organism. Many compounds known to have growth regulating activity also have the property of acting as oxygen or hydrogen acceptors or donators depending on the circumstances in which they find themselves. For example, in the search for compounds intended to prevent or delay the emergence of buds, the object has been to look for those which interfere with the oxygen supply to the cell and thus damp down metabolic activity. The most important substance with this attribute is iodoacetic acid which inhibits or retards respiration by forming loose molecular compounds with some of the chemical entities involved in cell oxidation, thus removing available oxygen from the growing plant cell.

Since the bibliography went to press a report of more recent findings on the effect of triiodobenzoic acid on flower formation in tomatoes has been published by P. W. Zimmerman and A. E. Hitchcock (*Contrib. Boyce Thompson Inst. Plant Research*, 1949, v. 15, pp. 353-361).

OTHER BIOCHEMICAL ASPECTS

ABSORPTION OF IODINE BY SEEDS (524-529). On page 8 we have already touched upon the literature concerning the soaking of seeds in iodine solutions before sowing with the object of stimulating germination. In the section now under review are grouped a number of studies in which seed treatments with iodine have been employed to elucidate certain purely physico-chemical questions relating to the permeability of the seed coat.

The majority of these investigations are concerned not so much with iodine *per se* as with the broad question of permeability of seed membranes to water and soluble chemical nutrients in general. The fact that free iodine and the iodides in solution have been selected for study in this connection is simply because the amount which passes through the membrane into the seed substance, or is left behind in the diffusing solution, is comparatively easy to determine by titration. Furthermore, the readily observable blue coloration which iodine forms with starch inside the seed reveals how far and in what directions penetration has taken place. The behaviour of the iodides may be assumed to give an indication of what probably happens with other soluble salts in like circumstances. In short, experiments of this kind use iodine as a test substance.

One investigator (Malhotra, 527), when studying questions of permeability in this way, took the opportunity to ascertain whether by the seed-soaking technique he could secure food plants with an increased iodine content to serve as prophylactic agents in the fight against human goitre. He concluded that seedlings obtained from seeds immersed in weak iodine solution showed somewhat better growth than controls; but he did not carry his studies far enough to prove whether the mere soaking of seed in iodine solution prior to sowing will produce plants with a distinctively higher iodine content than that of plants resulting from untreated seed.

PHOTOSYNTHESIS: ENZYME ACTION: RESPIRATION (530-546). Earlier reference has been made (p. 4) to Gautier's belief (207) that all plants which contain chlorophyll contain iodine and to Remington's finding (222) that iodine is most concentrated in those parts of the plant which contain most chlorophyll. That iodine seems to promote the development of chlorophyll is one of the interesting conclusions reached by Powers (393) after ten years of research on the role of iodine in plant life. In line with this is the observation by Richter and Vasileva (543) that spraying the leaves of beans in the evening with a weak solution of potassium iodide results in a marked increase in the rate of photosynthesis the following day.

Others have found quite opposite effects. Kohn, for example, inhibited photosynthesis in green algae by the application of iodoacetic acid or iodoacetamide (532). Similar findings were obtained by Greenfield (542, 544). His treatment of the cells of *Chlorella vulgaris* with an aqueous solution of potassium iodide inhibited photosynthesis over a wide range of light intensities.

Two other papers deserve mention in this connection. Rabinowitch and Weiss (535) when studying the reversible oxidation of chlorophyll found that a yellow oxidized solution of chlorophyll regains its original green colour on addition of potassium iodide. The relation of iodine to the assimilation of chlorophyll is also discussed by Freundler, Ménager and Laurent in entry 111.

What association or interdependence, if any, there may be between chlorophyll formation and trace amounts of iodine remains for future research to determine. Meanwhile nothing definite can be said. However, the references cited in this section may well serve as a starting point for those who will undoubtedly give further thought to the problem.

Consideration of the many studies involving the use of iodoacetate to elucidate enzyme action and the process of respiration in higher plants is appropriately deferred to a later section on page 21.

HYDROPONICS (547-548). So far as can be ascertained, of the many authors who have written practical handbooks on the new developments in soilless agriculture, only Professor D. R. Matlin includes iodine in the formulae of nutrient solutions used in plant chemiculture. His recommendations are cited in entries 547 and 548.

MICRO-ORGANISMS

EFFECT OF IODINE ON BACTERIA AND FUNGI

SOIL MICROFLORA: NITROGEN CYCLE (549-562). Before considering the published findings which purport to show that iodine influences the soil micro-organisms taking part in the nitrogen cycle, it will be helpful to refresh our minds regarding the nitrogen cycle itself, otherwise there will be much that will be difficult to understand. The nitrogen cycle is very clearly explained in a recent book (*The Chemical Activities of Bacteria.* London: University Tutorial Press Ltd., 2nd edition, 1948) by Dr. Ernest F. Gale, on whose admirable account we have freely drawn in preparing the following summary.

Certain bacteria have the power to fix gaseous atmospheric nitrogen and combine it in organic form as proteins (A). Through the action of proteolytic enzymes, these proteins are hydrolysed to their constituent amino-acids. Amino-acids are decomposed by other organisms with the production of ammonia (B). Ammonia is oxidized to nitrate in two stages by the nitrifying bacteria, *Nitrosomonas* and *Nitrobacter* (C). Finally, the Chromobacteria have the property of liberating gaseous nitrogen from nitrate (D). Thus, nitrogen completes the full cycle of build-up and break-down indicated in the diagram on page 19.

In greater detail the principal steps in the nitrogen cycle are these:

A. *Fixation of Atmospheric Nitrogen as Protein.* The organism mainly concerned in nitrogen fixation is *Azotobacter* which is able to utilize free atmospheric nitrogen as its sole source of nitrogen for growth. Its only other requirement is an ample supply of carbohydrate. The amount of carbohydrate available in the soil is often the limiting factor for growth, a fact which explains the practice in some countries of enriching soil by ploughing waste molasses into it. *Azotobacter* is the organism responsible for the natural replenishment of soil-nitrogen in fields left fallow for a season.

Atmospheric nitrogen is also fixed by the bacteria called *Rhizobia*. These are the organisms normally present in soils which give rise to the formation of the characteristic nodules on the roots of leguminous plants. The *Rhizobia* in contact with the plant within the nodules are able to fix nitrogen; but the process is essentially dependent on the symbiotic partnership between the organism and the leguminous plant. That is to say, neither the leguminous plant alone nor the free-living *Rhizobium* can fix nitrogen independently.

B. *Degradation of Amino-Acids to Ammonia.* The molecule of an amino-acid, $R.CHNH_2.COOH$, may be degraded to produce ammonia (1) by deamination, *i.e.*, the removal of the $-NH_2$ group; (2) by decarboxylation, *i.e.*, the removal of the $-COOH$ group; or (3) by splitting or hydrolysis of the molecule at some other position. Various organisms are responsible, and the particular type of process which will operate is profoundly influenced not only by the particular organism operating but by the hydrogen ion concentration of the medium.

Deamination may proceed in several different ways. For example, oxidative deamination is ac-

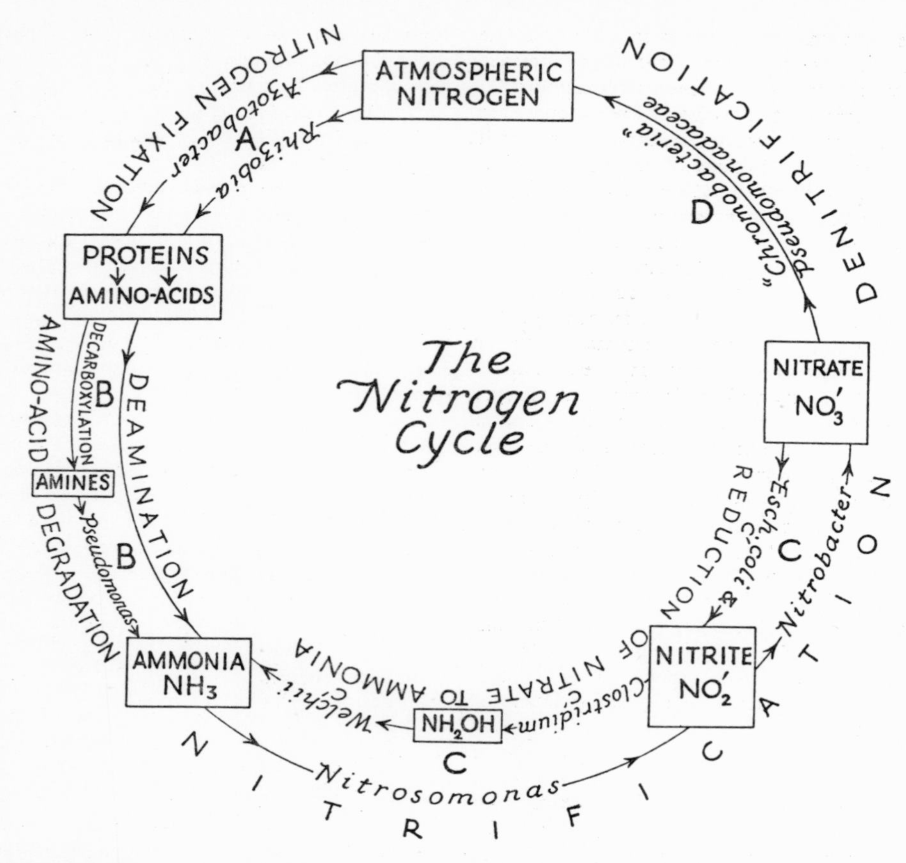

complished through the action of *Escherichia coli* and some other organisms according to the equation:

$$R.CHNH_2.COOH+O \rightarrow R.CO.COOH+NH_3$$

Reductive deamination is accomplished by certain strict aerobes (*Mycobacterium phlei*) according to the equation:

$$R.CHNH_2.COOH+2H \rightarrow R.CH_2.COOH+NH_3$$

Desaturation deamination, hydrolytic deamination and dehydration deamination are other forms of deamination which may occur with different organisms under varying conditions.

If decarboxylation occurs, the intermediate nitrogenous product is an amine:

$$R.CHNH_2.COOH \rightarrow R.CH_2NH_2+CO_2$$

which is subsequently oxidized by certain bacteria, particularly *Pseudomonas*, with the liberation of ammonia.

C. *Nitrification*. The oxidation of ammonia to nitrate in the soil is termed nitrification. The process takes place in two stages and two specific organisms are involved. The first step is the oxidation of ammonia to nitrite by *Nitrosomonas* and the second is the oxidation of nitrite to nitrate by *Nitrobacter*. The two phases of the process are distinct and non-interchangeable. Thus, *Nitrosomonas* must have ammonia as its source of nitrogen and cannot grow in a medium containing nitrite but no ammonia. Similarly, *Nitrobacter* cannot grow in a nitrite-free medium but relies entirely on the oxidation of nitrite to nitrate for its energy.

The oxidation of ammonia to nitrate (C) is a reversible process as is indicated in the diagram by the letter (C^1). The reverse change, namely, reduction of nitrate to ammonia may under certain conditions be carried out by *Escherichia coli*, which reduces nitrate to nitrite, and by both *Escherichia coli* and *Clostridium welchii* which are capable of carrying the backward reaction to completion with the re-formation of ammonia.

D. *Denitrification*. Providing the final link in the cycle is the process of denitrification. This is achieved by certain species of *Serratia*, Chromobacteria and *Pseudomonadaceae* which have the faculty of liberating free nitrogen gas from nitrate or nitrite. The process is non-reversible and occurs in the presence of nitrate or nitrite as the sole source of nitrogen.

With the foregoing preliminary introduction we are now in a better position to consider the part which iodine may play in the course of the nitrogen cycle.

Study of entries 549 to 562 leaves no doubt that iodine in trace quantities favourably influences the growth and activities of the soil bacteria involved in the fixation of atmospheric nitrogen, that is, the part of the cycle marked A in our schema. Five papers (553, 554, 556, 561, 562) refer specifically to *Azotobacter* and the greatly increased power of nitrogen fixation by this organism when iodine is added to the culture medium. Fedorov's experiments (562) register the increase as 25 per cent. Greaves (556) records an increase of as much as 200 per cent.

Two authors, Powers (557) and Leroux (559), mention particularly the stimulating effect of iodine on the micro-organisms (*Rhizobia*) concerned in nitrogen fixation by leguminous plants such as peas and beans and clovers.

The amount of iodine required to bring about these beneficial effects is exceedingly small. Itano and Matsuura (554) say that the optimum for stimulating *Azotobacter chroococcum* is about 1 part of iodine in 14,300 parts of culture medium. Greaves (556) got his 200 per cent increased fixation of nitrogen by adding 1 part of sodium iodide to 25,000 parts of Ashby's basal solution. Fedorov (562) used iodine (as iodoacetic acid) in concentrations between 1 part in 7800 and 1 part in 78,000 parts of the nutrient solution; and Leroux's (559) positive effects were obtained with soils containing added iodine in the proportion of 1 part in 200,000 to 1 part in 500,000 parts of soil.

So far as present knowledge goes, no phase of the nitrogen cycle other than fixation (A) is affected by iodine except perhaps the formation of nitrate nitrogen (C) as mentioned by Leroux (558). In addition to those authors specially mentioned in the foregoing paragraphs, there are some others cited in the bibliography who have investigated various aspects of iodine and the nitrogen cycle. Taking all the information as a whole, the general conclusion seems to be that iodine plays a positive role in the microbial activity of the soil and that this factor must be given due consideration when evaluating the effect of iodine on the growth of higher plants. Only one author (Dopter, 555) records negative results from his investigation of the action of iodine on soil microflora.

BACTERIA: YEASTS: FUNGI IMPERFECTI (563-646). Apart from the foregoing studies on the effect of iodine on the particular micro-organisms concerned with nitrogen fixation in the soil, very little has been done to determine whether traces of inorganic salts of iodine are necessary for the nutrition and growth of bacteria in general. In fact, we have been able to find only five papers (563, 564, 574, 577, 579) which may be said to have any bearing on this subject.

These relate to the possible influence of iodine on the metabolism of *Streptococcus haemolyticus*, *Staphylococcus albus*, *Brucella abortus*, *Bacillus anthracis* and other similar organisms which give rise to diseases in man and animals. In view of the meagre information available, however, no conclusions can be drawn and we do not know whether iodine in minute traces is essential to bacterial nutrition or not.

In this connection it must be remembered, of course, that elemental iodine and one or two of its organic compounds, even in great dilution, are among the best known and most effective of protoplasmic poisons. The very large literature on the practical applications of this property, namely, the consciously directed use of iodine as a germicide, does not belong here and has purposely been deferred to a later bibliography because the issues involved are almost exclusively of medical and pharmaceutical interest.

In contrast to our lack of knowledge as to whether iodine may be a positive nutritional factor in the life of pathogenic bacteria, there is considerable information and a striking unanimity of opinion that inorganic iodine in low concentrations stimulates the activity of yeasts. This literature is classified in entries 580 to 599, and of the fourteen different authors who have studied the question all except one are agreed that iodine somehow accelerates the energy metabolism of yeast cells, promotes a more intensive fermentation of sugar in the presence of yeast suspensions, and concomitantly increases yeast growth.

The stimulating effect is achieved only in low concentration of iodine. High concentrations are toxic to the yeast cell. "Low concentration" is however a term used with considerable latitude. Scharrer and Schwartz at Weihenstephan found that the activity of yeast in sugar solution was stimulated by putting 1 part of iodine (as sodium or potassium iodide) in 10,000 to 17,000 parts of sugar solution. This is in accord with Itano's finding (595) that the optimum dilution is 1 part in 14,000. Weber (598), on the other hand, speaks of concentrations of 1 part in one million, and Kooijmans's best results were obtained at an iodine concentration of about 1 part in ten million parts of the basal nutrient solution.

Entries 632 to 646 contain particulars of iodine studies on various organisms belonging to the class Fungi Imperfecti which includes *Penicillium* and *Aspergillus niger*. The last named is a useful test organism in experiments with trace elements when accuracy, speed and precision are necessary. Iodine does not appear to be one of its essential nutritional requirements.

Iodoacetic Acid. In 1930 Einar Lundsgaard (600) published his discovery, made in Copenhagen the previous year, that sodium monoiodoacetate inhibits glycolysis in muscle. Iodoacetate is a cellular poison and owes its toxic property to the fact that the iodine atom readily takes part in substitution reactions and combines with sulphydryl (–SH) groups in certain enzymes, such as the triosephosphate dehydrogenase of muscle, so that when muscle tissue is poisoned with this substance lactic acid formation is completely stopped. Iodoacetate has therefore provided a convenient biochemical tool with which to study intermediary carbohydrate metabolism in animal muscle.

Lundsgaard also pointed out that iodoacetic acid could be used equally well for elucidating analogous problems of carbohydrate breakdown and cellular respiration in plants. He himself applied the method particularly to investigate the mechanism of respiration and fermentation by yeast. The addition of monoiodoacetate stops the process and prevents the further breakdown of the intermediate products of fermentation which can then be isolated and examined. This can be done at any stage, and investigators have been able to isolate hexose diphosphate, dihydroxyacetone phosphate and 3-glyceraldehyde phosphate from fermentations of glucose by yeast extract.

Needless to say, a large literature has grown up around the use of iodoacetic acid and its salts as chemical instruments for studying respiratory and other mechanisms of plant and bacterial cells. In all, sixty-six papers pertaining to the subject are included in the bibliography. In harmony with the general design these are classified according to the plant groups concerned in the particular investigation cited. Proceeding in this manner, it is inevitable that relevant material is scattered over the five sections: Growth Regulating Substances, Enzyme Action, Bacteria, Yeasts, and Fungi Imperfecti. However, it may be easily found by referring to the annotations in these sections and to the subject index.

Since iodoacetate is not itself a substance of physiological or nutritional importance to plants but a laboratory reagent used to facilitate our understanding of certain special aspects of plant-cell biochemistry, no purpose is served here by considering the results of the various experiments in which it has been employed. Readers who may wish to go more fully into the question are recommended to consult Turner's excellent review on the relation between respiration and fermentation in yeast and the higher plants, the reference to which is given in entry 619.

PLANT PROTECTION

In the foregoing narrative we have considered the place of iodine in the chemical composition of plants and its possible relationship to their growth and development.

But iodine has a relevance to plant life in another important respect. It is the active agent in certain germicidal solutions, sprays, seed-dressings and insecticides used to prevent or control diseases in plants. The literature of these applied aspects is covered in the concluding sections of the bibliography.

VARIOUS SOIL AND PLANT TREATMENTS (653-694). Plant diseases associated with deficiency of particular micro-nutrients—manganese, boron, iron, and others—are well recognized. So far, however, no disease of plants specifically attributable to shortage of iodine is known. Nevertheless, one or two observers have expressed the belief that iodine applied to the soil in simple inorganic or organic form, or in Chilean nitrate of soda, enables plants better to resist the attacks of fungous and virus diseases.

As long ago as 1853, Rivet (653) was writing enthusiastically about the value of iodine-containing seaweed manure for preserving vines from spoilage by the fungus *Oidium*, and of the special quality of the wine from vines so treated. Eighty years later, Klein (660) found that after the application of iodized chalk and Chilean nitrate of soda to the soil of a greenhouse where tomato stem disease had been rife, no evidence of the disease appeared and the yield of fruit was greatly increased. This finding was confirmed by Gleisberg (659).

It must be conceded, however, that these views have been based on general observation rather than on the results of strictly controlled experimental research. We are on much surer ground when we consider situations in which iodine is used directly to kill the disease-producing agents which infest plant life.

One of the most effective disinfectants for potato cutting knives to prevent the spread of bacterial ring rot and other diseases of potatoes is a solution of iodine and potassium iodide in glycerine and water. A desirable concentration is 1 part of iodine in about 260 parts of solution as recommended by Iverson and Kelly (670) and by Ark (676). Glick (686), who prefers a 1 per cent solution, gives the obvious warning that the solution deteriorates with use and must be kept up to strength. In the continuous disinfection of rotary cutting knives, one gallon lots of 1 per cent iodine solution lost potency after cutting 800 lb. of potatoes.

Direct iodine treatment of the potato tuber itself is sometimes effective. According to Goodwin, Salmon and Ware (657), the zoospores of hop downy mildew and potato blight are rapidly killed on exposure to iodine vapour. On the other hand, the dipping of cut seed-potatoes in a fairly strong solution of iodine (1:200) does not appear to be lethal against ring rot caused by *Phytomonas sepedonica* (676, 680), although it is damaging to the starchy substance of the potato.

Iodine in dilute solution is very effective against nematode infestations of tubers and bulbs. Opinion here is unanimous. Dr Poate, an Australian authority on the cultivation of daffodils, finds iodine the only substance which will kill eelworms in bulbs. He uses a 1 in 4000 solution (662). For the hot-water treatment of narcissus bulbs, plant pathologists at Seale-Hayne Agricultural College recommend an iodine-iodide bath containing 1 part of free iodine in 8000 parts of water. This is effective against both eelworm and *Fusarium* bulb rot, and does no harm to the subsequent growth of the bulb (668). Wallace (674) reports a similar experience; but he uses a stronger solution, namely, 1 part of free iodine in about 1700 parts of water. Bud eelworms of strawberries may be killed by immersing the plants for thirty minutes in warm water containing iodine in the proportion 1 to 20,000. It is doubtful, however, whether this solution is sufficiently strong to be completely effective. Reid (692) reports that treated strawberry plants became re-infected a few months later.

Solutions containing free iodine applied to control fungous and parasitic diseases of plants are referred to by several other authors. For example, the sclerotia, or storage organs, of the fungus *Colletotrichum tabificum* which causes a root disease in tomatoes can be killed by immersion in aqueous iodine (656). Reichert and Littauer (666) have successfully applied an alcoholic iodine solution to control the fungus, *Diplodia natalensis*, responsible for wastage in oranges. Similarly, the tobacco mosaic virus can be inactivated by iodine solution (675, 690). And the chemical eradication of crown gall on almond trees has been satisfactorily accomplished by painting the gall with a liniment of iodine in glycerine (677).

All these treatments, and others like them, depend for their success on the fact that iodine is applied in the free state and thus acts directly as a protoplasmic poison. Little success has attended the use of iodides or iodates in this field. Potassium iodide and potassium iodate were among the hundred chemicals tested by Newton and his colleagues (661) for lethal effect on the nematode *Tylenchus dipsaci*. The results were not encouraging. Applied to soil, potassium iodide is useless as a killer of plant pests. It has been tried in this way without success to control cotton root rot (667), tomato eelworms (682, 685) and potato scab (691). The only evidence that potassium iodide may under certain circumstances exercise a fungicidal effect is found in the experiments of Raleigh (664) and of Krüger (671). Raleigh showed that this iodide increases the efficacy of mercury bichloride solution as a dip for seed potatoes in the control of *Rhizoctonia solani*. In Krüger's experiments, potassium iodide at a concentration of 1 in 6000 had a pronounced effect on the differentiation of zoospores in potato blight (*Phytophthora infestans*), inhibited their formation at a strength of 1 in 400, and completely stopped their development at 1 in 100. There is some evidence, too, that potassium periodate has fungistatic activity (689).

Organically combined iodine, however, is definitely fungicidal in one or two special forms. For example, ethyl mercuric iodide is a highly efficient soil disinfectant (672, 684), and has also been successfully used to inhibit the growth of *Fusarium oxysporum cubense* on banana plants (688). Iodoacetamide will inactivate the tobacco mosaic virus (675); and recent exhaustive tests at the Butterwick Research Laboratories of the Imperial Chemical Industries Limited (693, 694) have revealed that tetraiodoethylene and diiodoacetylene possess important fungistatic properties.

SEED DISINFECTION (695-721). For many years it has been known that seed-borne diseases of cereals and other crops can be controlled by dressing the seed with alkyl mercurials prior to sowing. Methyl mercury iodide and ethyl mercury iodide are among the active compounds in this group but owing to their poisonous nature and the consequent risk attending their use, efforts are continually being made to find safe and reliable substitutes.

In 1927, Sayre and Thomas, of the Ohio Agricultural Experiment Station, claimed excellent results against oat smut by applying an iodine dusting powder made from 5 parts of ground crystalline iodine mixed with 95 parts of kieselguhr or diatomaceous earth. This announcement stimulated considerable interest and the literature of 1928, 1929 and 1930 contains numerous reports from American research stations of trials with various simple inorganic iodine mixtures including elementary iodine dusts, powdered potassium iodide, salts of hydriodic acid, and solutions of iodine in carbon disulphide. These were tested against smut on oats, covered smut or bunt of wheat, barley stripe, and seed-borne disease of cotton, flax and other economic crops.

Opinions vary regarding the efficacy of these treatments. Earlier reports are almost unanimous in commending them; accounts subsequent to 1930 are less enthusiastic. In that year Dillon Weston (712) of the School of Agriculture, Cambridge, published his conclusion that iodine dust is of no use as a fungicide against bunt in wheat. And in 1937 we have the authority of Leukel (715) after twelve years' work with five different iodine dusts that "the corrosive nature of iodine and its detrimental effect on germination eliminate it from further consideration as a practical seed disinfectant."

The alkyl mercury iodides, however, are by no means ruled out as fungicidal seed dressings and are still used in considerable quantities for this purpose.

FRUIT PRESERVATION (722-745). To reduce the serious losses which constantly occur during the storage and transport of fruit due to the growth of moulds and fungi, R. G. Tomkins, of the Low Temperature Research Station, Cambridge, developed the idea of encasing fruit in iodine-impregnated wrappers.

His various tests (722, 723, 724, 727) showed that wraps treated with iodine retarded the germination and growth of mould fungi responsible for fruit spoilage without damaging the fruit or impairing its appearance and flavour. The most striking results were seen in the control of mould growth on grapes. Bunches of grapes wrapped in iodized paper remained free from mould for periods two to three times longer than when wrapped in plain paper. The same was found true of tomatoes and oranges. Rotting of plums and peaches was also reduced by iodized wraps, but some varieties of these were adversely affected by the treatment in that they ripened abnormally and even turned black. Passion fruit and melons wrapped in iodized wraps suffered no damage on storage, while the same varieties in plain wraps became mouldy.

In making these wraps the solution of iodine generally used consists of 12·7 grammes of iodine, 10 grammes of potassium iodide, 200 millilitres of water and 800 millilitres of rectified spirit. Sheets of tissue paper approximately 50 centimetres by 75 centimetres readily absorb 15 millilitres of this solution. A convenient method of iodinating the wrap is to place five sheets of tissue paper on a sheet of glass and pour on to them 75 millilitres of the iodine solution. Uniform absorption is achieved by wearing a rubber glove with which to smooth the wet paper. When dry, the sheets are cut into six smaller pieces 25 centimetres square. Each of these pieces will contain approximately 30 milligrammes of iodine.

Tomkins's experiments in England were eagerly watched by fruit exporting countries, with the result that more extensive and thorough practical trials were undertaken in South Africa, Cyprus, Trinidad, Palestine, India, the United States of America, and Russia. The results obtained were in substantial agreement with those of Tomkins.

Rattray (726, 730, 733) and du Plessis (728, 732, 737), who made investigations for the Union of South Africa Department of Agriculture and Forestry, found that wrappers treated with an iodine solution containing 1 or 1·5 per cent of iodine and 1 to 2 per cent of potassium iodide were most effective in controlling wastage in grapes caused by *Botrytis* infection. The iodized wrappers did not appear to inhibit to any extent the growth of this fungus within the grape, but they definitely prevented the spread of the infection from one grape to another. The efficacy of the iodized wrapper was increased when the wrapped bunches of grapes were further enclosed in non-porous "Crystalline" paper which prevents volatilization of the iodine to the outside atmosphere.

The use of iodized cottonwool plugs and crêpe-paper plugs as a means of controlling *Botrytis* wastage in grapes has also been studied by these South African investigators. Absorbent cottonwool rolls, one and a half inches in length and half an inch in diameter, and crêpe-paper plugs of the same dimensions are treated with an alcoholic solution of iodine and potassium iodide and allowed to dry for several days before being used. These are then inserted as far into the bunches as possible without damaging the berries, or, if the bunches are too compact, are merely laid on the top. The best results are obtained by using crêpe-paper plugs treated with an 0·5 N solution of iodine and then wrapping the bunch in "Crystalline" paper.

The extent to which iodized wraps might be used to reduce wastage in grapes transported under commercial conditions has been demonstrated by Dreyer (725) in a series of experimental consignments from South Africa to England. In every instance the result was a decrease in wastage, the spoilage in iodized wrapped grapes being about half that encountered in the plain wrapped grapes.

To obviate the inconvenience and labour of wrapping each fruit individually in iodized paper, Tomkins has suggested the employment of iodized wood shavings or iodized cork dust and has demonstrated that tomatoes stored in iodized shavings remain free from mould while those stored in the ordinary way produce luxuriant growths. This has been confirmed by Singh and Jakhanwal (735), who conclude that iodized wood shaving has a definite advantage over iodized paper wrap for preventing rot in tomatoes.

In spite of these many favourable results, it is still uncertain whether iodine is, after all, the ideal substance with which to treat wrappers. It is perhaps too volatile; it stains packing material yellow; and it cannot be applied to every variety of fruit without causing some injury. Tomkins himself, who originated the idea, is lukewarm in his most recent reports (727, 742); and others who do not regard the method as entirely satisfactory are Wardlaw (731), of the Imperial College of Tropical Agriculture, Trinidad, and Gerhardt and Ryall (738) whose tests with various volatile chemicals used for impregnating fruit-packing materials showed that elementary iodine effectively checks *Penicillium* and *Rhizopus* rot but only when used in concentrations sufficient to produce some surface injury to the fruit.

An interesting patent in this field is that cited in entry 739 covering the use of betaine iodide for treating air which comes in contact with fruit.

WEED KILLERS (746-753). Chemical methods for killing weeds and noxious plants have already been referred to briefly on page 16 in connection with the practical application of growth regulating substances. In this section are grouped some additional references in that sphere and also one or two dealing specially with the weed-killing effect of inorganic iodine compounds. Treatment of soil at sowing time with an aqueous solution of potassium iodide at the rate of 5 kilogrammes of iodine per hectare effectively controlled weeds and insect pests in sugar beet plots (747). A solution containing 1 part of mercuric chloro-iodide in 10,000 parts of water is sufficient to kill the more important aquatic plants which inhabit the canals of the Gezira cotton area of the Anglo-Egyptian Sudan (748). According to Hessenland and his co-workers (746), sodium iodate is ineffective as a weed killer owing to its high stability.

IODINE INSECTICIDES (754-818). Studies undertaken to determine the insecticidal value of iodine comprise the final section of the bibliography. They number sixty-five, and together refer to more than one hundred iodine compounds tested for insecticidal effect. These are chiefly organic iodine derivatives but the list includes such inorganic preparations as iodine in aqueous or alcoholic solution and the iodides of potassium, cadmium, copper, mercury and silver.

The citations cover every insecticidal aspect of iodine and are not confined solely to those which deal with the insect pests of plant life. To have selected only those papers which apply particularly to the plant world would have left a small residue of interesting border-line studies inappropriate to classify by themselves in any subsequent bibliography. They are therefore included here in their proper setting so that insecticidal knowledge of iodine may be considered as a whole.

So far as organic iodine derivatives are concerned, the wide variety of compounds tested and the dissimilarity of the methods in which they have been employed make it difficult to draw conclusions which apply generally to the entire field. Each substance must be considered on its own merits in relation to the circumstances of its use and the particular insect against which it is being applied.

Nevertheless, it seems that chemical structure does have some positive relationship to insecticidal efficiency if we accept the conclusions of Frear and Seiferle (811). Their study of the data to 1947 justified them in arranging iodine compounds containing the groupings named in the following descending order of toxicity: iodoxy, iodoso, monoiodo, diiodo, triiodo. Inorganic iodides showed a toxicity rather less than the monoiodo compounds but much greater than the diiodo compounds.

It is apparent, too, that some iodine compounds possess greater insecticidal efficiency than their bromine or chlorine analogues. For example, Roark and Cotton (768) found that *n*-propyl iodide is nearly two-and-one-half times more toxic against rice weevils than *n*-propyl bromide. On the other hand, there is plenty of evidence that the iodine analogues of DDT are not as effective as DDT itself (800, 802, 807, 808, 817, 818).

A useful alphabetical index of 108 organic and inorganic iodine compounds which have been tested as insecticides and fungicides is included in *Iodine Information* No. 7, entitled "Plant Protection", published in December 1946 by the Chilean Iodine Educational Bureau, London.

ANNOTATED BIBLIOGRAPHY
1813-1949

IODINE AND PLANT LIFE

ANNOTATED BIBLIOGRAPHY 1813-1949

REVIEWS AND GENERAL PAPERS

1-20

1926. ORR, J. B., and I. LEITCH, *Rowett Research Institute, Aberdeen.* Iodine in relation to plant and animal life. *J. Roy. Agric. Soc. England*, 1926, v. 87, pp. 43–57. **1**

A literature survey. Further work is necessary to prove the essentiality of iodine for plant life and to determine the effect of iodine manuring.

1928. SCHARRER, *Dr.* KARL, *Institute of Agricultural Chemistry, College of Agriculture and Brewing, Weihenstephan, near Munich.* Chemie und Biochemie des Jods. [Chemistry and biochemistry of iodine.] Stuttgart: *Ferdinand Enke*, 1928, vii + 192 pp. **2**

The literature on iodine in relation to plants is reviewed on pp. 83–111.

1929. EDDELBÜTTEL, H., *Rostock.* Das Jod als biogenes Element. [Iodine as a biogenic element.] *Ztschr. phys. chem. Unterricht*, 1929, v. 42, pp. 32–42. **3**

A discussion of some of the literature, with brief reference to the significance of iodine in plant nutrition.

1929. GREAT BRITAIN. MEDICAL RESEARCH COUNCIL. Iodine in nutrition. A review of existing information up to 1927. By John Boyd Orr, *M.D., D.Sc.*, and Isabella Leitch, *D.Sc.*, *Rowett Research Institute, Aberdeen.* Special Report Series No. 123. London: *H.M. Stationery Office*, 1929, 108 pp. **4**

A critical survey of the literature on iodine in relation to plant nutrition forms part of this important bulletin. Data on the iodine content of vegetable foods are tabulated.

1930. ORR, J. B., *M.D., D.Sc.*, and I. LEITCH, *M.A., D.Sc.*, *Rowett Research Institute, Aberdeen.* Iodine in practical agriculture. *Internat. Rev. Agric.* 1. *Monthly Bull. Agric. Sci. Pract.*, 1930, v. 21, pp. 197–208. **5**

Contemporary investigations on the effect of iodine manuring on growth and iodine content of plants are briefly reviewed and discussed on pp. 199–200.

1932. SCHARRER, *Dr.* KARL, *Institute of Agricultural Chemistry, College of Agriculture and Brewing, Weihenstephan, near Munich.* Neuere Forschungen über die Bedeutung des Jods für Boden und Pflanze. [Recent researches on the importance of iodine for soils and plants.] *Biedermanns Zentralbl., Abt. A*, 1932, New Series, v. 2, pp. 1–12. **6**

A review article with 100 references to the literature.

1934. NIKLAS, *Prof.* H., *director, Institute of Agricultural Chemistry and Agricultural Experiment Station, Weihenstephan, near Munich, Dr.* A. HOCK, *director, Bureau of Soil Science and Soil Survey, Weihenstephan, Dr.* F. CZIBULKA and *Dr.* F. KOHL. Literatursammlung aus dem Gesamtgebiet der Agrikulturchemie. Band 3. Pflanzenernährung. [Bibliography of the whole field of agricultural chemistry. Volume 3. Plant nutrition.] Weihenstephan, near Munich: *Verlag der Bodenuntersuchungsstelle*, 1934, xlv + 1114 pp. **7**

On pp. 391–396 ninety references to the literature on iodine in relation to plant nutrition are listed.

1934. THATCHER, *Prof.* R. W., *Massachusetts State College, Amherst.* A proposed classification of the chemical elements with respect to their functions in plant nutrition. *Science*, 1934, v. 79, pp. 463–466. **8**

Position and grouping in the periodic table are used as a basis from which to study the functions of chemical elements in plant nutrition. Fluorine, chlorine, bromine and iodine are classed as "anion formers with fixed valence."

1935. BERTRAM, *Dr.* PAUL, *scientific adviser, Chilesalpeter G.m.b.H., Berlin.* Die Bedeutung einiger Spurelemente fuer die Pflanzen. [The importance of some trace elements in plants.] *C. R. 4e Congr. Internat. Techn. Chim. Indust. Agric.*, Brussels, 1935, v. 2, pp. 396–414. **9**

Includes a brief review of the literature on iodine in relation to plant nutrition.

1938. NIKLAS, *Prof.* H., *director, Institute of Agricultural Chemistry and Agricultural Experiment Station, Weihenstephan, near Munich*, F. ADER, F. KISSEL, F. KOHL and F. CZIBULKA. Literatursammlung aus dem Gesamtgebiet der Agrikulturchemie. Band 4. Düngung und Düngemittel. [Bibliography of the whole field of agricultural chemistry. Volume 4. Manuring and fertilizers.] Leipzig: *Helingsche Verlagsanstalt*, 1938, xxxix + 1144 pp. **10**

Fifty-five references to the literature on iodine manuring are included.

1938. WASICKY, *Dr.* R., *Vienna*. Die biologische Rolle der Mikroelemente. [Biological role of the trace elements.] *Österreich. Chemikerztg.*, 1938, v. 41, pp. 1–9. **11**

The distribution and significance of iodine in the plant kingdom are discussed.

1942. LEROUX, DÉSIRÉ, *director, agricultural chemistry laboratory, Conservatoire National des Arts et Métiers, Paris.* Contribution à l'étude agronomique de divers "oligo-éléments." [Contribution to the study of some trace elements in agriculture.] Alençon: *Imprimerie Alençonnaise, Maison Poulet-Malassis*, 1942, [iii]+176 pp. **12**

Contains a very extensive review of the literature on trace elements in relation to plant growth (with a bibliography of 941 references).

1943. BRENCHLEY, WINIFRED E., *D.Sc., Rothamsted Experimental Station, Harpenden, Herts.* Minor elements and plant growth. *Biol. Rev.*, 1943, v. 18, pp. 159–171. **13**

General review. "It has not yet been proved whether iodine is essential to plants as it is to animals."

1944. SCHARRER, *Dr.* KARL, *professor and director of the Agricultural Chemistry Institute, Giessen University*. Biochemie der Spurenelemente. [Biochemistry of the trace elements.] Berlin: *Paul Parey*, 1944, 2nd edition, viii + 319 pp. **14**

The first edition of this work, which includes a brief section on the biochemistry of iodine, appeared in 1941.

1946. STILES, WALTER, *Sc.D., F.R.S., Mason Professor of Botany in the University of Birmingham.* Trace elements in plants and animals. *Cambridge University Press*, 1946, xi + 189 pp. **15**

Undoubtedly the most thoughtful and stimulating modern survey of knowledge in this field. The question of iodine in relation to plant and animal physiology and pathology is considered in several sections of the book.

1947. LEHR, *Dr.* J. J., *agricultural chemist*, with the co-operation of *Prof.* J. HUDIG, *director, laboratory for agricultural chemistry, College of Agriculture, Wageningen, Netherlands.* Chilisalpeter. Een monografie over de oudste minerale meststof ter wereld. [Chilean nitrate of soda. A monograph on the oldest mineral fertilizer in the world.] The Hague: *Inlichtingenbureau voor Chilisalpeter*, 1947, 224 pp. **16**

The significance of iodine in plant nutrition with special reference to the iodine content of Chilean nitrate of soda is briefly discussed on pp. 127–128. The authors conclude that although it still remains doubtful whether iodine is a physiological necessity to the plant itself, it can be said with certainty that addition of iodine to the soil increases the iodine content of crops and that human and animal needs for iodine can be met in this way.

1948. CHILEAN NITRATE EDUCATIONAL BUREAU, INC., *New York*. Bibliography of the literature on the minor elements and their relation to plant and animal nutrition. New York: *Chilean Nitrate Educational Bureau, Inc.*, 1948, 4th edition, v. 1, 1037 pp. **17**

A comprehensive bibliography, with abstracts, covering the literature on 45 elements up to June, 1947. The *Iodine* section lists 354 papers, 105 of which deal directly with the role of iodine in plant nutrition.

1948. CHILEAN NITRATE EDUCATIONAL BUREAU, INC., *New York*. Bibliography of the literature on sodium and iodine in relation to plant and animal nutrition. New York: *Chilean Nitrate Educational Bureau, Inc.*, 1948, 1st edition, v. 1, 123 pp. **18**

The *Iodine* and *Sodium* sections of the larger bibliography cited in the preceding entry have been reprinted under separate cover for the convenience of workers in these two fields of enquiry.

1948. CORRIE, FRANK EWART, *B.Sc., N.D.A., N.D.D., East Grinstead, Sussex*. Some elements of plants and animals. The mineral elements in plant and animal nutrition. London: *Fertiliser Journal Ltd.*, 1948, x + 120 pp. **19**

Collection in book form of articles previously published serially in *Fertiliser and Feeding Stuffs Journal*, including two on iodine in relation to plant nutrition.

1948. GILBERT, FRANK A., *M.A., Ph.D., agricultural sciences research division, Battelle Memorial Institute, Columbus, Ohio*. Mineral nutrition of plants and animals. Norman: *University of Oklahoma Press*, 1948, xii+131 pp. **20**

The essential facts about 21 different elements are summarized in as many chapters, that on iodine occupying 6 pages. A selected bibliography of 329 references includes 21 on iodine covering the years 1917–1941. The text is well illustrated.

MARINE PLANTS

IODINE CONTENT OF SEAWEEDS

21-182

QUALITATIVE AND QUANTITATIVE DATA 21-107

1813. COURTOIS, BERNARD (1777–1838). Découverte d'une substance nouvelle dans le vareck. [Discovery of a new substance in kelp.] *Ann. Chim.*, 1813, v. 88, pp. 304–310. **21**

Courtois discovered iodine in seaweed ash towards the end of 1811 or early in 1812. The exact date is unknown. Announcement of the discovery was not made until November 29, 1813. This is not only the first paper concerning iodine in a plant substance, but the first in the whole vast field of iodine literature.

1814. DAVY, *Sir* HUMPHRY, *F.R.S.* (1778–1829), *professor of chemistry, Royal Institution, London.* Further experiments and observations on iodine. *Phil. Trans. Roy. Soc.*, 1814, v. 104, pp. 487–507. **22**

Paper read before the Royal Society on June 16, 1814. Author found slight indications of the presence of iodine in the ash from each of the following Italian seaweeds: *Fucus cartilagineus, F. membranaceus, F. rubens, F. filamentosus, Ulva pavonia* and *U. linza*. Examination of 3 specimens of alkali formed by the combustion of vegetables that grow on the seashore gave no evidence of the presence of iodine.

1815. GAULTIER DE CLAUBRY, H. Recherches sur l'existence de l'iode dans l'eau de la mer et dans les plantes qui produisent la soude de varecks, et analyse de plusieurs plantes de la famille des algues. [The presence of iodine in seawater and in plants which yield kelp soda, and analysis of several algae.] *Ann. Chim.*, 1815, v. 93, pp. 75–110; 113–137. **23**

Seaweeds analysed can be arranged in decreasing order of iodine content as follows: *Laminaria saccharina, L. digitata, Fucus serratus, F. vesiculosus, Halidrys siliquosa, Chorda filum.* No quantitative data are given.

1839. GROSSE, —, *Leipzig*. Brom- und Jodgehalt in *Sphaerococcus crispus* Ag. (Carageen). [Bromine and iodine content of *Sphaerococcus crispus* Ag. (carrageen).] *Pharm. Centralbl.*, 1839, v. 10, pp. 159–160. **24**

Presence of iodine in carrageen is recorded.

1843. DUPASQUIER, ALPHONSE. Sur l'existence du brôme et de l'iode dans le *Fucus crispus*, et sur un procédé propre à y faire reconnaître par une seule expérience, ainsi que dans les éponges, les coraux, la mousse de Corse et les autres substances marines analogues, la présence de ces deux principes. [A procedure to determine by a single experiment the existence of bromine and iodine in *Fucus crispus* and also in sponges, corals, Corsican moss and other similar marine matter.] *J. Pharm. Chim.*, Paris, 1843, 3rd Series, v. 29, pp. 112–118. **25**

Fucus crispus contains a considerable amount of iodine in the form of iodide. No quantitative data are given.

1848. BONET, MAGIN, *professor of chemistry, University of Oviedo, Asturias.* Abondance de l'iode dans les algues des Asturies. [Plentiful iodine in the seaweeds of Asturias.] *J. Chim. Méd.*, 1848, 3rd Series, v. 4, p. 431. **26**

A brief note that iodine has been obtained in quantity from *Fucus palmaticus* L. along the Asturian coasts, Bay of Biscay. No quantitative data are given.

1851. MARSSON, TH., *chemist, Wolgast, North Germany.* Ueber den bedeutenden Bromgehalt der Asche des *Fucus vesiculosus* aus der Ostsee so wie über die Entdeckung des Broms neben Jod. [The significant bromine content of the ash of *Fucus vesiculosus* from the Baltic and the detection of bromine in the presence of iodine.] *Arch. Pharm.*, Hanover, 1851, v. 116, pp. 281–285. **27**

Ash of *Fucus vesiculosus* contains 0·031 per cent of iodine.

1856. ANDERSON, THOMAS, *M.D., chemist to the Highland and Agricultural Society of Scotland.* On the composition of seaweeds, and their use as manure. *Trans. Highland Agric. Soc. Scot.*, 1856, v. 21, pp. 349–364. **28**

Percentage figures are given for the iodine content of the ash of Scottish *Fucus nodosus, Fucus vesiculosus* and *Laminaria digitata*. Manurial value of seaweed and of kelp is discussed.

1862. STANFORD, EDWARD C. C., *F.C.S., Glasgow.* On the economic applications of seaweed. *J. Soc. Arts*, 1862, v. 10, pp. 185–195; discussion pp. 195–199. **29**

Data are given for the iodine content of the soluble ash in several species of *Laminaria, Fucus, Zostera* and *Rhodomela*, and of the products of destructive distillation of these seaweeds. On an average 3·26 lb. of iodine were obtained by the distillation of a ton of the dried weed.

1865. MARCHAND, EUGÈNE. Composition des cendres de *Fucus*. [Composition of *Fucus* ash.] *J. Pharm. Chim.*, Paris, 1865, 4th Series, v. 2, pp. 276–278. **30**

Five species of *Fucus* were analysed for the iodine content of the ash. Values ranged from 0·659 per cent in *Fucus siliquosus* to 5·352 per cent in *Fucus digitatus*.

1877. STANFORD, EDWARD C. C., *F.C.S., Glasgow.* Ueber Jodfabrikation. [Iodine production.] *Dingler's polytechn. J.*, 1877, v. 226, pp. 85–94. **31**

The average iodine contents of ten species of seaweed from various localities are given. Values for dried weed ranged from 0·0297 per cent in *Fucus vesiculosus* to 0·4535 per cent in *Laminaria digitata.*

1877. STANFORD, E. C. C. On the manufacture of iodine. *Chem. News*, 1877, v. 35, pp. 172–175. **32**

Deep sea algae have a greater proportion of iodine than those growing in shallow water.

1878. PELLIEUX, J., and A. MAZÉ-LAUNAY, *Kerhuon, France*. L'industrie française de l'iode à l'Exposition de 1878. [The French iodine industry at the 1878 Exhibition.] Brest: *Imprimerie et Lithographie J.-P. Gadreau*, 1878, 38 pp. **33**

Original analytical data are given for the iodine content of several species of *Fucus* and *Laminaria*, as well as of *Alaria esculenta*, *Halidrys siliquosa* and *Saccorhiza bulbosa*.

1879. SCHOTT, *Dr*. OTTO. Jodbestimmung im Varec. [The determination of iodine in kelp.] *Ztschr. anal. Chem.*, 1879, v. 18, pp. 443–446. **34**

Kelp from Cudillero (Asturias, north coast of Spain) had an average iodine content of 0·35 per cent.

1881. ALLARY, E. Analyses d'algues marines. [Analysis of marine algae.] *Bull. Soc. Chim. Paris*, 1881, v. 35, pp. 11–12. **35**

The iodine contents of various species of *Laminaria* and *Fucus* collected on the Breton coast are recorded.

1884. STANFORD, EDWARD C. C., *F.C.S., Glasgow*. On the economic applications of seaweed. *J. Soc. Arts*, 1884, v. 32, pp. 717–730; discussion pp. 730–732. **36**

Gives extensive and interesting statistics of the Scottish kelp industry, and tabulates the iodine content of several species of seaweed.

1889. ITALLIE, L. VAN, *apothecary, Harlingen, Holland*. Über das Vorkommen von Iodium in *Fucus Vesiculosus* und *Chondrus Crispus*. [The occurrence of iodine in *Fucus vesiculosus* and *Chondrus crispus*.] *Arch. Pharm.*, Berlin, 1889, v. 227, pp. 1132–1134. **37**

Iodine is present in *Fucus vesiculosus* as iodide. Percentage on a dry matter basis was 0·0113. Amount in *Chondrus crispus* was too small to estimate.

1894. BRIONES, N. Sur le cochayuyo. [On cochayuyo.] *Actes Soc. Sci. Chili*, 1894, v. 4, pp. cviii–cix. **38**

A sample of *Durvillea utilis* was analysed for iodine content. None was found.

1895. GAUTIER, FERDINAND. Rapport de la Commission nommée par la Société Scientifique du Chili pour la détermination de l'iode dans le cochayuyo. [Report of the Commission appointed by the Scientific Society of Chile for the determination of iodine in cochayuyo (*Durvillea utilis*).] *Actes Soc. Sci. Chili*, 1895, v. 5, pp. cxiv–cxix (published 1897). **39**

Results of supervised repeat investigations indicate that iodine is not present merely in traces but in quantity (up to 0·0028 per cent) easily capable of determination.

1895. LEON, CRISÓLOGO. Yodo y cochayuyo. [Iodine and cochayuyo.] *Actes Soc. Sci. Chili*, 1895, v. 5, p. cviii (published 1897). **40**

1895. LEON, CRISÓLOGO. El yodo del cochayuyo. [The iodine in cochayuyo.] *Actes Soc. Sci. Chili*, 1895, v. 5, p. cx (published 1897). **41**

This and the preceding entry contribute to a discussion initiated by Martens (see following entry). Iodine in cochayuyo is found mostly in the root and stalk, but not in the branches.

1895. MARTENS, PABLO. ¿Hay yodo en el cochayuyo? [Is there iodine in cochayuyo?] *Actes Soc. Sci. Chili*, 1895, v. 5, p. xcii (published 1897). **42**

The author found 0·08 per cent of iodine in the ash of this Chilean seaweed food.

1895. MARTENS, PABLO, and FRANCISCO SERVAT. De la existencia del yodo en el cochayuyo (*Durvillea utilis*). [The presence of iodine in *Durvillea utilis*.] *Actes Soc. Sci. Chili*, 1895, v. 5, pp. 188–197 (published 1897). **43**

Iodine content in eight samples of air-dried weed varied from 0·00114 to 0·01376 (average 0·00596) per cent, the highest values being obtained for samples ashed in the presence of sodium carbonate.

1900. CUNIASSE, L. Analyse des algues marines. [Analysis of marine algae.] *Ann. Chim. Anal.*, 1900, v. 5, pp. 213–215. **44**

Iodine content of the ash of six species of *Fucus* rich in iodine varied from 0·382 to 1·408 per cent, and of three species poor in iodine from 0·070 to 0·157 per cent.

1907. TUNMANN, *Dr*. —. Ueber das Jod und den Nachweis desselben in der *Laminaria*. [Detection of iodine in the *Laminaria*.] *Pharm. Zentralhalle*, 1907, v. 48, pp. 505–509. **45**

Percentage of iodine, on a dry matter basis, varied in the stems from 0·059 to 0·108 and in the leaves from 0·071 to 0·154.

1908. WHITE, C. J., *B.Sc., University of Sydney, N.S.W.* On the composition of the ash of a New South Wales seaweed *Ecklonia exasperata*, and the percentage of iodine present. *J. Proc. Roy. Soc. New South Wales*, 1908, v. 41, pp. 95–99. **46**

Dried weed contains 0·89 per cent of iodine.

1909. BALCH, DAVID M., *S.B., Coronado Beach, California*. On the chemistry of certain algae of the Pacific coast. *J. Indust. Engin. Chem.*, 1909, v. 1, pp. 777–787. **47**

Data are given for the iodine content of the ash in *Pelagophycus porra*, *Nereocystis luetkeana* and *Macrocystis pyrifera*.

1912. TURRENTINE, J. W., *Bureau of Soils, U.S. Department of Agriculture, Washington, D.C.* The composition of the Pacific kelps. *J. Indust. Engin. Chem.*, 1912, v. 4, pp. 431–435. **48**

Original data are given for the iodine content of about 30 different varieties of seaweeds found on the Pacific coast of N. America. Seaweeds from southern regions appeared to be richer in iodine than those from northern regions.

1913. KNUDSEN, HENRIK. Determination of iodine in seaweed. *Chem. Engin.*, 1913, v. 17, pp. 119–122. **49**

Gives the percentage of ash and of iodine in the ash

of three species each of *Laminaria* and *Fucus* found on the Norwegian coast.

1913. PARKER, E. G., and J. R. LINDEMUTH, *Bureau of Soils, U.S. Department of Agriculture, Washington, D.C.* Analyses of certain of the Pacific coast kelps. *J. Indust. Engin. Chem.*, 1913, v. 5, pp. 287–289. **50**

Original data are tabulated for the iodine content of 16 samples of *Nereocystis luetkeana* and 23 of *Macrocystis pyrifera*. Percentage figures, on a dry matter basis, varied from 0·13 to 0·30 in *Nereocystis* and from 0·14 to 0·27 in *Macrocystis*.

1914. CAMERON, A. T., *University of Manitoba*. Contributions to the biochemistry of iodine. 1. The distribution of iodine in plant and animal tissues. *J. Biol. Chem.*, 1914, v. 18, pp. 335–380. **51**

Iodine contents of various plants (mostly marine) were determined by Hunter's method. Marine algae contained amounts greater than 0·001 per cent, the *Laminaria* showing a higher average value than other brown algae. On account of their environment marine algae contain more iodine than freshwater or land plants.

1914. MERZ, A. R., *Bureau of Soils, U.S. Department of Agriculture, Washington, D.C.* On the composition of giant kelps. *J. Indust. Engin. Chem.*, 1914, v. 6, pp. 19–20. **52**

Original data are recorded on the iodine content of *Macrocystis, Nereocystis, Alaria* and *Fucus*.

1915. BURD, JOHN S. The economic value of Pacific coast kelps. *California Agric. Exp. Stat.*, Bulletin No. 248, 1915, pp. 183–215. **53**

Gives the percentage iodine content of fresh, oven-dried and water-free samples of *Macrocystis pyrifera, Pelagophycus porra, Egregia laevigata, Nereocystis luetkeana, Egregia menziesii, Laminaria andersonii* and *Iridaea*.

1915. CAMERON, A. T., *University of Manitoba*. Contributions to the biochemistry of iodine. 2. The distribution of iodine in plant and animal tissues. Part 2. *J. Biol. Chem.*, 1915, v. 23, pp. 1–39. **54**

Iodine is invariably present in all marine algae. Of the brown algae only the *Laminariaceae* (and one or two *Fucaceae*) contain amounts greater than 0·1 per cent. Of the red algae only the *Rhodymeniaceae* and *Delesseraceae* contain as much.

1916. HENDRICK, JAMES, *B.Sc., F.I.C., professor of agriculture, Aberdeen University*. The composition and use of certain seaweeds. *J. Board Agric.*, London, 1916, v. 22, pp. 1095–1107. **55**

Gives the iodine content of *Laminaria digitata, L. stenophylla, Fucus vesiculosus, F. nodosus* and *F. serratus*. *Laminaria* have a much higher iodine content than *Fucus*. A paper read to the British Association, Manchester, 1915.

1916. HENDRICK, JAMES. The value of seaweeds as raw materials for chemical industry. *J. Soc. Chem. Indust.*, London, 1916, v. 35, pp. 565–574. **56**

The stems of *Laminaria digitata* and *L. stenophylla* are rich in iodine. Seaweeds of the *Fucus* family contain considerably less. Quantitative data are given.

1916. ITALLIE, L. VAN, and J. VAN DER ZANDE, *pharmacy laboratory, Leiden University*. Het iodiumgehalte van zeegras. [The iodine content of seaweed.] *Pharm. Weekblad Nederland*, 1916, v. 53, pp. 705–708. **57**

Iodine content of dried *Zostera marina* collected on the shores of the Zuider Zee was 0·0019 per cent.

1916. MIYAMA, KISABURO, *Kōgakuhakushi, Japan*. [Seaweeds.] *J. Chem. Indust.*, Tokyo, 1916, v. 19, pp. 1044–1066. In Japanese: English summary in Abstract Section, p. 48. **58**

Of all Japanese seaweeds, species of *Laminaria* and *Arthrothamnus* contain the most iodine; for example, dried *Arthrothamnus bifidus* Rupr. contains 0·6 per cent. Other very good sources of iodine are *Kjellmaniella gyrata* Miyabe and *Ecklonia cava* Okam.

1917. [AVERKIEV, N. D.] АВЕРКІЕВЪ, Н. Д., *Ekaterinoslav (Dnepropetrovsk) Experimental Station for the production of Russian iodine for army needs*. Изслѣдованіе водорослей морей россійскаго государства. [Researches on seaweeds of the seas of the Russian realm.] *Zhurnal Russkovo Fis.-Khim. Obshchestva*, 1917, v. 49, pp. 175–183. **59**

Air-dried Black Sea *Phyllophora* contain from 18–26 per cent of ash (average 20 per cent). The iodine content of the ash varies between 0·14 and 1·5 (average 0·5) per cent, and is higher in the spring and early summer than in the winter months. Black Sea *Phyllophora* contain 50 per cent more iodine than those in the White Sea.

1917. DESMOIRES, A., *pharmacist*. De la teneur en iode des algues de Bretagne. [The iodine content of the seaweeds of Brittany.] *Thesis, Montpellier College of Pharmacy*, 1917, 111 pp. **60**

Original analytical data are given for the iodine content of the ash in members of the *Chlorophyceae, Phaeophyceae, Laminariaceae, Fucaceae* and *Florideae* found on the Breton coast. Variations with age, season and locality are also shown for several species of *Fucus* and *Laminaria*.

1917. [SHKATELOV, V.] ШКАТЕЛОВЪ, В. О содержаніи солей калія, брома и іода въ Черноморской водоросли *Cystoseira barbata*. [The contents of potassium, bromine and iodine salts in the Black Sea seaweed *Cystoseira barbata*.] *Zhurnal Russkovo Fis.-Khim. Obshchestva*, 1917, v. 49, pp. 122–130. **61**

Cystoseira barbata contains 0·00772 per cent of iodine on a dry matter basis.

1917. WIEBULL, MATS. Om halten af jod i svensk tång och bestämning däraf. [The iodine content of Swedish seaweed and its determination.] *Svensk Kem. Tidskr.*, 1917, v. 29, pp. 79–82. **62**

Percentages of iodine in the ash of *Laminaria saccharina, Fucus serratus, Fucus vesiculosus, Halidrys siliquosa* and *Furcellaria* were 0·0–5·0, 0·07–0·2, 0·0–0·12, 0·08 and 0·06, respectively.

1918. DOHERTY, WILLIAM. Seaweed as a source of iodine. *Chem. Engin. Mining Rev.*, 1918, v. 11, p. 53. **63**

A sample of *Ecklonia radiata* collected on the Australian coast contained 0·06 and 0·40 per cent of iodine in the fresh and dry weed, respectively.

1919. ALBERT, *Dr*. R., and *Dr*. M. KRAUSE, *Forstakademie, Eberswalde*. Untersuchungen deutscher Seetange. [Investigations of German seaweeds.] *Chemikerzeitung*, 1919, v. 43, pp. 97–99. **64**

The iodine content of samples of ten species of seaweed collected in Heligoland varied from 0·01 per cent (dry matter basis) in *Himanthalia lorea* to 1·15 per cent in *Laminaria hyperborea*.

1919. BOAS, I. H., *M.Sc., lecturer in chemistry, Perth Technical School*. Examination of Western Australian seaweeds for potash and iodine. *Western Australia Geological Survey*, Bulletin No. 77, 1919, pp. 35–38. **65**

Appendix I to "Sources of industrial potash in Western Australia", by E. S. Simpson. Five samples of *Ecklonia radiata* gave iodine contents of dry matter varying between 0·26 and 0·86 per cent, and of ash from 0·97 to 3·39 per cent.

1923. LOSANA, L., and P. E. CROCE, *laboratory for the chemistry of building materials, Royal Polytechnic, Turin*. Utilizzazione di ceneri di piante marine della Libia. [Utilization of the ashes of marine plants from Libya.] *Ann. Chim. Appl*., 1923, v. 13, pp. 37–39. **66**

From 25 kilogrammes of the ash of *Zostera marina* mixed with other algae characteristic of the Libyan coast 32 grammes of iodine were obtained.

1923. MOLISCH, *Dr*. HANS, *professor and director, Institute of Plant Pathology, Vienna University*. Mikrochemie der Pflanzen. [Microchemistry of plants.] Jena: *G. Fischer*, 1923, 3rd edition, xii + 438 pp. **67**

Iodine in plants is dealt with on pp. 84–88, and the iodine contents of 30 species of seaweed are tabulated.

1926. COLLADO, ESTEBAN G., *University of the Philippines, Manila*. Studies on the nutritive properties of seaweed. *Philippine Agric*., 1926, v. 15, pp. 129–148. **68**

Gracilaria confervoides, *Laurencia* and *Sargassum* contained, respectively, 0·020, 0·439 and 0·390 per cent of iodine.

1927. PARGA PONDAL, ISIDRO, *professor, Faculty of Science, Santiago, Spain*. El contenido en iodo de las principales algas marinas de las costas de Galicia. [The iodine content of the principal marine algae of the Galician coasts.] Santiago, Spain: *Tip. de "El Eco Franciscano"*, 1927, 30 pp. **69**

Original data are given on the iodine content of dried (at 105° C) samples of 22 species. Percentage values varied between 0·001 in *Codium tomentosum* and 0·55 in *Laminaria flexicaulis*.

1927. READ, BERNARD E., and GEORGE K. HOW, *department of pharmacology, Peking Union Medical College, Peking*. The iodine, arsenic, iron, calcium and sulphur content of Chinese medicinal algae. *Chinese J. Physiol*., 1927, v. 1, pp. 99–108. **70**

The percentage iodine contents of dried Chinese algae were as follows: *Laminaria japonica*, 1·234; *L. religiosum*, 1·158; Hai-pai-t'sai, 0·212; *Nostoc commune flagelliforme*, 0·142; *Sargassum siliquastrum*, 0·339.

1929. DANGEARD, PIERRE, *Faculty of Science, University of Paris*. Sur quelques algues iodifères nouvelles. [Some new iodiferous algae.] *C. R. Acad. Sci*., Paris, 1929, v. 189, pp. 862–864. **71**

More than 120 species of marine algae from Roscoff and Quiberon were examined qualitatively for iodine by microchemical methods. The results are discussed.

1930. [AVERKIEV, N. D.] АВЕРКИЕВ, Н. Д. О добыче иода из водорослей Черного Моря "красная Филлофора." [Extraction of iodine from the red *Phyllophora* of the Black Sea.] *Zhurnal Priklad. Khim*., 1930, v. 3, pp. 589–604. **72**

Air-dried Black Sea *Phyllophora* contain an average of 20 per cent of ash and 0·5 per cent of iodine in the ash. The ash content falls from 24·6 to 19·1, and the iodine content of the ash rises from 0·22 to 1·32 per cent as one proceeds from coastal waters to the open sea. Statistics of Russian iodine production are given.

1930. BUEN, VICTOR DE, *engineer-director, Sociedad Española del Yodo, S.A*. El valor industrial de la flora marina. [The industrial value of marine flora.] *Rev. Ingen. Indust*., 1930, v. 1, no. 6, pp. 5–12. **73**

Contains valuable original data on the iodine content of various species of seaweed. It requires 1000 tons of *fresh* Laminarian weed to obtain 1 ton of iodine. This is in good agreement with other authorities.

1930. DIXIT, S. C., *Wilson College, Bombay*. A note on the percentage of iodine in certain algae. *J. Indian Chem. Soc*., 1930, v. 7, p. 959. **74**

The iodine contents of air-dried samples of *Fucus*, *Sargassum*, *Halymenia* and *Gracilaria* and of *Asparagopsis sansfordiana* collected on the coast of the Bombay Presidency compare favourably with those of seaweeds from other countries.

1931. BUTLER, MARGARET R., *department of biochemistry, Dalhousie University, Halifax, N.S*. Comparison of the chemical composition of some marine algae. *Plant Physiol*., 1931, v. 6, pp. 295–305. **75**

Percentage iodine content on a dry weight basis, determined by Kendall's method in twelve species of seaweed collected on the North Atlantic coast, varied from 0·0085 in *Porphyra laciniata* to 0·349 in *Laminaria digitata*. Average value was less than 0·1 per cent.

1931. CLOSS, KARL. Über das Vorkommen des Jods im Meer und in Meeresorganismen. [Occurrence of iodine in the sea and in marine organisms.] *Arch. Math. Naturvidenskab*., 1931, v. 40, no. 5, 150 pp. **76**

Original data are tabulated on the iodine contents of small marine algae, such as *Diatomaceae*, as well as of *Zostera marina* and the various parts of *Laminaria digitata*.

1931. DONOVAN, W., *M.Sc., F.I.C., dominion analyst and chief gas examiner*. New Zealand seaweed (dried) and seaweed gels. *Dominion Laboratory, Department of Scientific and Industrial Research, New Zealand*, 65th Annual Report, for 1931 (1932), pp. 9–10. **77**

Dried *Gigartina clarifera* contains 0·0120 per cent of iodine.

1931. SUZUKI, KOZO, TETSUSABURO NISHIKAWA and SADAO AOKI [Seaweeds as animal feed. 1. Chemical

composition of the seaweeds.] *J. Agric. Chem. Soc. Japan*, 1931, v. 7, pp. 622–628. In Japanese. **78**
Iodine content of eight Pacific coast seaweeds ranged from 0·00066 per cent in *Gracilaria confervoides* Grev. to 0·67106 per cent in *Eisenia bicyclis* Kjellm.

1932. [LIPSKI, V. I.] Липский, В. И., *Botanical Garden, Odessa.* Иод и агар-агар из водорослей Черного Моря. [Iodine and agar-agar from seaweeds of the Black Sea.] *Dokladi Akad. Nauk SSSR*, 1932, Series A, pp. 60–64. **79**
Phyllophora from shallow water and coastal belt deposits contain less iodine than open sea *Phyllophora*. No quantitative data are given.

1933. [BRUEVICH, S. V., A. V. TROFIMOV and A. N. GARTMAN.] Бруевич, С. В., А. В. Трофимов and А. Н. Гартман, *State Oceanographic Institute, Moscow.* Содержание иода в водорослях Белого Моря и Мурманского побережья. [The iodine content of seaweeds of the White Sea and Murman Coast.] *Trudi Gos. Okeanogr. Inst.*, 1933, v. 3, no. 3, pp. 61–76; English summary pp. 77–78. **80**
Average percentage iodine contents of the most important species, for all regions were: *Laminaria saccharina*, 0·264; *L. digitata*, 0·347; *Alaria esculenta*, 0·059; *Desmarestia aculeata*, 0·463; *Ascophyllum nodosum*, 0·052.

1933. FABRIS, *Dr.* UGO. L'utilizzazione delle alghe marine della Somalia Italiana. [Utilization of the marine algae of Italian Somaliland.] *Riv. Ital. Essenze Profumi*, 1933, v. 15, pp. 87–93. **81**
Data are given on the iodine content of various types of seaweed found along the coast of Somaliland.

1933. HERCUS, C. E., and H. A. A. AITKEN, *University of Otago, New Zealand.* Miscellaneous studies on the iodine and goitre problem in New Zealand. *J. Hyg.*, Cambridge, 1933, v. 33, pp. 55–79. **82**
The iodine contents of Pacific coast seaweeds on a dry weight basis (pp. 60–64) range from 0·0023 per cent in *Durvillea antarctica* to 0·103 per cent in *Cystophora retroflexa*. Dialysis experiments indicate that probably 70 to 80 per cent of the total iodine in *Cystophora retroflexa* is in inorganic form.

1933. ITANO, ARAO, *Ph.D., Ōhara Institute for Agricultural Research, Kurashiki, Okayama.* Reports on general survey and investigation on agar. *Ber. Ōhara Inst. landwirtsch. Forsch. Kurashiki*, 1933, v. 6, pp. 59–72. In English. **83**
On pp. 62–69 results are given of investigations on the iodine contents of agar and some seaweeds used in its manufacture. In three different samples of commercial agar values ranged from 11·8 to 42·8 parts per million of dried material and in four species of *Gelidium* from 430·2 to 796·2 parts per million.

1933. ITANO, ARAO. Investigation on agar as to its iodine content. *Proc. Imp. Acad. Japan*, 1933, v. 9, pp. 398–401. **84**
See preceding entry.

1933. [KOMAROVSKI, A. S., A. F. TYULPINA and G. B. FISHER.] Комаровський, А. С., А. Ф. Тюльпіна and Г. Б. Фішер, *iodine laboratory, Ukrainian Scientific Research Institute of Chemistry and Radiology, Odessa.* Визначення вмісту йоду у водоростях Чорного Моря. [The determination of the iodine content of the seaweeds of the Black Sea.] *Ukrainski Khem. Zhurnal*, 1933, v. 8, scientific part, pp. 151–154. **85**
Open sea, deep water and shallow water *Phyllophora* contain, respectively, 0·519, 0·272 to 0·520 and 0·150 to 0·270 per cent of iodine on a dry matter basis.

1933. MCCLENDON, J. F., *laboratory of physiological chemistry, University of Minnesota, Minneapolis.* Iodine and goiter with especial reference to the Far East. *J. Biol. Chem.*, 1933, v. 102, pp. 91–99. **86**
Original data on the iodine contents of 79 species of seaweed from 14 localities on the Japanese coast are given.

1933. [SKOPINTSEV, B. A.] Скопинцев, Б. А., *State Oceanographic Institute, Moscow.* Об иодосодержащих водорослях. Краткий обзор журнальной литературы за период 1920–1930 г. [The iodine-containing seaweeds. A short review of the periodical literature for the period 1920 to 1930.] *Trudi Gos. Okeanogr. Inst.*, 1933, v. 3, no. 3, pp. 52–60. **87**
Gives 51 references (15 to Russian papers).

1934. HAWAII AGRICULTURAL EXPERIMENT STATION. Iodine content of some Hawaiian marine food products. *Hawaii Agric. Exp. Stat.*, Report for 1934 (1935), p. 27. **88**
Iodine contents of twelve of the most widely used seaweeds are tabulated. Values range from 1970 parts per 1000 million of dry sample in Huna seaweed to 487,000 parts per 1000 million in Kala seaweed.

1934. [OPOTSKI, V., S. POGREBINSKA and A. TYULPINA.] Опоцький, В., С. Погребінська and А. Тюльпіна, *iodine laboratory, Ukrainian Scientific Research Institute of Chemistry, Odessa.* До характеристики Чорноморської Філофори. [Characteristics of the Black Sea *Phyllophora*.] *Ukrainski Khem. Zhurnal*, 1934, v. 9, scientific-technical part, pp. 73–78. **89**
The iodine contents of *Phyllophora* from bay deposits and the open sea ranged from 0·150 to 0·294 and 0·311 to 0·367 per cent, respectively, on a dry matter basis.

1934. [ZINOVA, E. S.] Зинова, Е. С. Новые обследования водорослей Белого моря по Летнему берегу и их использование. [New studies of White Sea algae along the Letni coast and their utilization.] *Gos. Hidrol. Inst. Issled. Morei SSSR*, 1934, no. 20, pp. 65–84; French summary p. 85. **90**
Average iodine content of the ash of seaweeds collected on the Letni coast was usually 0·3 per cent and occasionally as high as 0·5 per cent.

1935. TANG, PEI-SUNG, and PAO-CHUN WHANG, *Wuhan University, Wuchang; and Soochow University, Soochow.* Iodine contents of ten species of Chinese marine algae. *Chinese J. Physiol.*, 1935, v. 9, pp. 285–290. **91**
Values obtained by von Fellenberg's method ranged from 21 parts per million dry weight in *Porphyra suborbiculata* Kjellm. to 1600 parts per million in *Gelidium amansii*.

1935. Tang, Pei-Sung, and C. S. Chang, *Wuhan University, Wuchang*. Further observations on the iodine contents of Chinese marine algae. *Chinese J. Physiol.*, 1935, v. 9, pp. 369–374. **92**

Twelve more species were analysed (see preceding entry). Values varied from 9 parts per million dry weight in *Eucheuma gelatinae* to 1104 parts per million in *Sargassum graminifolium*.

1936. Fester, Gustavo A., and Jose Cruellas. El alga *Macrocystis pyrifera* y el salitre de Chile. [The alga *Macrocystis pyrifera* and Chile saltpetre.] *Rev. Fac. Quim. Indust. Agric. Univ. Santa Fé*, 1936, v. 4, pp. 202–205. **93**

The fresh material contains 0·03 per cent of iodine.

1936. Madras Fisheries Department. Kelp and iodine. *Madras Fisheries Department*, Administration Report for 1935–36 (1937), pp. 25–26. **94**

Samples of *Sargassum* and *Turbinaria* from Krusadai Island contain, respectively, 0·017 and 0·014 per cent of iodine on a fresh matter basis. *Enhaulis koenigi* contains only a trace.

1936. Tang, T. H., F. C. Kou and P. S. Tang, *Shantung University, Tsingtao; and Wuhan University, Wuchang*. Iodine content of some marine algae of the Shantung coast. *Chinese J. Physiol.*, 1936, v. 10, pp. 377–378. **95**

A continuation of earlier work (see entries **91** and **92**). Values ranged from 16·8 parts per million dry weight in *Ulva lactuca* L. to 462·0 parts per million in *Sargassum* sp.

1936. Tseng, C. K., *Shantung University*, and P. S. Tang, *Wuhan University, Wuchang*. On the occurrence of two laminariaceous plants on China coast with a note on their iodine content. *Lingnan Sci. J.*, 1936, v. 15, pp. 219–224. **96**

Percentage of iodine, on a dry matter basis, varies from 0·08 to 0·20 in *Laminaria japonica* and from 0·0020 to 0·0044 in *Undaria pinnatifida*.

1937. Lunde, *Dr.* Gulbrand, *research laboratory, Norwegian Canning Industry, Stavanger*. Der Meerestang als Rohstoffquelle. [Seaweed as a source of raw materials.] *Angewandte Chem.*, 1937, v. 50, pp. 731–734. **97**

Ash of *Laminaria digitata* contains 1·5 to 2·0 per cent of iodine.

1938. Weber, *Prof.* Ulrich, *Würzburg*, and H. Gerhard, *Pharmaceutical Institute, Würzburg*. Die Fucusarten der deutschen Küsten und ihr Jodgehalt. [*Fucus* species of the German coast and their iodine content.] *Deutsche Apotheker-Ztg.*, 1938, v. 53, pp. 1351–1354; 1373–1375. **98**

Iodine contents of *Fucus vesiculosus, F. serratus, F. platycarpus* and *F. mytili* collected on the North Sea coast were, respectively, 0·109, 0·107, 0·046 and 0·083 per cent on a dry matter basis. The corresponding values for *F. vesiculosus* and *F. serratus* collected on the Baltic coast were, respectively, 0·033 and 0·019 per cent.

1939. McClendon, J. F., *professor of physiological chemistry, University of Minnesota*. Iodine and the incidence of goiter. Minneapolis: *The University of Minnesota Press*. London: *Oxford University Press*, 1939, vi + 126 pp. **99**

A large number of published data on the iodine content of seaweeds are tabulated in convenient form on pp. 30–32.

1939. Narasimham, M., and S. N. Pal, *Pittapur Rajah's College, Cocanada, Madras*. A note on the analysis of certain algae. *J. Indian Chem. Soc.*, 1939, v. 16, p. 161. **100**

Four species of drift seaweeds collected on the Coromandel coast of the Madras Presidency were analysed for iodine content. None was found in *Padina, Ulva* and *Enteromorpha*; but there was 0·044 per cent in an air-dried sample of *Polysiphonia*.

1939. Seifert, *Dr.* Rudolf, *scientific department, Caesar and Loretz, Halle-on-Saale*. Zur Jodbestimmung in *Fucus vesiculosus*. [Determination of iodine in *Fucus vesiculosus*.] *Süddeutsche Apotheker-Ztg.*, 1939, v. 79, pp. 555–558. **101**

Values for the air-dried weed range from 0·01 to 0·06 per cent.

1941. Bombay Province. Department of Industries. Recovery of iodine from seaweeds. *Bombay Province, Department of Industries*, Annual Report for 1940–41 (1942), p. 15. **102**

One or two unspecified varieties of seaweed collected on the west coast of India were found to contain iodine. Percentage in the ash varied from 0·1 to 0·3.

1941. Rasmussen, H. Baggesgaard, and Gudrun Bjerresø, *Pharmaceutical School of Denmark, Copenhagen*. Om iodindholdet i tang, samt lidt om tangens øvrige indholdsstoffer. [The iodine content of seaweed, with notes on other constituents.] *Dansk Tidsskr. Farm.*, 1941, v. 15, pp. 121–158. **103**

Samples (air-dried) of several species of *Fucus* and *Laminaria*, as well as of *Ascophyllum nodosum* and *Zostera marina*, were analysed. Percentage of iodine varied from 0·310 in *Laminaria hyperborea* to 0·016 in *Zostera marina*.

1942. Kollo, Constantin, and Konstanta Anitescu, *Pharmaceutical Faculty, University of Bucharest*. Die Meeresalgen der rumänischen Schwarze-Meer-Küste und ihr Jodgehalt. (Vorläufige Mitteilung.) [The iodine content of the marine algae of the Rumanian Black Sea coast. Preliminary communication.] *Arch. Pharm.*, Berlin, 1942, v. 280, pp. 317–320. **104**

A sample of *Cystoseira barbata* contained 0·0367 per cent of iodine on a dry matter basis and a composite sample of *Ceramium* spp. and *Enteromorpha* spp. 0·0478 per cent.

1942. Rigg, George B., *department of botany, University of Washington*. Plant resources of the sea along the northwest coast and Alaska. *California Fish and Game*, 1942, v. 28, pp. 206–209. **105**

Fresh samples of *Nereocystis luetkeana* and *Macrocystis pyrifera* contain, respectively, 0·0110 and 0·0305 per cent of iodine. *Alaria fistulosa* contains only a trace.

1942. WEI, WEN-TEH. [The composition of Chinese marine algae.] *Golden Sea Research Inst. China*, Bulletin No. 24, 1942, 4 pp. In Chinese. **106**

Iodine content ranged from 0·0043 to 0·4595 per cent in 35 seaweeds examined.

1944. TAKAHASHI, TAKEO. [Studies on the chemical composition of Japanese brown seaweeds. 3. Chemical composition of Japanese seaweeds serving as a source of potassium.] *J. Agric. Chem. Soc. Japan*, 1944, v. 20, pp. 183–186. In Japanese. Cited from *Chem. Abstr.*, 1947, v. 41, col. 4897. **107**

Dried samples of ten species of edible Japanese seaweeds were analysed for iodine content. The three highest percentages were 0·416, 0·297 and 0·227 for *Arthrothamnus bifidus*, *Ecklonia cava* and *Eisenia bicyclis*, respectively.

SEASONAL VARIATION 108–121

1906. SCURTI, F. Sulla funzione del iodio nelle alghe marine. [The role of iodine in seaweeds.] *Gazz. Chim. Ital.*, 1906, v. 36, part 2, pp. 619–625. **108**

Iodine content varies seasonally according to the reproductive development of the plant. Scurti believes that iodine excites reproductive development.

1919. LAPICQUE, LOUIS. Variation saisonnière dans la composition chimique des algues marines. [Seasonal variation in the chemical composition of seaweeds.] *C. R. Acad. Sci.*, Paris, 1919, v. 169, pp. 1426–1428. **109**

From spring to September the mineral content of *Laminaria flexicaulis* decreases. There is no specific mention of iodine.

1921. FREUNDLER, P., Y. MÉNAGER and Y. LAURENT. L'iode chez les Laminaires. [The iodine content of *Laminaria*.] *C. R. Acad. Sci.*, Paris, 1921, v. 173, pp. 931–932. **110**

Determinations were made on a large number of samples of *Laminaria flexicaulis*, *L. saccharina* and *L. cloustoni*. During drying, the algae lost up to 50 per cent of their iodine content. Samples collected in July had a higher content than those collected in March. Iodine content decreased with age of the plant.

1921. FREUNDLER, P., Y. MÉNAGER and Y. LAURENT. La composition des Laminaires. [Composition of *Laminaria*.] *C. R. Acad. Sci.*, Paris, 1921, v. 173, pp. 1116–1118. **111**

Maximum iodine content coincides with the period of maximum sun. The relation of iodine to the assimilation of chlorophyll is discussed.

1922. FREUNDLER, P., Y. LAURENT and Y. MÉNAGER. Étude biochimique des Laminaires. Variations des principaux constituants. Leur relations; leur dépendance des conditions extérieures; leur rôle. [Biochemical study of *Laminaria*. Variations of the principal constituents, their relationships, their dependence on external conditions and their role.] *Bull. Soc. Chim. France*, 1922, 4th Series, v. 31, pp. 1341–1347. **112**

Wide variations were noted in the iodine content of young plants of *Laminaria cloustoni* and *L. saccharina* collected at different times of the year off the Breton coast. The influence of ocean current movements on the iodine content of *Laminaria* is discussed. (See preceding entries.)

1924. FREUNDLER, P. Sur l'iode dosable des *Laminaria flexicaulis*. [Determinable quantities of iodine in *Laminaria flexicaulis*.] *C. R. Acad. Sci.*, Paris, 1924, v. 178, pp. 515–517. **113**

Laminaria flexicaulis contains 0·6 to 0·7 per cent of iodine on a dry matter basis. Slight variations are noted in samples collected between August and December.

1924. FREUNDLER, P. Variation de l'iode chez les *L. flexicaulis* à l'époque de la repousse annuelle; rôle de la zone stipo-frondale. [Variation in iodine content of *L. flexicaulis* at the time of the annual new growth: role of the stipo-frondal zone.] *C. R. Acad. Sci.*, Paris, 1924, v. 178, pp. 1625–1628. **114**

Variations observed in the iodine content of the frond and stipe (both with and without the stipo-frondal zone) of *Laminaria flexicaulis* collected during February to April are attributed to differences in diastatic activity as the season advances.

1924. FREUNDLER, P. Sur les conditions de stabilisation de l'iode chez *L. flexicaulis*. [The conditions of stabilization of iodine in *L. flexicaulis*.] *C. R. Acad. Sci.*, Paris, 1924, v. 179, pp. 1421–1422. **115**

Three methods of stabilizing the iodine in *Laminaria* are described. No definite conclusion is drawn from the results.

1925. FREUNDLER, P., Y. MÉNAGER, Y. LAURENT and J. LELIÈVRE. L'iode dissimulé des Laminaires. [The concealed iodine in *Laminaria*.] *Bull. Soc. Chim. France*, 1925, 4th Series, v. 37, pp. 1466–1482. **116**

Laminaria, especially *L. flexicaulis*, which have been stored in a closed container for 10 to 30 days give on analysis a value for iodine content 50 to 150 per cent higher than the fresh weed.

1925. LELIÈVRE, J., and Y. MÉNAGER. Application aux *L. flexicaulis* de la méthode d'analyse par combustion. [Application to *L. flexicaulis* of the combustion method of analysis.] *C. R. Acad. Sci.*, Paris, 1925, v. 180, pp. 536–538. **117**

Values for iodine content obtained by the authors' combustion method (*C. R. Acad. Sci.*, Paris, 1924, v. 178, pp. 1315–1316) confirm those obtained by incineration and by treatment with bisulphite. From the results of analysis of samples collected in November, with and without the stipo-frondal zone, it is shown that the latter acts as a stabilizer of the iodine content.

1938. [VEDRINSKI, A. I.] ВЕДРИНСКИЙ, А. И. Химический состав промышленных видов водорослей Белого Моря. [The chemical composition of industrially important seaweeds of the White Sea.] *Trudi Arkhangelskovo Vodoroslevovo Nauch.-Issled. Inst.*, 1938, pp. 61–79; English summary p. 79. **118**

Seaweeds collected in late autumn have an iodine content four times greater than those collected in summer.

1948. BLACK, W. A. P., *Scottish Seaweed Research Association, Institute of Seaweed Research, Mussel-*

burgh, Midlothian. The seasonal variation in chemical constitution of some of the sub-littoral seaweeds common to Scotland. 1. *Laminaria cloustoni.* 2. *Laminaria digitata.* 3. *Laminaria saccharina* and *Saccorhiza bulbosa. J. Soc. Chem. Indust.*, 1948, v. 67, pp. 165–168; 169–172; 172–176. **119**

1. Iodine content shows a somewhat erratic seasonal variation between 0·5 and 1·0 per cent on a dry matter basis. It is at a maximum in the spring and in general is higher in the frond than in the stipe.

2. Iodine content of the fronds of *Laminaria digitata* varies, on a dry matter basis, from 0·8 to 1·1 per cent in open sea samples and from 0·6 to 0·7 per cent in sea loch samples, being at a maximum at the beginning of the year. In the stipes the variation throughout the year is from 0·3 to 0·7 per cent.

3. In *Laminaria saccharina* iodine content of the fronds varies from 0·20 to 0·50 per cent in sea loch samples and from 0·25 to 0·50 per cent in open sea samples, being at a maximum at the beginning of the year. In the stipes the variation throughout the year is from 0·20 to 0·50 per cent. In *Saccorhiza bulbosa* iodine content varies from 0·05 to 0·16 per cent in the fronds and from 0·09 to 0·13 per cent in the stipes.

1948. BLACK, W. A. P. The seasonal variation in chemical composition of some of the littoral seaweeds common to Scotland. 1. *Ascophyllum nodosum. J. Soc. Chem. Indust.*, 1948, v. 67, pp. 355–357. **120**

Iodine content varies between 0·07 and 0·20 per cent on a dry matter basis, and, in general, is highest from January to March. It is lower in loch samples than in open sea samples.

1949. BLACK, W. A. P., *Scottish Seaweed Research Association, Institute of Seaweed Research, Musselburgh, Midlothian.* Seasonal variation in chemical composition of some of the littoral seaweeds common to Scotland. 2. *Fucus serratus, Fucus vesiculosus, Fucus spiralis* and *Pelvetia canaliculata. J. Soc. Chem. Indust.*, 1949, v. 68, pp. 183–189. **121**

Iodine content showed very slight seasonal variation and was appreciably lower in all four species than in the *Laminaria* seaweeds previously examined (see entry 119).

FORM: LIBERATION: DISTRIBUTION 122–182

1894. GOLENKIN, M. Algologische Notizen. [Notes on algae.] *Bull. Soc. Imp. Nat. Moscou*, 1894, v. 8, pp. 257–270. **122**

On pp. 257–259 the liberation of free iodine by special cells in *Bonnemaisonia asparagoides* is noted.

1897. ESCHLE, *Dr. —, director of the District Health Institute, Baden.* Ueber den Jodgehalt einiger Algenarten. [The iodine content of certain algae.] *Ztschr. physiol. Chem.*, 1897, v. 23, pp. 30–37. **123**

Extraction and solubility tests with different solvents indicate that most if not all iodine in *Fucus vesiculosus* and *Laminaria digitata* is present in organic combination. There is no evidence as to the nature of the compounds.

1903. WEIS, EDMUND, *Institute of Pharmacology and Pharmacognosy, Vienna University.* Nachweis des Jods in *Fucus vesiculosus* und in den daraus hergestellten Präparaten. [Detection of iodine in *Fucus vesiculosus* and in the preparations made from it.] *Ztschr. allgem. österreich. Apotheker-Vereines*, 1903, v. 41, pp. 429–433. **124**

A dry extract of *Fucus vesiculosus*, prepared by Merck, contained 0·0889 per cent of iodine, present in organic combination.

1911. OSWALD, A., *agricultural chemistry laboratory, Zurich Technical College.* Gewinnung von 3, 5-Dijodtyrosin aus Jodeiweiss. 4. Die Verhältnisse beim Gorgonin und Spongin. [3:5-Diiodotyrosine from iodoproteins. 4. Gorgonin and spongin.] *Ztschr. physiol. Chem.*, 1911, v. 75, pp. 353–362. **125**

On pages 361–362 it is recorded that dried *Fucus vesiculosus* contained 0·1 per cent of iodine. There was no evidence of the presence of organically combined iodine.

1915. HOAGLAND, D. R., *Agricultural Experiment Station, University of California.* Organic constituents of Pacific coast kelps. *J. Agric. Research*, 1915, v. 4, pp. 39–58. **126**

The iodine of dried kelp was found to be almost entirely soluble in cold water or in 90 per cent alcohol.

1915. KYLIN, HARALD, *School of Medicine, University of Uppsala.* Über die Blasenzellen einiger Florideen und ihre Beziehung zur Abspaltung von Jod. [The bladder cells of certain *Florideae* and their relation to the liberation of iodine.] *Ark. Botanik*, 1915, v. 14, no. 5, pp. 1–13. **127**

Iodine content of the bladder cells of *Spermothamnion roseolum* was negligible. None was found in the cells of *Ceramium tenuissimum* and *Antithamnion plumula.*

1915. KYLIN, HARALD. Untersuchungen über die Biochemie der Meeresalgen. [Investigations on the biochemistry of marine algae.] *Ztschr. physiol. Chem.*, 1915, v. 94, pp. 337–425. **128**

Iodine is present in the younger but not in the older parts of the *Fucoideae*. It is present as free iodine or at least as labile iodine compounds in *Bonnemaisonia asparagoides* and *Spermothamnion roseolum.*

1916. OKUDA, YUZURU, and TOKU ETO. On the form of iodine in algae. *J. College Agric. Univ. Tokyo*, 1916, v. 5, pp. 341–353. **129**

Most of the iodine in species of *Ecklonia, Turbinaria* and *Sargassum* is in organic combination.

1925. SAUVAGEAU, CAMILLE (1861–1936), *professor of botany, University of Bordeaux.* Sur quelques algues floridées renfermant de l'iode à l'état libre. [Some *Florideae* containing free iodine.] *Bull. Stat. Biol. Arcachon*, 1925, v. 22, pp. 5–45. **130**

Free iodine exists in special vacuoles inside the young cells of *Asparagopsis armata, Bonnemaisonia asparagoides* and *Falkenbergia doubletii* and, probably, also in other species of *Asparagopsis.*

1925. SAUVAGEAU, CAMILLE. Sur la naturalisation en France d'une Floridée australasienne (*Asparagopsis armata* Harv.) et sur ses ioduques. [The naturalization in France of one of the Australasian Florideae (*Asparagopsis armata* Harv.) and its iodine-containing gland cells.] *C. R. Acad. Sci.*, Paris, 1925, v. 180, pp. 1887–1890. **131**

Free iodine is probably present in vacuoles in the cells of the fronds of *Asparagopsis armata* Harv.

1925. SAUVAGEAU, CAMILLE. Sur une Floridée (*Polysiphonia Doubletii* mscr.) renfermant de l'iode à l'état libre. [One of the Florideae (*Polysiphonia doubletii* mscr.) containing iodine in the free state.] *C. R. Acad. Sci.*, Paris, 1925, v. 181, pp. 293–295. **132**

The presence of free iodine in the young cells of *Polysiphonia doubletii* is demonstrated.

1926. CHEMIN, E., and R. LEGENDRE. Observations sur l'existence de l'iode libre chez *Falkenbergia Doubletii* Sauv. [Observations on the occurrence of free iodine in *Falkenbergia doubletii* Sauv.] *C. R. Acad. Sci.*, Paris, 1926, v. 183, pp. 904–906. **133**

Contrary to the findings of Sauvageau (see preceding entry) free iodine was not present in the samples of *Falkenbergia doubletii* examined, but was liberated when the plant was treated with an acid.

1926. SAUVAGEAU, CAMILLE, *professor of botany, University of Bordeaux*. À propos d'une note à MM. Chemin et Legendre sur l'existence de l'iode libre chez *Falkenbergia Doubletii* Sauv. [On Chemin and Legendre's paper concerning the occurrence of free iodine in *Falkenbergia doubletii* Sauv.] *C. R. Acad. Sci.*, Paris, 1926, v. 183, pp. 1006–1007. **134**

Chemin and Legendre's results (preceding entry) do not in any way invalidate this author's earlier findings.

1927. MANGENOT, G., *Botanical Library, Faculty of Science, University of Paris*. Les travaux récents sur la localisation de l'iode et du brome dans les cellules des algues marines. [Recent work on the localization of iodine and bromine in the cells of marine algae.] *Bull. Histol. Appl. Physiol. Path. Techn. Microsc.*, 1927, v. 4, pp. 52–71. **135**

A review of the literature on the form and distribution of iodine in marine algae and the localization of free iodine in some red algae.

1927. OLLIVIER, G. Sur les tetrasporanges du *Falkenbergia doubletii* Sauv. [The tetraspores of *Falkenbergia doubletii* Sauv.] *C. R. Acad. Sci.*, Paris, 1927, v. 184, pp. 469–470. **136**

No free or combined iodine is present in either the tetraspores or young plants of *Falkenbergia*.

1927. SAUVAGEAU, CAMILLE, *professor of botany, University of Bordeaux*. Sur le "*Fucus lutarius*" et sur l'iode libre de certaines algues. [*Fucus lutarius* and the free iodine in certain algae.] *Bull. Stat. Biol. Arcachon*, 1927, v. 24, pp. 75–84. **137**

The author replies to criticism by Chemin and Legendre (see entries **132** and **133**) and maintains the correctness of his previous findings.

1928. CHEMIN, E. Quelques précisions sur l'état de l'iode chez *Falkenbergia doubletii* Sauv. [The form of the iodine in *Falkenbergia doubletii* Sauv.] *Bull. Soc. Botan. France*, 1928, v. 75, pp. 540–542. **138**

Iodine does not exist in a free state and volatilization does not occur as a normal function in *Falkenbergia*.

1928. CHEMIN, E. Sur l'état de l'iode chez quelques Floridées. [The form of the iodine in certain *Florideae*.] *Rev. Gén. Botan.*, 1928, v. 40, pp. 129–145. **139**

In the *Florideae* studied, iodine is not present in the free state but in unstable combination from which it is liberated by weak acids in some species and only by stronger reagents in others.

1928. DANGEARD, PIERRE, *Faculty of Science, University of Paris*. Contribution à la connaissance du cycle de l'iode chez les algues marines. [The iodine cycle in marine algae.] *Botaniste*, 1928, v. 20, pp. 69–115. **140**

During their life processes brown algae liberate free iodine from cells situated in a layer of the thallus near the periphery. The liberation is apparently not affected by light or movements of the tide.

1928. DANGEARD, PIERRE. Notes au sujet de l'émission d'iode libre par les algues. [The liberation of free iodine by algae.] *Bull. Soc. Botan. France*, 1928, v. 75, pp. 509–519. **141**

See preceding entry.

1928. DANGEARD, PIERRE. Sur l'évolution de l'iode chez les Laminaires. Réponse à *M.* Freundler. [The evolution of iodine in *Laminaria*. Reply to *M.* Freundler.] *Bull. Soc. Botan. France*, 1928, v. 75, pp. 980–986. **142**

Author maintains that the results obtained by Freundler (see entries **116** and **148**) cannot be attributed to iodine volatilization. Iodine volatilization takes place in *Laminaria* 1 to 3 metres below the surface of the sea.

1928. DANGEARD, PIERRE. Sur le dégagement d'iode libre chez les algues marines. [The liberation of free iodine in marine algae.] *C. R. Acad. Sci.*, Paris, 1928, v. 186, pp. 892–894. **143**

Various species of *Laminaria* and *Fucus* in their natural habitat liberate appreciable quantities of free iodine. This is due to a special activity of the peripheral cortical cells.

1928. DANGEARD, PIERRE. Sur les conditions du dégagement de l'iode libre chez les Laminaires. [Conditions for the liberation of free iodine in the *Laminaria*.] *C. R. Acad. Sci.*, Paris, 1928, v. 186, pp. 1371–1373. **144**

Conditions affecting the liberation of free iodine in *Laminaria flexicaulis* are discussed.

1928. DANGEARD, PIERRE. Sur l'iodovolatilisation et ses caractères chez les algues septentrionales. [Volatilization of iodine in northern algae.] *C. R. Acad. Sci.*, Paris, 1928, v. 187, pp. 899–901. **145**

Volatilization of iodine in *Laminaria* and *Fucus* can take place in localities where the temperature of the seawater is approximately zero.

1928. DANGEARD, PIERRE. Action favorisante de l'iodure de potassium sur l'iodovolatilisation.

[Favourable action of potassium iodide on the volatilization of iodine.] *C. R. Acad. Sci.*, Paris, 1928, v. 187, pp. 1156–1158. **146**

Seawater containing 0·1 per cent of potassium iodide greatly increases the volatilization of iodine from certain seaweeds.

1928. FREUNDLER, P., *Faculty of Science, University of Paris.* Introduction à l'étude des complexes biologiques. [Introduction to the study of the biological complexes.] Paris: *E. Belin*, 1928, 224 pp. **147**

Deals with the iodine complex in *Laminaria flexicaulis.*

1928. FREUNDLER, P. Sur l'évolution de l'iode chez les Laminaires. [Evolution of iodine in *Laminaria.*] *Bull. Soc. Chim. Biol.*, 1928, v. 10, pp. 1123–1128. **148**

Criticism of Dangeard's conclusions, and a restatement of the author's earlier findings concerning the existence of concealed iodine in *Laminaria.* (See entries **116** and **140.**)

1928. KYLIN, HARALD, *botanical laboratory, University of Lund.* Über *Falkenbergia hillebrandii* und ihre Beziehung zur Abspaltung von Jod. [*Falkenbergia hillebrandii* and its relation to the liberation of iodine.] *Botan. Notiser*, 1928, part 4, pp. 233–254. **149**

Living cells of *Falkenbergia* contain no free iodine but may occasionally contain some combined iodine which, in the presence of certain acids, decomposes into free iodine.

1928. MANGENOT, G. Sur la localisation des iodures dans les cellules des algues. [Localization of iodides in the cells of algae.] *Bull. Soc. Botan. France*, 1928, v. 75, pp. 519–540. **150**

Localization of iodides in the cells of different species of algae was studied by means of the cresyl blue test.

1928. MANGENOT, G. Sur la signification des cristaux rouges apparaissant, sous l'influence du bleu de crésyl, dans les cellules de certaines algues. [Significance of the red crystals appearing under the influence of cresyl blue in the cells of certain algae.] *C. R. Acad. Sci.*, Paris, 1928, v. 186, pp. 93–95. **151**

Results obtained for the distribution of iodine in the thallus of *Laminaria* agree with those of Tunmann. (See entry **45.**)

1928. SAUVAGEAU, CAMILLE, *professor of botany, University of Bordeaux.* Un dernier mot sur les ioduques et les bromuques. [Final note on the iodine- and bromine-containing gland cells.] *Bull. Stat. Biol. Arcachon*, 1928, v. 25, pp. 3–24. **152**

Confirms the presence of free iodine in *Falkenbergia.*

1929. CHEMIN, E. Variations de l'iode chez une Floridée: *Trailliella intricata* Batt. [Variations of iodine in one of the Florideae (*Trailliella intricata*).] *C. R. Acad. Sci.*, Paris, 1929, v. 188, pp. 1624–1625. **153**

Filaments of *Trailliella intricata* gathered in March gave a test for iodine when dipped in acidified starch paste. It is considered that the iodine is present in a combined form.

1929. DANGEARD, PIERRE, *Faculty of Science, University of Paris.* L'iodovolatilisation chez les algues marines et les problèmes de l'iode. [Volatilization of iodine in marine algae and problems of iodine.] *Botaniste*, 1929, v. 21, pp. 129–266. **154**

Iodogenic cells in the epidermis of *Laminaria* have a delicate mechanism which produces free iodine according to the amount of iodide in the tissues. The mechanism is affected by external factors such as temperature and chemical agents.

1929. DILLON, THOMAS, *University College, Galway.* An iodine liberator from Laminariae. *Nature*, London. 1929 v. 123 pp. 161–162. **155**

Method is described for preparing an aqueous extract of fresh fronds of *Laminaria* which, when acidified, liberates iodine from potassium iodide. Active agent appears to be a dialysable organic substance.

1929. KAY, H. D., *Medical Unit, London Hospital.* An iodine liberator from Laminariae. *Nature*, London, 1929, v. 123, p. 317. **156**

Criticism of paper by Dillon (see preceding entry). His evidence is considered insufficient to warrant the conclusion that the active agent is an organic substance.

1929. KYLIN, HARALD, *botanical laboratory, University of Lund.* Über das Vorkommen von Jodiden, Bromiden und Jodidoxydasen bei den Meeresalgen. [The occurrence of iodides, bromides and iodide-oxidases in seaweeds.] *Ztschr. physiol. Chem.*, 1929, v. 186, pp. 50–84. **157**

Iodine is present in marked degree in some *Phaeophyceae* and *Rhodophyceae* and is absent in others. Amounts, on a fresh matter basis, ranged from 0·0008 to 0·53 per cent, the maximum being for *Trailliella intricata.* The iodine is present in both organic and inorganic forms. The presence of iodide-oxidases in several species is reported.

1929. LUNDE, GULBRAND, and KARL CLOSS, *research laboratory, Norwegian Canning Industry, Stavanger.* An iodine liberator from Laminariae. *Nature*, London, 1929, v. 124, p. 578. **158**

A preliminary report that most of the iodine in the fresh aqueous extract of *Laminaria digitata* is present in such a form that the iodine is liberated by an "iodine liberator" which is also present in the extract and acts only in acid solution.

1930. DANGEARD, PIERRE, *Faculty of Science, University of Paris.* Recherches sur les iodures, l'iodovolatilisation et les oxydases chez les algues marines. [Iodides, the volatilization of iodine and the oxidases in marine algae.] *Botaniste*, 1930, v. 22, pp. 33–73. **159**

See entries **71** and **160.**

1930. DANGEARD, PIERRE. Sur l'influence de l'oxygène dans l'iodovolatilisation. [Influence of oxygen on the volatilization of iodine.] *C. R. Acad. Sci.*, Paris, 1930, v. 190, pp. 131–133. **160**

External oxygen is necessary for the volatilization of iodine from fresh seaweeds.

1930. DANGEARD, PIERRE. Sur l'obtention, aux dépens des Laminaires, d'un complexe iodé labile. [A labile iodine complex from *Laminaria.*] *C. R. Acad. Sci.*, Paris, 1930, v. 191, pp. 337–339. **161**

Two or three days following the immersion of a stalk of *Laminaria flexicaulis* in seawater a complex iodine compound is obtained which liberates free iodine on acidification.

1930. Kylin, Harald, *botanical laboratory, University of Lund.* Über die Blasenzellen bei *Bonnemaisonia, Traillieliella* und *Antithamnion.* [The bladder cells of *Bonnemaisonia, Trailliella* and *Antithamnion.*] *Ztschr. Botanik*, 1930, v. 23, pp. 217-226. **162**

Most of the iodine in the bladder cells of *Bonnemaisonia asparagoides* and *Trailliella intricata* is in the form of potassium iodide.

1930. Kylin, Harald. Über die Jodidspaltende Fähigkeit der Phäophyceen. [The iodide-splitting capacity of the *Phaeophyceae.*] *Ztschr. physiol. Chem.*, 1930, v. 191, pp. 200–210. **163**

Extracts of *Laminaria digitata* gave no evidence of the presence of an iodine liberator. There was evidence, however, of the presence of an iodide-oxidase in the surface cells of the plant.

1930. Lami, Robert. Libération de l'iode des ioduques de *Bonnemaisonia asparagoides* sous l'action des rayons ultraviolets. [The liberation of iodine from the iodine-containing gland cells of *Bonnemaisonia asparagoides* by the action of ultraviolet light.] *C. R. Acad. Sci.*, Paris, 1930, v. 191, pp. 863–865. **164**

Irradiation of the iodine-containing gland cells of *Bonnemaisonia asparagoides* with ultraviolet light liberates free iodine.

1930. Lunde, Gulbrand, and Karl Closs, *University of Oslo; and the research laboratory of the Norwegian Canning Industry, Stavanger.* Über die Bindungsart des Jods bei *Laminaria digitata.* [The nature of the iodine compound in *Laminaria digitata.*] *Biochem. Ztschr.*, 1930, v. 219, pp. 198–217. **165**

Figures are given for the iodine content of the leaves, stems and roots expressed as total iodine and the following fractions: water soluble, water and alcohol soluble, iodide, iodine combined with calcium, iodine combined with alginic acid, and residual iodine.

1931. Dangeard, Pierre. La sensibilité des Laminaires aux actions extérieures et l'iodovolatilisation. [The sensitivity of *Laminaria* to external actions and the volatilization of iodine.] *C. R. Acad. Sci.*, Paris, 1931, v. 192, pp. 500–501. **166**

Volatilization of free iodine from *Laminaria* is excited by a number of external actions.

1931. Kylin, Harald, *botanical laboratory, University of Lund.* Über die jodidspaltende Fähigkeit von *Laminaria digitata.* [The iodide-splitting capacity of *Laminaria digitata.*] *Ztschr. physiol. Chem.*, 1931, v. 203, pp. 58–65. **167**

No iodine liberator was found in sterile aqueous extracts of the fresh weed. The iodine liberation observed in ordinary extracts is due to the presence of nitrite formed from nitrate by bacterial action.

1932. Suneson, Svante, *University of Lund.* Beitrag zur Frage von der Jodverflüchtigung bei den Laminariaarten. [Iodine volatilization in *Laminaria* species.] *Ztschr. physiol. Chem.*, 1932, v. 213, pp. 270–272. **168**

Discusses the work of Kylin and Dangeard on this subject and favours Kylin's results.

1933. Dangeard, Pierre, *University of Bordeaux.* Sur le mécanisme de l'iodovolatilisation et le rôle des cellules iodogènes chez les Laminaires. [Mechanism of iodine volatilization and the role of the iodogenic cells of *Laminaria.*] *C. R. Soc. Biol.*, Paris, 1933, v. 113, pp. 1203–1205. **169**

Mechanism of iodine volatilization in *Laminaria flexicaulis* is simple but its determination is quite the reverse. When the normal physiological activity of the cells is temporarily modified the mechanism ceases to function.

1933. Masuda, Etsuo, *laboratory of the Koei-Kabushikikaisha, Osaka.* Über die Jodverbindungen in Meeres-tangen. (Vorläufige Mitteilung.) [Iodine compounds in seaweeds. Preliminary communication.] *Proc. Imp. Acad. Japan*, 1933, v. 9, pp. 599–601. **170**

Five decomposition products obtained by oxidizing with hydrogen peroxide the organic iodine compound from *Ecklonia cava* are described.

1933. [Opotski, V. F., G. B. Fisher and A. F. Tyulpina.] Опоцький, В. Ф., Г. Б. Фішер and А. Ф. Тюльпіна, *iodine laboratory, Ukrainian Scientific Research Institute of Chemistry and Radiology, Odessa.* Сухий перегін Чорноморської Філофори. [Dry distillation of Black Sea *Phyllophora.*] *Ukrainski Khem. Zhurnal*, 1933, v. 8, scientific-technical part, pp. 237–241. **171**

Iodine in Black Sea *Phyllophora* is in organic form, insoluble in water and difficult to hydrolyse, but readily decomposed on burning the weed.

1933. Toryu, Yoshiyuki, *Biological Institute, Tôhoku Imperial University, Sendai.* On the organic iodine in *Laminaria ochotensis* Miyabe, with especial reference to protein iodine and the search for diiodotyrosine. *Sci. Rep. Tôhoku Imp. Univ.*, 1933, 4th Series, v. 8, pp. 107–110. **172**

About 6 per cent of the total iodine in *Laminaria ochotensis* is alcohol insoluble, 5 per cent being protein and 1 per cent non-protein iodine.

1933. [Trofimov, A. V.] Трофимов, А. В., *State Oceanographic Institute, Moscow.* О формах иода в морских водорслях. [The form of iodine in seaweed.] *Trudi Gos. Okeanogr. Inst.*, 1933, v. 3, no. 3, pp. 88–93; English summary p. 94. **173**

In all samples of brown seaweed the iodine is in a form which can be precipitated by silver.

1934. Masuda, E., and K. Nishida, *laboratory of the Koei-Kabushikikaisha, Osaka.* [Iodine compounds in seaweeds. 2. Dialysis of seaweeds and their infusions.] *J. Pharm. Soc. Japan*, 1934, v. 54, pp. 497–508. In Japanese: German summary in Abstract Section, pp. 90–91. **174**

Ecklonia cava Kjellm. and *Laminaria ochotensis* Miyabe contain larger quantities of inorganic than of organic iodine compounds.

1934. MASUDA, E., and K. NISHIDA. [Iodine compounds in seaweeds. 3.] *J. Pharm. Soc. Japan*, 1934, v. 54, pp. 952–956. In Japanese: German summary in Abstract Section, pp. 243–245. **175**

From 13 to 85 (average 48) per cent of the iodine in *Laminaria japonica* Aresch is in the form of organic compounds.

1934. [TROFIMOV, A. V.] Трофимов, А. В., *State Oceanographic Institute, Moscow*. Über das mineralische Jod in Meeresalgen. [Inorganic iodine in marine algae.] *Planta*, 1934, v. 23, pp. 56–70. **176**

Data are given for the iodine content of the different tissues of several species of White Sea algae.

1935. MASUDA, E., *laboratory of the Koei-Kabushikikaisha, Osaka*. [Iodine compounds in seaweeds. 4. Triiodoacetaldehyde (Iodal).] *J. Pharm. Soc. Japan*, 1935, v. 55, pp. 625–627. In Japanese: German summary in Abstract Section, pp. 97–98. **177**

One of the five compounds obtained from *Ecklonia cava* (see entry **170**) is said to be triiodoacetaldehyde.

1937. [KORENTSVIT, A.] Коренцвит, А., *Botanical Garden, Odessa State University*. О комплексном использовании Черноморской водоросли *Phyllophora nervosa*. [Utilization of the Black Sea alga *Phyllophora nervosa*.] *Zhurnal Priklad. Khim.*, 1937, v. 10, pp. 2064-2067. **178**

Iodine is present, in a percentage of from 0·130 to 0·726 on a dry basis, in the form of an insoluble organic compound which can be made soluble by steaming the seaweed and then extracting with water.

1937. JACQUES, A. G., *Rockefeller Institute for Medical Research, New York, and Bermuda Biological Station for Research, Inc., Bermuda*. The kinetics of penetration. 14. The penetration of iodide into *Valonia*. *J. Gen. Physiol.*, 1937, v. 20, pp. 737–766. **179**

When *Valonia macrophysa* is immersed in seawater containing 0·1 *M* sodium iodide, iodine appears in the sap, entering largely as sodium iodide.

1937. OSTERHOUT, W. J. V., *Rockefeller Institute for Medical Research, New York*. The protoplasmic surface in certain plant cells. *Trans. Faraday Soc.*, 1937, v. 33, pp. 997–1002. **180**

An examination of the cell surface in three marine plants. Iodine enters *Valonia* chiefly as sodium iodide.

1938. JACQUES, A. G., and W. J. V. OSTERHOUT. The accumulation of electrolytes. 10. Accumulation of iodine by *Halicystis* and *Valonia*. *J. Gen. Physiol.*, 1938, v. 21, pp. 687–693. **181**

Iodide concentration in the cell sap of *Halicystis osterhoutii* and *Valonia macrophysa* is, respectively, $3{\cdot}61 \times 10^{-4}$ and $1{\cdot}1 \times 10^{-5}$ *M*.

1939. FELDMANN, JEAN, and GENEVIÈVE FELDMANN. Additions à la flore des algues marines de l'Algérie. [Additions to the flora of marine algae in Algeria.] *Bull. Soc. Hist. Nat. Afrique du Nord*, 1939, v. 30, pp. 453–464. **182**

Authors state that *Laminaria ochroleuca* liberates appreciable quantities of free iodine *in vivo*.

LAND PLANTS

IODINE CONTENT OF LAND PLANTS

183-270

IODINE OCCURRING NATURALLY 183-230

1819. FYFE, ANDREW, *M.D., lecturer on chemistry, Edinburgh University*. Account of some experiments, made with the view of ascertaining the different substances from which iodine can be procured. *Edinburgh Phil. J.*, 1819, v. 1, pp. 254–258. **183**

Having found iodine in various species of *Fucus* gathered near Leith, Fyfe turned his attention to land plants but could not find any iodine in *Plantago maritima* (seaside plantain), *Arenaria peploides* (sea-purslane), or *Salsola kali* (saltwort). Nor did he discover any in ferns, mushrooms and lichens. Fyfe was one of the first to detect the presence of iodine in sponges. For information on the production of iodine in 1814 from *soda hishanica* (barilla) made from *Salsola kali* and *Salicornia perbacea*, see *Iodine Facts*, 1943, v. 1, no. 243.

French and German translations of Fyfe's paper appeared in *Ann. Chim. Phys.*, 1819, v. 12, pp. 405–411 and *Ann. Phys.*, 1820, v. 66, pp. 241–248, respectively.

1836. ANNALES DE CHIMIE ET DE PHYSIQUE. Présence de l'iode dans differérens minerais et dans des plantes croissant loin de la mer. [Presence of iodine in various minerals and in some plants growing far from the sea.] *Ann. Chim. Phys.*, 1836, v. 62, pp. 110–111. **184**

Presence of iodine in "sabila" (agaves) and "roméritos" (kind of barilla) is recorded.

1842. DICKIE, GEORGE, *M.D., lecturer on botany, King's College, Aberdeen University*. Notice of the occurrence of *Gelidium rostratum* (Harv.) at Aberdeen, with remarks; and of the presence of iodine in some plants growing near the sea. *Trans. Botan. Soc. Edinburgh* (for 1842), 1844, v. 1, pp. 165–168. **185**

Iodine was present in considerable quantities in some of the plants examined. A summary of this paper was published by Dickie in *Chem. Gaz.*, 1843, v. 1, pp. 146–147, under the title "Iodine in Plants."

1843. MÜLLER, —, *apothecary, Kosswein, Germany*. Prüfung des *Nasturtium aquaticum* auf Jod. [Testing watercress for iodine.] *Arch. Pharm.*, Hanover, 1843, v. 85, p. 40. **186**

Iodine was found in the ash of watercress.

1845. RIGHINI, GIOVANNI. Note sur l'existence de l'iode et sur sa présence dans quelques végétaux du genre *Adianthum* L. [The existence of iodine and its occurrence in some plants of the genus *Adiantum* L.] *J. Chim. Méd.*, 1845, 3rd Series, pp. 644–645. **187**

Presence of iodine in the leaves of dead and rotting plants in mountainous districts is confirmed. Chlorides, iodates, sulphates and carbonates with an alkaline-earth base were produced by a gradual rotting process. Iodine was also found in dried specimens of *Adiantum capillus veneris* and *Asplenium trichomanes* L. collected from rocks on the mountains of Comasco (Italy).

1847. MARCK, W. VON DER, *apothecary, Lüdenscheid, Germany*. Vorkommen von Jod in *Jungermannia albicans* L. [Occurrence of iodine in *Jungermannia albicans* L.] *Arch. Pharm.*, Hanover, 1847, v. 101, pp. 154–156. **188**

Iodine was detected in the ash of this liverwort.

1849. VOELCKER, *Dr*. AUGUSTUS. On the composition of the ash of *Armeria maritima*, grown in different localities, and remarks on the geographical distribution of that plant; and the presence of fluorine in plants. *Report Brit. Assoc.* (for 1849), 1850, Trans. Section, pp. 43–45. **189**

In the analysis of seapinks from three different localities iodine was detected in only those specimens grown near the seashore.

1850. CHATIN, GASPARD ADOLPHE (1813–1901), *professor of botany, School of Pharmacy, Paris*. Existence de l'iode dans les plantes d'eau douce. Conséquences de ce fait pour la géognosie, la physiologie végétale, la thérapeutique et peut-être pour l'industrie. [The occurrence of iodine in freshwater plants. The importance of this fact in geology, vegetable physiology, therapeutics and perhaps n industry.] *C. R. Acad. Sci.*, Paris, 1850, v. 30, pp. 352–354. **190**

Chatin carried out the first systematic chemical enquiry into the distribution of iodine in the terrestrial mass, including plants. This is his abbreviated version of a paper delivered before the Académie des Sciences, Paris, in March 1850. Iodine is present in cress and in all plants growing in running water. It could not be detected in land crops. The proportion of iodine in aquatic plants is, in general, not related to their nature but to their habitat.

1850. CHATIN, G. A. Recherches sur l'iode des eaux douces (suite); de la présence de ce corps dans les plantes et les animaux terrestres. [Studies on iodine in fresh waters (continuation); the presence of this substance in terrestrial plants and animals.] *C. R. Acad. Sci.*, Paris, 1850, v. 31, pp. 280–283. **191**

Includes further data on the distribution of iodine in plants. (See preceding entry.)

1850. CHATIN, G. A. Existence de l'iode dans toutes les plantes d'eau douce. Conséquences de ce fait pour la géognosie, la physiologie végétale, la thérapeutique, et peut-être pour l'industrie. [The occurrence of iodine in freshwater plants. The importance of this fact in geology, vegetable physiology, therapeutics and perhaps in industry.] *J. Pharm. Chim.*, Paris, 1850, 3rd Series, v. 17, pp. 418–430. **192**

Full version of a paper delivered before the Académie des Sciences, Paris, in March 1850. (See entry **190**.)

1850. FEHLING, HERMANN VON (1812–1885), *professor of chemistry, Technical College, Stuttgart*. Ueber das Vorkommen von Jod in Landpflanzen. [The occurrence of iodine in land plants.] *Ann. Chem. Pharm.*, 1850, v. 75, p. 67. **193**

Traces of iodine were detected in sugar beet ash.

1850. MARCHAND, E. Sur la présence de l'iode dans les eaux douces et dans les plantes terrestres. [The presence of iodine in fresh waters and in land plants.] *C. R. Acad. Sci.*, Paris, 1850, v. 31, pp. 495–496. **194**

Without citing any evidence the author states that in well-wooded country iodine may be removed from natural waters by the vegetation and that the ash of most forest trees contains iodine.

1850. MEYRAC, V., *pharmacist, Dax, France*. Note sur l'existence des iodures et bromures alcalins, dans les plantes de la famille des Oscillariées, qui vivent dans les eaux thermales de Dax (département des Landes). [The occurrence of alkaline iodides and bromides in plants of the *Oscillariae* family, found in the thermal waters at Dax (Landes).] *C. R. Acad. Sci.*, Paris, 1850, v. 30, pp. 475–477. **195**

Species of *Anabaina* and *Oscillaria* growing in thermal waters were found to be rich in iodine.

1850. PERSONNE, J. Note sur l'existence de l'iode dans certaines plantes d'eau douce. [Note on the presence of iodine in certain freshwater plants.] *C. R. Acad. Sci.*, Paris, 1850, v. 30, p. 478. **196**

Presence of iodine in *Jungermannia pinguis* L. is recorded.

1851. VYVERE, E. VAN DE. De la présence de l'iode dans les plantes des dunes. [The presence of iodine in plants of the dunes.] *Ann. Soc. Méd.-Chirurg. Bruges*, 1851, v. 12, pp. 125–144. **197**

Author found iodine present in species of *Cakile, Eryngium, Zostera, Hippophaë, Salsola, Salicornia, Plantago, Limonium, Statice, Cynoglossum* and *Convolvulus*, as well as in grasses belonging to the *Cyperaceae* and *Juncaceae* families. The latter contained more iodine than watercress.

1852. MACADAM, STEVENSON, *Ph.D., teacher of chemistry, Philosophical Institution, Edinburgh*. On the presence of iodine in various plants, with some remarks on its general distribution. *Trans. Botan. Soc. Edinburgh* (for 1852), 1853, v. 4, pp. 151–156. Also in *Chem. Gaz.*, 1852, v. 10, pp. 281–286. **198**

The author, who was an authority on the general distribution of iodine in nature, was able to detect iodine in a large number of plants, including species of *Myosotis, Mentha, Menyanthes, Equisetum, Ranunculus, Potamogeton, Chara, Iris* and *Phragmites*.

1852. WINCKLER, *Dr*. F. L. Ueber den vermeintlichen Jodgehalt der Sassaparilla. [Supposed iodine content of sarsaparilla.] *Chem.-pharm. Centralbl.*, 1852, v. 23, p. 479. **199**

The author was unable to detect the presence of iodine in sarsaparilla roots.

1853. CASASECA, JOSÉ LUIS, *director, Institute of Chemical Research, Havana*. Note sur la faible quantité d'iode contenue dans l'eau de la rivière Almendares, qui fournit aux besoins de la population de la Havane, ainsi que dans les plantes terrestres et dans l'atmosphère des tropiques. [Note on the small quantity of iodine in the waters of the river Almendares, which serves the population of Havana, and in terrestrial plants and the atmosphere of the tropics.] *C. R. Acad. Sci.*, Paris, 1853, v. 37, pp. 348–350. **200**

No trace of iodine was found in the ashes of bananas or maize, and the quantity in watercress was too small to be determined.

1853. CHATIN, GASPARD ADOLPHE, *professor of botany, School of Pharmacy, Paris*. Présence de l'iode dans les eaux pluviales, les eaux courantes, et les plantes des Antilles et des côtes de la Méditerranée. [The occurrence of iodine in rainwater, running waters and plants in the Antilles and on the Mediterranean coast.] *C. R. Acad. Sci.*, Paris, 1853, v. 37, pp. 723–724. **201**

Presence of iodine in French and Havana tobaccos is reported.

1855. CASASECA, JOSÉ LUIS, *director, Institute of Chemical Research, Havana*. Recherches sur la quantité d'iode contenue dans des tabacs de diverses qualités, cultivés à l'île de Cuba, sur la perte en matières volatiles qu'éprouvent ces tabacs dans leur déssiccation, ainsi que sur la quantité de cendres qu'ils fournissent; suivies de quelques observations sur la méthode de *M*. de Luca, pour le dosage de l'iode. [The iodine content of tobaccos of different qualities grown in the island of Cuba; the loss of volatile materials which these tobaccos undergo during drying, as well as the quantity of ash which they yield: followed by some observations on de Luca's method for the determination of iodine.] *Ann. Chim. Phys.*, 1855, New Series, v. 45, pp. 477–485. **202**

Iodine was present, but only in small amount, in one of three varieties of tobacco analysed.

1860. ALSCHINGER, *Prof.* A., *Zara, Dalmatia*. Die jodhaltigen Pflanzen Dalmatiens. [The iodine-containing plants of Dalmatia.] *Österreich. botan. Ztschr.*, 1860, v. 10, pp. 122–123. **203**

Lists 59 species of algae and phanerogams occurring on the Dalmatian coast which are said to contain iodine, but gives no details.

1866. NADLER, *Dr.* G. Ueber den angeblichen Jodgehalt der Luft und verschiedener Nahrungsmittel. [The reported iodine content of the atmosphere and various foodstuffs.] *J. prakt. Chem.*, 1866, v. 99, pp. 183–206. **204**

Curly pondweed and watercress from Lake Zurich were examined for iodine content. None was found.

An extract from this paper appeared in *Schmidt's Jahrb. in- u. ausländ. ges. Med.*, 1868, v. 137, pp. 3–5.

1875. ZENGER, H., *Munich*. Eine bis jetzt vernachlässigte Jodquelle. Jod und Brom in den Süsswasserpflanzen. [A neglected source of iodine. Iodine and bromine in freshwater plants.] *Arch. Pharm.*, Halle, 1875, v. 206, pp. 137–148. **205**

Freshwater plants contain considerable quantities of iodine. No quantitative data given.

1899. BOURCET, PAUL. Sur l'absorption de l'iode par les végétaux. [The absorption of iodine by plants.] *C. R. Acad. Sci.*, Paris, 1899, v. 129, pp. 768–770. **206**

In 28 plants analysed, amounts varied from nil in potatoes and some other vegetables to 0·94 milligramme per kilogramme in garlic. *Chenopodiaceae* and *Liliaceae* absorb more iodine than *Solanaceae* and *Umbelliferae*.

1899. GAUTIER, *Prof.* ARMAND (1837–1920), *University of Paris*. Présence de l'iode en proportions notables dans tous les végétaux à chlorophylle de la classe des algues et dans les sulfuraires. [Occurrence of iodine in considerable quantities in all chlorophyll-containing plants of the algal class and in sulphur bacteria.] *C. R. Acad. Sci.*, Paris, 1899, v. 129, pp. 189–194. **207**

Freshwater algae belonging to the orders *Chlorophyceae*, *Cyanophyceae* and *Florideae* contained from 0·25 to 2·40 milligrammes of iodine per 100 grammes of dried material. A sample of *Beggiatoa* contained 36 milligrammes per 100 grammes.

1900. BOURCET, PAUL. Sur l'absorption de l'iode par les végétaux. [The absorption of iodine by plants.] *Bull. Soc. Chim. Paris*, 1900, 3rd Series, v. 23, pp. 40–41. **208**

See entry **206**.

1902. JUSTUS, *Dr.* J., *skin specialist, Jewish Hospital, Budapest*. Ueber den physiologischen Jodgehalt der Zelle. [The physiological iodine content of cells.] *Arch. path. Anat.*, 1902, v. 170, pp. 501–517. **209**

Investigation of many cellular tissues convinces the author that iodine is always present in the nucleus of animal and plant cells.

1913. BABIY, JOHANNA, *Institute of Plant Physiology, Vienna University*. Über das angeblich konstante Vorkommen von Jod im Zellkern. [The supposed constant occurrence of iodine in the cell nucleus.] *Ber. deutschen botan. Ges.*, 1913, v. 31, pp. 35–47. **210**

From the examination of a large number of plants the author was unable to confirm the conclusion of Justus (see preceding entry) that iodine is always present in the nucleus of animal and plant cells.

1914. CAMERON, A. T., *department of physiology and physiological chemistry, University of Manitoba*. The distribution of iodine in plant and animal tissues. *Proc. Trans. Roy. Soc. Canada*, 1914, 3rd Series, v. 8, Trans. Section 4, pp. 7–10 (published 1915). **211**

Iodine is an almost invariable constituent of all organisms, plant and animal.

1918. WINTERSTEIN, E., *agricultural chemistry laboratory, Zurich Technical College*. Über das Vorkommen von Jod in Pflanzen. [The occurrence of iodine in plants.] *Ztschr. physiol. Chem.*, 1918, v. 104, pp. 54–58. **212**

Of 38 phanerogams examined, iodine was detected only in beetroot, potatoes, celery roots, lettuce and carrots. It could not be found in the fruits, seeds, tubers or leaves of the other 33. Three fungi showed no evidence of the presence of iodine.

1923. FELLENBERG, THEODOR VON, *chemist, Public Health Laboratory, Berne*. Untersuchungen über das Vorkommen von Jod in der Natur. 1. [Investigations on the occurrence of iodine in nature. 1.] *Biochem. Ztschr.*, 1923, v. 139, pp. 371–451. Also in *Mitt. Geb. Lebensmitteluntersuch. Hyg.*, 1923, v. 14, pp. 161–240. **213**

Fellenberg's iodine studies are among the most extensive and comprehensive on the subject. This paper contains original data on the iodine content of water plants, plant products, and foodstuffs of vegetable origin.

1925. HEYMANN, *Dr.* J. A., *chemist and bacteriologist, Municipal Waterworks, Amsterdam*. Het jodium in het waterleidingbedrijf. [Iodine in water supply undertakings.] *Water en Gas*, 1925, v. 9, pp. 39–54. **214**

Original data are given for the iodine content of several plants. The author thinks it is very probable that plants absorb more iodine from the air than from the soil.

1926. FELLENBERG, THEODOR VON, *chemist, Public Health Laboratory, Berne*. Das Vorkommen, der Kreislauf und der Stoffwechsel des Jods. [The occurrence, cycle and metabolism of iodine.] *Ergebn. Physiol.*, 1926, v. 25, pp. 178–363. **215**

Summary of the author's published work carried out over a period of years. Includes a section on iodine in relation to plants, together with a review of the literature.

1930. SCHWAIBOLD, JULIUS, *Kaiser Wilhelm Biochemistry Institute, Berlin-Dahlem*. Über den Jodgehalt frischer, dachreifer und fermentierter Tabakblätter. [The iodine content of fresh, roof-cured and fermented tobacco leaves.] *Biochem. Ztschr.*, 1930, v. 218, pp. 318–320. **216**

Iodine occurs in all tobaccos but varies in quantity according to variety and to the iodine content of the soil. Roof-cured leaves have a reduced iodine content compared with fresh tobacco.

1930. SIMPSON, B. W., *Rowett Research Institute, Aberdeen*. Iodine content of some New Zealand pastures. *New Zealand J. Agric.*, 1930, v. 41, pp. 179–182. **217**

Wide seasonal variations in samples from different parts of the country are noted.

1930. WRANGELL, M. VON, *Agricultural College, Hohenheim, Germany*. Das atmosphärische Jod und die Pflanze. [Atmospheric iodine and the plant.] *Umschau*, 1930, v. 34, pp. 805–806. **218**

Contrary to most other evidence, this author concludes that it is probable that plants obtain their principal supply of iodine from the atmosphere by absorption through the leaves.

1931. GLIMM, E., and ST. HALASA, *Agricultural Chemistry Institute, Technical College, Danzig-Langfuhr*. Über die Verteilung des Jods im Getreidekorn. [Distribution of iodine in cereal grains.] *Biochem. Ztschr.*, 1931, v. 243, pp. 88–96. **219**

The iodine content of cereal grains is highest at the tip and lowest in the middle portion. In the whole plant the absolute amount of iodine is fairly uniformly distributed, but the percentage is relatively lowest in the ear and highest in the root. Malt is poorer in iodine than the barley from which it is prepared. Figures are given for the iodine content of a number of cereals from the Danzig district.

1931. KENTUCKY AGRICULTURAL EXPERIMENT STATION. Iodine in Kentucky soils, limestones, waters and forage crops. *Kentucky Agric. Exp. Stat.*, 44th Annual Report, for 1931 (1932), part 1, p. 24. **220**

Watercress was found to be rich in iodine.

1931. MCHARGUE, J. S., *Kentucky Agricultural Experiment Station, Lexington*. Report on less common elements in plants. *J. Assoc. Official Agric. Chem.*, 1931, v. 14, pp. 222–223. **221**

The iodine content of 8 samples of red clover ranged from 211 to 388 (mean 310) parts per thousand million.

1931. REMINGTON, ROE E., *Ph.D., director of laboratory, South Carolina Food Research Commission and professor of nutrition, Medical College of the State of South Carolina*. A nutritional research in the South. *South. Med. J.*, 1931, v. 24, pp. 49–53. **222**

Iodine appears to be most concentrated in those plants, or parts of plants, which contain most chlorophyll.

1931. [SERGEEV, L. V.] Сергеев, Л. В., *agricultural chemistry laboratory, Nikitsky Botanical Garden; and biochemical laboratory, Institute of Plant Industry*. Нахожтение иода в плодах *Feijoa Selloviana* Berg. [The occurrence of iodine in the fruit of *Feijoa sellowiana* Berg.] *Trudi Priklad. Botan. Genetike i Selektsi*, 1931, v. 25, no. 1, pp. 279–288; English summary p. 289. **223**

Iodine content of the fruit of *Feijoa sellowiana* varied between 10·20 and 7·69 milligrammes per kilogramme of dried fruit and between 3·90 and 1·65 milligrammes per kilogramme of fresh fruit. It fluctuated considerably from year to year and is present in a combination soluble in water.

1932. MCHARGUE, J. S., W. R. ROY and J. G. PELPHREY, *Kentucky Agricultural Experiment Station, Lexington*. The iron, manganese, copper, zinc and iodine content of some important forage crops. *J. Amer. Soc. Agron.*, 1932, v. 24, pp. 562–565. **224**

In five forage crops analysed the average iodine content per 1000 million of dry matter ranged from 66·9 parts in wheat straw to 117·3 parts in orchard grass hay.

1934. BLOM, I. J. B., *M.Sc., Ph.D., department of biochemistry, Onderstepoort, South Africa*. Studies in mineral metabolism. 30. Variations in the iodine content of grasses at different stages of growth and a note on the iodine content of milk. *Onderstepoort J. Vet. Sci.*, 1934, v. 2, pp. 139–150. **225**

Five pure species of grass were cut and analysed at monthly stages of development over 12 months. At the end of the 3rd month, when grass is dry and brown, iodine content is at a minimum. Following spring rains, a stage of active growth coincides with increased iodine content which reaches a maximum about the 8th or 9th month, and thereafter diminishes. In general, leaves and flowers contain more iodine than stalks.

1934. FISCHER, G. Untersuchungen über Veränderungen des Mineralstoffgehalts und des Mineralstoffverhältnisses in Gemüsearten, unter besonderer Berücksichtigung des Jods. [Changes in the content and proportions of mineral substances in vegetables with special reference to iodine.] *Dissertation, Jena University*, 1934. Cited from *Biedermanns Zentralbl., Abt. A*, 1934, v. 63, pp. 484–485. **226**

Iodine content and capacity for iodine absorption of individual species varies considerably. Iodine occurs principally in organic combination and is possibly related to the chlorophyll, carotene or vitamin A content.

1934. SCHWARZ, H., *Munich*. Brunnenkresse und Jod. [Watercress and iodine.] *Heil- u. Gewürzpflanzen*, 1934, v. 16, pp. 57–59. **227**

A sample of watercress contained 448 microgrammes of iodine per kilogramme. Figures for the iodine content of other fresh-water, salt-water, and land plants are given.

1935. MCHARGUE, J. S., *Kentucky Agricultural Experiment Station, Lexington*. Report on less common elements in plants. *J. Assoc. Official Agric. Chem.*, 1935, v. 18, pp. 377–378. **228**

Data are given on the iodine content of some eighteen plant materials.

1939. MENON, *Dr.* A. S., *University Biochemical Laboratory, Chepauk, Madras*. Mineral and nitrogen content of some South Indian pasture grasses. *Current Sci.*, 1939, v. 8, pp. 230–231. **229**

In nine common grasses analysed at the post-flowering stage the iodine content per 100 grammes of dry matter ranged from 15 microgrammes in *Cyanodon dactylon* to 118 microgrammes in *Setaria verticillata*.

1939. THIEL, HERMANN, *Reichenbach, Germany*. Beiträge zur Kenntnis der Verbreitung des Jodes in Gemüsepflanzen. [The distribution of iodine in vegetables.] *Inaugural Dissertation, Jena University*, 1939, 24 pp. **230**

Original data are tabulated for the iodine content of several samples each of kale, beetroot, watercress, radishes, rose hips and celery (roots and leaves). Results of investigations on the form of iodine in watercress are also reported.

IODINE CONTENT INFLUENCED BY IODINE APPLICATION

231–270

1926. HILTNER, *Dr.* E., and MARIANNE BERGOLD, *Bavarian State Institute for Plant Cultivation and Plant Protection, Munich*. Jodanreicherung von Pflanzen durch Düngung und Bespritzung und Kropfproblem. [Iodine enrichment of plants by manuring and spraying and its relation to the goitre problem.] *Prakt. Blätter Pflanzenbau*, 1926, New Series, v. 3, pp. 249–259. **231**

In pot experiments with ryegrass, oats and spinach, watering or spraying with a 0·1 per cent solution of potassium iodide increased the iodine content to a much higher level than did the application to the soil of 10 to 25 milligrammes of potassium iodide per pot. Similar results were obtained in a trial on meadowland fertilized with potassium iodide at the rate of 600 grammes per hectare or sprayed with a 0·1 per cent solution of potassium iodide.

1926. STROBEL, A., *Institute of Agricultural Chemistry, College of Agriculture and Brewing, Weihenstephan, Munich*. Joddüngungs- und Fütterungsversuche als Voraussetzung der Ermöglichung natürlicher Kropfverhütung durch Nahrungsjod. [Experiments on the use of iodine in fertilization and feeding, and the possibility of preventing goitre naturally by dietary iodine.] *Ztschr. angewandte Chem.*, 1926, v. 39, pp. 1208–1209. **232**

Iodine content of sugar beet, turnips and maize was increased by manuring with sodium iodide.

1927. HERCUS, C. E., and K. C. ROBERTS, *University of Otago, New Zealand*. The iodine content of foods, manures and animal products in relation to the prophylaxis of endemic goitre in New Zealand. *J. Hyg.*, Cambridge, 1927, v. 26, pp. 49–83. **233**

It is recorded (pp. 71–72) that lettuce leaves and turnip tops from plants manured with potassium iodide (0·2 to 5 grammes per square yard) or Chilean nitrate of soda (10 grammes per square yard) had a much higher iodine content than those from untreated plants.

1927. KLEIN, *Dr.* GUSTAV, *Vienna*. Zur Frage der Joddüngung: eine kritische Zusammenfassung. [The question of iodine manuring: a critical summary.] *Fortschr. Landwirtsch.*, 1927, v. 2, pp. 424–430. **234**

The author reviews the literature on the effect of iodine on the growth and iodine content of plants and concludes that it is purposeless to attempt enriching plants by iodine manuring.

1927. SCHARRER, K., and J. SCHWAIBOLD, *Institute of Agricultural Chemistry, College of Agriculture and Brewing, Weihenstephan, Munich*. Zur Kenntnis des Jods als biogenes Element. 10. Mitteilung. Untersuchung einige Kulturpflanzen auf ihren natürlichen Jodgehalt und dessen Steigerung durch Joddüngung. [Iodine as a biogenic element. 10. The natural iodine content of some cultivated plants and its increase by manuring with iodine.] *Biochem. Ztschr.*, 1927, v. 185, pp. 405–413. **235**

In pot trials and under farming conditions application of small amounts of potassium iodide to the soil caused marked increases in the iodine contents of the plants tested. In sugar beet the contents of both leaves and roots were increased.

1927. SCHARRER, K., and A. STROBEL. Die Jodanreicherung der Pflanzen durch Jodzufuhr. [The iodine enriching of plants by the application of iodine.] *Angewandte Botanik*, 1927, v. 9, pp. 187–199. **236**

In field experiments with sugar beet and spinach, and in pot experiments with barley, oats, peas and meadow grasses, iodine content was increased by iodine manuring.

1927. STROBEL, A., and K. SCHARRER, *Institute of Agricultural Chemistry, College of Agriculture and Brewing, Weihenstephan, Munich.* Die Beeinflussung des Jodgehaltes der Pflanzen durch Jodgaben. [The effect of added iodine on the iodine content of plants.] *Deutsche landwirtsch. Presse*, 1927, v. 54, p. 458. **237**

A reply to M. von Wrangell (see entry **332**).

1928. HILTNER, *Dr.* E., *Bavarian State Institute for Plant Cultivation and Plant Protection, Munich.* Ist eine wesentliche Jodanreicherung in Pflanzen möglich? [Is a substantial increase of iodine in plants possible?] *Fortschr. Landwirtsch.*, 1928, v. 3, pp. 1–4. **238**

Results given in an earlier paper (see entry **231**) are again recorded.

1928. KÖHLER, *Dr.* R., *Prussian Geological Institute, Berlin.* Untersuchungen über den Jodgehalt der Böden und die Aufnahme von Jod durch Pflanzen. [Studies of the iodine content of soils and the uptake of iodine by plants.] *Mitt. Lab. preuss. geol. Landesanst.*, 1928, no. 7, pp. 11–29. **239**

Rye seedlings grown on various types of soil for 18 days absorbed an appreciable amount of iodine.

1928. MAURER, *Dr.* E., W. SCHROPP and *Dr.* H. DUCRUE, *Faculty of Medicine, Munich University; and Institute of Agricultural Chemistry, Weihenstephan.* Ueber den Einfluss der Joddüngung auf Wachstum und Zusammensetzung der Nahrungspflanzen. [The influence of iodine manuring on the growth and composition of food plants.] *Münchener med. Wochenschr.*, 1928, v. 75, pp. 1246–1247. **240**

Applications of potassium iodide at the rate of 2·5 kilogrammes per hectare increased the iodine content of eight vegetables tested by amounts varying from 25 to 7900 per cent.

1928. ORR, J. B., F. C. KELLY and G. L. STUART, *Rowett Research Institute, Aberdeen.* The effect of iodine manuring on the iodine content of plants. *J. Agric. Sci.*, 1928, v. 18, pp. 159–161. **241**

Experiments with plants grown in culture solution and also in soil confirm the results of other workers that manuring with potassium iodide increases the iodine content of food plants.

1929. GAUS, W., and R. GRIESSBACH, *I. G. Farbenindustrie A.-G., Ludwigshafen-on-Rhine.* Jodfrage und Landwirtschaft. [The iodine question and agriculture.] *Ztschr. Pflanzenernähr. Düng.* [A], 1929, v. 13, pp. 321–425. **242**

See entry **340**.

1929. GUM, ROBERT, *Munich.* Ein Beitrag zur Frage der Joddüngung. [A contribution to the question of iodine manuring.] *Thesis, Munich Technical College*, 1929, 67 pp. **243**

See entry **341**.

1929. KÖHLER, *Dr.* R., *Prussian Geological Institute, Berlin.* Zur Kenntnis des Jodes in Boden und Pflanze. [Iodine in soil and plants.] *Ztschr. angewandte Chem.*, 1929, v. 42, pp. 192–197. **244**

See entry **239**.

1929. PFEIFFER, G., and H. COURTH, *department of animal physiology, Agricultural College, Bonn-Poppelsdorf.* Der Transport und die Transformation organisch gebundenen Pflanzenjods im Tierkörper. [The passage and transformation of organic iodine from plants in the animal body.] *Biochem. Ztschr.*, 1929, v. 213, pp. 74–85. **245**

Carrots and radishes show the greatest capacity for storing iodine applied to the soil. Their iodine content rises to 500–700 times that of normal plants. Plant iodine fed to dogs is transformed and utilized to a very large extent, the iodine content of the thyroid being greatly increased.

1929. REITH, J. F., *chemist, State Institute of Public Health, Utrecht.* Over het iodiumgehalte der planten, voornamelijk beschouwd in verband met het iodium in den bodem. [The iodine content of plants, considered especially in connection with the iodine in the soil.] *Landbouwkundig Tijdschr.*, 1929, v. 41, pp. 236–242. **246**

More quantitative data are needed before one can say whether the amount of iodine in plants is directly proportional to the iodine content of the soil. Two important factors which have not been sufficiently considered are the absorption of atmospheric iodine and the correct determination of assimilable (inorganic) iodine in the soil.

1929. REITH, J. F. De bemesting van planten met iodide. Doel der proefnemingen nieuwere gezichtspunten. [The manuring of plants with iodide. Object of the experiments and more recent points of view.] *Landbouwkundig Tijdschr.*, 1929, v. 41, pp. 287–299. **247**

Although results to date are inconclusive and often contradictory, it is premature to "adopt an attitude of refusal to every kind of significance of iodine for the plant." It is unlikely that a simple direct relationship will be found between the quantity of iodine in soils and the percentage of iodine in plants grown thereon.

1929. SOUTH CAROLINA AGRICULTURAL EXPERIMENT STATION. Iodine fertilization of plants. *South Carolina Agric. Exp. Stat.*, 42nd Annual Report, for 1928–29 (1929), p. 45. **248**

The iodine content of plants can be increased by iodine manuring. In some instances the increase is as high as 100 per cent. Potassium iodide and potassium iodate gave the best results. Iodine had a toxic effect on plants when applied at the rate of 3 lb. per acre in pot experiments.

1929. STOKLASA, JULIUS (1857–1936), *director, State Experiment Station, Prague.* Die Resorption des Jods durch das Wurzelsystem der Pflanze. [The absorption of iodine by the root system of plants.] *Protoplasma*, 1929, v. 8, pp. 199–214. **249**

Pot experiments with numerous species of plants grown in neutral or slightly alkaline soils showed that the amount of iodine absorbed increased with the iodine content of the soil within the range tested. Each type of plant has its own peculiarities regarding iodine absorption and the hydrogen ion concentration of the cell sap of the various organs plays an important part.

1930. KÖHLER, *Dr.* R., *Prussian Geological Institute, Berlin.* Untersuchungen über die Verteilung des Jodes im Abwasser und die Anwendung des Abwasserschlammes als Joddünger. [Studies on the distribution of iodine in sewage and the use of sewage sludge as iodine fertilizer.] *Mitt. Lab. preuss. geol. Landesanst.*, 1930, no. 11, pp. 1–14. **250**

Berlin sewage has an iodine content of 30 to 60 microgrammes per litre. Some iodine remains in the sludge, and when this is used as a fertilizer plants are likely to have an increased iodine content.

1930. KÖHLER, *Dr.* R. Untersuchungen über den Jodgehalt des Abwassers. [The iodine content of sewage.] *Ztschr. angewandte Chem.*, 1930, v. 43, pp. 503–507. **251**

Plants fertilized with sewage sludge show increased iodine content. The preceding entry gives a more detailed account of these findings.

1931. CONNER, W. H., *Florida Agricultural Experiment Station, Gainesville.* Study of the iodine content of Florida-grown crops. *Florida Agric. Exp. Stat.*, 45th Annual Report, for 1930–31, p. 65. **252**

A brief note on the year's work. Iodine content can be materially increased by the addition of 5 lb. of potassium iodide per acre. The iodine content of 26 different fruits and vegetables examined was uniformly lower than in the previous season. It was not possible to determine the cause of this.

1931. HERCUS, C. E., H. A. A. AITKEN, H. M. S. THOMSON and G. H. COX, *University of Otago, New Zealand.* Further observations on the occurrence of iodine in relation to endemic goitre in New Zealand and on iodine metabolism. *J. Hyg.*, Cambridge, 1931, v. 31, pp. 493–522. **253**

On pp. 497-498 it is recorded that the iodine content of pasture was increased by the application of potassium iodide or commercial fertilizers (including Chilean nitrate of soda) to the soil before sowing.

1931. MALHOTRA, R., *Hull Botanical Laboratory, University of Chicago.* Permeability of iodine in some economic plants. *Protoplasma*, 1931, v. 12, pp. 1–22. **254**

Intake of iodine by crops depended upon the nature of the plant and on the iodine content and hydrogen ion concentration of the soil. Root crops showed the greatest capacity for absorbing and retaining iodine. Of these, carrots gave the highest values and showed a maximum absorption when grown in soil containing 8000 parts of iodine per 1000 million. Tomatoes absorbed and retained least iodine.

1931. MITCHELL, J. H., *South Carolina Agricultural Experiment Station, Clemson College.* Factors influencing the iodine content of plants. *South Carolina Agric. Exp. Stat.*, 44th Annual Report, for 1930–31 (1931), p. 56. **255**

A brief note outlining investigations in progress on the effect of iodine manuring on the iodine content of pasture grasses. No results are given.

1931. SIMPSON, B. W., *chemistry section, New Zealand Department of Agriculture (seconded from the Rowett Research Institute, Aberdeen, Scotland).* Mineral feeding experiments. Iodine, lime, and salt-lick questions. *New Zealand J. Agric.*, 1931, v. 42, pp. 18–23. **256**

On pp. 18–19 original data recorded show that plants grown on soil which had been watered with a dilute solution of potassium biniodate before planting contained up to 17 times as much iodine as those grown on untreated soil. Amounts of iodine assimilated varied with the species.

1931. STOKLASA, JULIUS, *director, State Experiment Station, Prague.* Die Bedeutung des Jods für die Kraft- und Stoffwechselprozesse im menschlichen Organismus. [The significance of iodine for energy and metabolic processes in the human organism.] *Ztschr. Ernähr.*, 1931, v. 1, pp. 3–15. **257**

This communication is mainly concerned with plant metabolism and covers ground dealt with by the author in earlier papers. He again shows that the amount of iodine absorbed by the plant and the relative amounts of inorganically and organically bound iodine in the plant vary with species and with the iodine content of the soil.

1931. WACHE, R. Untersuchungen über das Vorkommen von Jod in Wässern und Kohlen und über einige Düngeversuche mit Jodsalzen. [Investigations on the occurrence of iodine in waters and coal and some experiments on the use of iodine as a fertilizer.] *Mitt. Lab. preuss. geol. Landesanst.*, 1931, no. 13, pp. 43–52. **258**

Both water and coal contain iodine, the latter in a relatively high degree. Fertilizer experiments with organic iodine on rye crops showed an increase in the iodine content of the harvested plants.

1932. BEAUMONT, A. B., *Massachusetts Agricultural Experiment Station, Amherst,* and GEORGE M. KARNS, *Mellon Institute of Industrial Research, Pittsburgh.* Effect of an iodide fertilizer on iodine content of a food plant. *Science*, 1932, v. 76 p. 567. **259**

Turnips grown on soil dressed with potassium iodide at the rate of 2 kilogrammes per hectare contained 441 and 950 parts of iodine per 1000 million in the roots and tops, respectively.

1933. SCHARRER, K., W. SCHROPP and J. SCHWAIBOLD, *Institute of Agricultural Chemistry, College of Agriculture and Brewing, Weihenstephan, Munich.* Milchertrag und Milchjodspiegel von Milchkühen auf jodgedüngten Weiden. [Milk yield and iodine content of the milk of dairy cows on pastures manured with iodine.] *Biedermanns Zentralbl., Abt. B*, 1933, v. 5, pp. 676–700. **260**

Pastures manured with iodine, as potassium iodide, at the rate of 2·5 kilogrammes per hectare contained up to 9090 microgrammes of iodine per 100 grammes of dry matter. The corresponding value for pastures manured at the rate of 1 kilogramme per hectare was 3934 microgrammes.

1934. TESKE, HEINZ, *food chemist, Gotha, Germany.* Untersuchungen über den Jodgehalt einiger Arzneipflanzen und über ihr Jodanreicherungsvermögen. [The iodine content of some medicinal plants and the possibility of increasing it.] *Inaugural Dissertation, Jena University*, 1934, 37 pp. **261**

In 15 common medicinal plants analysed, the iodine content varied from 1·39 microgrammes per 100 grammes in hyssop to 52·66 microgrammes in iceland moss. Application of iodine as potassium iodide, potassium iodate or potassium periodate at the rate of 0·25 gramme per square metre had a stimulating effect on germination and early development of valerian but not of peppermint. It increased the iodine content of both plants, very markedly in valerian and only slightly or not at all in peppermint, and usually decreased crop yield, more especially of valerian.

1936. EISENMENGER, WALTER S., and EDWARD B. HOLLAND. The absorption by food plants of chemical elements important in human nutrition. *Massachusetts Agric. Exp. Stat.*, Bulletin No. 339 (Annual Report for 1936), 1937, p. 11. **262**

Iodine was one of several elements applied to plots growing spinach, lettuce, onions, beets and carrots.

1936. MACK, WARREN B., and EUGENE P. BRASHER, *Pennsylvania Agricultural Experiment Station, State College*. The influence of commercial fertilizers, potassium iodide, and soil acidity on the iodine content of certain vegetables. *J. Agric. Research*, 1936, v. 53, pp. 789–800. **263**

Application of potassium iodide to the soil at the rate of 2·356 kilogrammes per acre increased the iodine contents of wax beans (green pods) and turnips (whole plant) 3-fold and from 10- to 120-fold, respectively. In turnips the largest increases occurred on alkaline soils. Yield of beans was markedly decreased and that of turnips was slightly increased.

1937. BERTRAM, *Dr.* PAUL, *scientific adviser, Chilesalpeter G. m. b. H., Berlin*. Neuere Erfahrungen über die Bedeutung der Spurenelemente für die Pflanzenernährung. [New research on the importance of trace elements in plant nutrition.] *C. R. 5e Congr. Internat. Techn. Chim. Indust. Agric.*, Scheveningen, 1937, v. 1, pp. 267–289. **264**

A useful tabulation of contemporary data on the iodine enrichment of plants is included.

1937. EISENMENGER, WALTER S., and KAROL J. KUCINSKI. The absorption by food plants of chemical elements important in human nutrition. *Massachusetts Agric. Exp. Stat.*, Bulletin No. 347 (Annual Report for 1937), 1938, p. 20. **265**

A brief report on iodine manuring experiments in progress. No results are given.

1938. BROWN, H. D., and C. DIETZ. Iodine content of lettuce. *Ohio Agric. Exp. Stat*, Bulletin No. 592, 1938, pp. 65–66. **266**

Great variation occurs in the iodine content of lettuce grown in different parts of Ohio. Iodine content can be increased to nearly 100,000 parts per 1000 million by iodine manuring.

1938. DIETZ, CARL, *department of horticulture, Ohio State University, Columbus*. Iodine content of some Ohio vegetables. *Food Research*, 1938, v. 3, pp. 359–365. **267**

Iodine content of lettuce was very greatly, and that of tomatoes only slightly, increased by the application of potassium iodide to the soil during cultivation.

1938. EISENMENGER, WALTER S., and KAROL J. KUCINSKI. The absorption by food plants of chemical elements important in human nutrition. *Massachusetts Agric. Exp. Stat.*, Bulletin No. 355 (Annual Report for 1938), 1939, p. 13. **268**

Iodine was applied, at the rate of 200 parts per million, to the soil on which lettuce and cabbages were grown. No results are given.

1943. MCHARGUE, J. S. Iodine in soils, waters, and farm products of Kentucky. *Kentucky Agric. Exp. Stat.*, Bulletin No. 447, 1943, 28 pp. **269**

Iodine content of maize was greatly increased by the addition of potassium iodide to the soil at rates varying from 0·10 to 4·20 grammes per plant.

1947. ØDELIEN, *Prof.* M., *College of Agriculture, Aas, Oslo*. Mikroelementenes betydning for planteproduksjonen og husdyrbruket i Norge. [Importance of trace elements for plant production and animal husbandry in Norway.] *Beretning 7e Kongr. Nord. Jordbrugsforsk. Forenings*, Oslo, 1947 (1948), part 3, pp. 711–721. **270**

It is briefly recorded that in pot trials with potatoes the use of a complete fertilizer, containing 5 to 62·5 grammes of iodine (as potassium iodide) per 100 kilogrammes, greatly increased the iodine content of the stems and leaves but had no effect on that of the tubers.

EFFECT OF IODINE ON GROWTH AND DEVELOPMENT

271–523

IODINE: IODIDES: IODATES

271–418

1834. GOEPPERT, H. R., *Breslau*. Versuche über die Einwirkung des Chlor, Jod, Brom, der Säuren und Alkalien auf das Keimen der Saamen. [The action of chlorine, iodine, bromine, acids and alkalis on the germination of seeds.] *Notizen Geb. Natur- u. Heilk.*, 1834, v. 40, pp. 33–38. **271**

It is briefly stated (without any details) that iodine solutions and hydriodic acid cause seeds to germinate more quickly.

1839. BLENGINI, DOMENICO. Sur l'influence du brôme, du bromure et de l'iodure de potassium dans la germination. [The effect of bromine, and of potassium bromide and iodide on germination.] *J. Pharm.*, Paris, 1839, 2nd Series, v. 25, pp. 28–29. **272**

Author concludes that if seawater is responsible for the germination of marine plants, this is for the most part due to the bromides and iodides contained therein.

1869. KNOP, W., *agricultural chemistry laboratory, Leipzig University*. Ueber die Bedeutung des Eisens, Chlors, Broms, Jods und Natrons als Pflanzennährstoffe. [The significance of iron, chlorine, bromine, iodine and sodium as plant nutrients.] *Ber. Verhandl. königl. sächsischen Ges. Wissensch. Leipzig*, 1869, v. 21, pp. 1–27. **273**

Potassium iodide in a concentration of 0·25 gramme per litre of water was toxic to maize, cress, *Psamma arenaria* (sand-oats) and buckwheat; cress was more resistant than the other plants. All the plants were found to have assimilated iodine [experiments by

Dircks]. Experiments carried out by Weigelt to determine the effect of a potassium-free solution containing sodium iodide on sand-oats gave no definite result.

1875. HECKEL, E. De l'action de quelques composés sur la germination des graines (bromure de camphre, borate, silicate et arséniate de soude). [The action on seed germination of certain compounds (bromide of camphor, borate, silicate and arsenate of soda).] *C. R. Acad. Sci.*, Paris, 1875, v. 80, pp. 1170–1172. **274**

Chlorine, bromine and iodine hastened the germination of radish seeds. This effect decreased from chlorine to iodine.

1878. RABUTEAU, —. Sur les propriétés anesthésiques et le mode d'élimination de l'iodure d'éthyle; influence de cet agent sur la germination. [The anaesthetic properties and mode of excretion of ethyl iodide: the effect of this substance on germination.] *Gaz. Méd. Paris*, 1878, 49th year, 5th Series, v. 7, pp. 506–507. Also in *C. R. Soc. Biol.*, Paris, 1880, 6th Series, v. 5 (année 1878), pp. 57–60. **275**

Ethyl iodide inhibited germination of garden cress seeds.

1898. DEMOUSSY, E. Sur l'absorption des sels halogénés du potassium par les plantes. [Absorption of potassium halides by plants.] *C. R. Acad. Sci.*, Paris, 1898, v. 127, pp. 771–774. **276**

When roots of colza were immersed in a solution containing 10 milligrammes of potassium iodide in 50 millilitres of water the amount of iodide absorbed was equal to that which would have been absorbed owing to transpiration. The iodide had toxic effects and after several weeks the plants died.

1900. COUPIN, HENRI. Sur la toxicité des composés du sodium, du potassium et de l'ammonium à l'égard des végétaux supérieurs. [The toxicity of compounds of sodium, potassium and ammonium to higher plants.] *Rev. Gén. Botan.*, 1900, v. 12, pp. 177–193. **277**

The amount of potassium iodide required to kill wheat plantlets in water culture is 0·05 gramme per 100 grammes of solution. The figure for sodium iodide is the same (0·05 g.), and for ammonium iodide, 0·33 gramme.

1900. VOELCKER, J. AUGUSTUS, *M.A., Ph.D., F.I.C., consulting chemist to the Royal Agricultural Society of England.* The Woburn pot-culture station. The Hills experiments. *J. Roy. Agric. Soc. England*, 1900, v. 61, pp. 566–591. **278**

In trials over two successive years, application of sodium iodide in quantities of 0·5 hundredweight per acre at the time of sowing or even later as a top-dressing had a harmful effect on wheat and barley. Soaking the seed in 1 per cent sodium iodide solution for 10 minutes before sowing stimulated growth and increased crop yield. Results with clover were inconclusive.

1901. COUPIN, HENRI. Sur la sensibilité des végétaux supérieurs à des doses très faibles de substances toxiques. [Sensitiveness of higher plants to very weak solutions of toxic substances.] *C. R. Acad. Sci.*, Paris, 1901, v. 132, pp. 645–647. **279**

Roots of young wheat plants failed to grow properly in distilled water containing magnesium iodide or calcium iodide at dilutions of 1 in 10,000.

1901. VOELCKER, J. AUGUSTUS, *M.A., Ph.D., F.I.C., consulting chemist to the Royal Agricultural Society of England.* The Woburn pot-culture experiments. The Hills experiments. 3. The soaking of seed wheat in solutions of sodium iodide, sodium bromide, and sodium chloride. 4. The soaking of seed barley in solutions of sodium iodide, sodium bromide, and sodium chloride. *J. Roy. Agric. Soc. England*, 1901, v. 62, pp. 326–328; 328–329. **280**

3. Soaking wheat seeds in 1, 10 or 20 per cent solutions of sodium iodide before sowing had no significant effect on growth or crop yield at the lowest concentration and appeared to have a harmful effect at the higher concentrations.

4. Similar treatment of barley had neither a beneficial nor a harmful effect at all three concentrations.

1902. SUZUKI, S. On the action of highly diluted potassium iodid on agricultural plants. *Bull. College Agric. Tokyo Imp. Univ.*, 1902, v. 5, pp. 199–201. **281**

In pot experiments with peas 0·006 gramme of potassium iodide added to 2300 grammes of soil significantly increased the yield.

1903. LOEW, OSCAR (1844–1941), *professor of agricultural chemistry, Tokyo Imperial University.* Über Reizmittel des Pflanzenwachstums und deren praktische Anwendung. [Plant growth stimulants and their practical application.] *Landwirtsch. Jahrb.*, 1903, v. 32, pp. 437–448. **282**

Pot experiments with peas and oats showed that potassium iodide added to the soil appreciably increased the yield above that of controls. Field experiments with radishes gave similar results.

1903. SUZUKI, S., and K. ASO. On the physiological action of iodine and fluorine compounds on agricultural plants. *Bull. College Agric. Tokyo Imp. Univ.*, 1903, v. 5, pp. 473–479. **283**

Potassium iodide, even in such small quantities as 2·6 grammes in 10,000 kilogrammes of soil, increased the yield of oats. Similar results were obtained with radishes.

1903. VOELCKER, J. AUGUSTUS, *M.A., Ph.D., F.I.C., consulting chemist to the Royal Agricultural Society of England.* Pot-culture experiments, 1902. The Hills experiments. *J. Roy. Agric. Soc. England*, 1903, v. 64, pp. 348–364. **284**

Wheat seeds sown in soil treated with manganese iodide gave a very small percentage of germination. Surviving seedlings produced luxuriant vegetative growth but the development of the ear was retarded. Seeds soaked in a 1 per cent manganese iodide solution derived considerable benefit. Barley seeds were less sensitive to iodine than wheat.

1904. ASO, K., and S. SUZUKI. On the stimulating effect of iodine and fluorine compounds on agricultural plants. *Bull. College Agric. Tokyo Imp. Univ.*, 1904, v. 6, pp. 159–160. **285**

Potassium iodide applied at a rate of 25 grammes per hectare stimulated seed production in rice; at a rate of 250 grammes per hectare results were indecisive.

1904. LOEW, OSCAR, *professor of agricultural chemistry, Tokyo Imperial University*. On the treatment of crops by stimulating compounds. *Bull. College Agric. Tokyo Imp. Univ.*, 1904, v. 6, pp. 161–175. **286**

A review and discussion of previous work, including that on the effect of potassium iodide on oats, radishes and rice.

1904. VOELCKER, J. AUGUSTUS, *M.A., Ph.D., F.I.C., consulting chemist to the Royal Agricultural Society of England*. Pot-culture experiments, 1903. The Hills experiments. *J. Roy. Agric. Soc. England*, 1904, v. 65, pp. 306–315. **287**

Iodides of manganese, potassium, sodium and lithium applied at the rate of 1 hundredweight per acre had an injurious effect on wheat, most marked with manganous iodide. The same four iodides were applied to barley at the rate of 2 hundredweights per acre. All were harmful, the injurious effect being more pronounced than with wheat. In water cultures the iodides of manganese and lithium had an injurious effect on the roots of barley.

1905. UCHIYAMA, S. On the stimulating action of potassium iodide upon sesamum and spinach. *Bull. Imp. Central Agric. Stat. Japan*, 1905, v. 1, no. 1, pp. 35–37. **288**

Potassium iodide applied in pot experiments at a rate of 123·7 and 1237 grammes per hectare, and in field tests at a rate of 25 grammes per hectare increased the yield of sesame. Potassium iodide at a rate of 120 grammes per hectare increased the yield of spinach more than when applied at 1200 grammes per hectare.

1907. UCHIYAMA, S. Influence of stimulating compounds upon the crops under different conditions. *Bull. Imp. Central Agric. Exp. Stat. Japan*, 1907, v. 1, no. 2, pp. 37–79. **289**

Potassium iodide applied at rates of up to 376 grammes per hectare increased the yield of millet. The optimal dose of potassium iodide for increasing the yield of barley is 500 grammes per hectare.

1908. HOLLRUNG, —. Increased beet yields with various stimulations. *Sugar Beet*, 1908, v. 29, no. 1, pp. 24–25. **290**

Watering with a 0·01 per cent solution of potassium iodide had no stimulating effect.

1908. MACDOUGAL, *Dr.* D. T., *director, department of botanical research and laboratory for plant physiology, Carnegie Institution of Washington*. Heredity and environic forces. *Science*, 1908, v. 27, pp. 121–128. **291**

Experiments included the injection of plant ovaries with potassium iodide in concentrations varying from 1 in 250 to 1 in 50,000 parts of distilled water. Results are not given.

1910. STUART, WILLIAM, *Vermont Agricultural Experiment Station, Burlington*. The role of anesthetics and other agents in plant forcing. *Vermont Agric. Exp. Stat.*, Bulletin No. 150, 1910, pp. 451–480. **292**

Treatment of astilbe and lily of the valley in the dormant state with ethyl iodide (2 millilitres per cubic foot of air space) accelerated growth.

1912. LIPMAN, JACOB G., AUGUSTINE W. BLAIR, IRVING L. OWEN and HARRY C. MCLEAN. The availability of nitrogenous materials as measured by ammonification. *New Jersey Agric. Exp. Stat.*, Bulletin No. 246, 1912, 36 pp. Also in *New Jersey Agric. Exp. Stat.*, Report for 1910–11 (1912), pp. 159–192. **293**

The addition of "so-called stimulants" (including potassium iodide) gave varying and inconclusive results.

1913. RIVIÈRE, GUSTAVE, *director of Agricultural Services, Seine-et-Oise*, and GABRIEL BAILHACHE, *Agricultural Station, Versailles*. De l'influence des substances catalytiques. [The effect of catalytic substances.] *J. Soc. Nationale Hort. France*, 1913, 4th Series, v. 14, pp. 782–788. **294**

Sodium iodide had a harmful effect on wheat even when applied in small quantities. Yield per hectare was decreased by 400 kilogrammes.

1915. ALBANO, SOTERO FLORDELIZA, *College of Agriculture, Los Baños*. The effect of fertilizers and stimulants upon the growth and production of *Corchorus capsularis* L. *Philippine Agric. Forester*, 1915, v. 3, pp. 218–226. **295**

Applications of 0·5, 5 and 10 grammes of potassium iodide per square metre accelerated the growth of jute plants.

1915. MACDOUGAL, *Dr.* D. T., *director, department of botanical research and laboratory for plant physiology, Carnegie Institution of Washington*. The effect of potassium iodide, methylene blue and other substances applied to the embryo sacs of seed-plants. *Proc. Soc. Exp. Biol. Med.*, 1915, v. 12, pp. 1–3. **296**

Treatment of the ovaries of *Scrophularia* with a solution of one part of potassium iodide in 40,000 parts of distilled water produced permanent modification of the germ plasm.

1915. MAZÉ, P. Détermination des éléments minéraux rares nécessaires au développement du maïs. [Determination of the trace elements necessary for the development of maize.] *C. R. Acad. Sci.*, Paris, 1915, v. 160, pp. 211–214. **297**

Water culture experiments showed that iodine is one of the trace elements essential for the growth of maize. Solutions containing 4 to 20 milligrammes of potassium iodide per litre were used.

1916. MOORE, P. W. Plant stimulation with non-essential elements. *Arizona Agric. Exp. Stat.*, 27th Report, for 1915–16 (1916), p. 300. **298**

A brief summary of an unpublished review of work by Japanese and French investigators. Unquestionable stimulation of the growth of radishes, especially of the root system, is said to have been obtained with boric acid and potassium iodide. The optimum application of potassium iodide was 750 grammes per acre.

1917. FREE, E. E. Symptoms of poisoning by certain elements, in Pelargonium and other plants. *Johns Hopkins Univ. Circular*, 1917, New Series, no. 3, pp. 195–198. **299**

Potassium iodide solution applied to soil in a concentration of 500 parts per million caused yellowing of geranium leaves.

1918. Loew, *Prof.* Oscar, *biochemical department, Botanical Institute, Munich University*. Das Jod als mineralischer Nährstoff. [Iodine as a mineral food.] *Prometheus*, 1918, v. 30, pp. 1–2. **300**

A general article in which brief reference is made to the results of earlier experiments (see entries **282** and **289**).

1918. Söderbaum, H. G. Tioåriga försök med växtretmedel, särskilt manganföreningar, 1908–1917. [Ten years' experiments with plant stimulants, with special reference to manganese compounds, 1908–1917.] *Meddel. Centralanst. Försöksv. Jordbruks.*, 1918, no. 166, 20 pp. **301**

In small-scale pot experiments potassium iodide, at a rate of 0·0025 gramme per 25 to 30 kilogrammes of soil, had no effect on the yield of oats and beans.

1919. Mazé, P. Recherche d'une solution purement minérale capable d'assurer l'évolution complète du mais cultivé à l'abri des microbes. [A purely mineral solution capable of assuring the complete development of maize grown under bacteria-free conditions.] *Ann. Inst. Pasteur*, 1919, v. 33, pp. 139–173. **302**

A more detailed account of earlier work (see entry **297**).

1924. Brenchley, Winifred E., *D.Sc., Rothamsted Experimental Station, Harpenden, Herts*. The effect of iodine on soils and plants. *Ann. Appl. Biol.*, 1924, v. 11, pp. 86–111. **303**

One of the most important British contributions to knowledge of this subject. Application of sodium iodide had no measurable effect on the subsequent germination of tomato seeds in "sick" soils or on the loss from "damping-off" of tomato seedlings. Mustard was sensitive to iodides, its germination being inhibited or badly checked by heavy doses. Barley was more sensitive than mustard and its germination was inhibited by smaller dressings.

1924. Costa, T., *Experiment Station for Sugar Beet Cultivation, Rovigo, Italy*. I sali di manganese, di alluminio e di jodo nella fertilizzazione della barbabietola. [The salts of manganese, of aluminium, and of iodine in the manuring of sugar beet.] *Staz. Sper. Agrarie Ital.*, 1924, v. 57, pp. 430–434. **304**

Potassium iodide applied at a rate of 5 kilogrammes per hectare had no effect on the yield of sugar beet.

1924. Loew, *Prof.* Oscar, *biochemical department, Botanical Institute, Munich University*. Das physiologische Verhalten der Pflanzen gegen Reizwirkungen. [The physiological behaviour of plants to stimulation.] *Beitr. Pflanzenzucht*, 1924, no. 7, pp. 65–69; discussion pp. 69–72. **305**

A paper read to the *Gesellschaft zur Förderung deutscher Pflanzenzucht*, Munich, June 1924. Briefly mentions that even 25 grammes of potassium iodide per hectare increases the yield of crops, while the maximum stimulation is achieved with 160 to 500 grammes per hectare, according to the soil type.

1924. Loew, *Prof.* Oscar. Biologische Möglichkeiten zur Hebung des Ernteertrages. [The possibility of increasing the harvest yield by biological methods.] *Biol. Zentralbl.*, 1924, v. 44, pp. 188–193. **306**

Author refers to Uchiyama's experiments with potassium iodide (see entry **289**).

1924. Loew, *Prof.* Oscar. Über Reizmittel des Pflanzenwachstums. [Stimulants of plant growth.] *Chemikerzeitung*, 1924, v. 48, pp. 391–392. **307**

Reference is made to work, undertaken during 1902 to 1907 by the author and his Japanese colleagues, on the stimulating effect of potassium iodide (see entries **281–283, 285, 286, 288** and **289**).

1924. Rafaïlesco, M., *University of Cernauti*. Action de l'eau iodée sur la germination. [The effect of iodized water on germination.] *C. R. Soc. Biol.*, Paris, 1924, v. 90, pp. 24–25. **308**

Water containing small amounts of iodine is beneficial for germination. With stronger concentrations (7 and 8 milligrammes per millilitre) the process is retarded or completely inhibited according to the length of contact.

1924. Stoklasa, Julius (1857–1936), *director, State Experiment Station, Prague*. De la fonction physiologique de l'iode dans l'organisme de la betterave à sucre. [The physiological function of iodine in the organism of the sugar beet.] *C. R. Acad. Sci.*, Paris, 1924, v. 178, pp. 120–122. **309**

Application of potassium iodide to soil at the rate of 0·02 gramme per 12 kilogrammes in pot experiments and 1·72 kilogrammes per hectare in field experiments markedly increased the yield of leaves and roots and improved the quality and quantity of seed, but had no significant effect on the percentage of sugar in the roots. Doses of 4 to 5 kilogrammes per hectare considerably reduced the sugar content of the roots.

1925. Fellenberg, Theodor von, *chemist, Public Health Laboratory, Berne*. Joddüngung und Jodfütterung. [Iodine manuring and iodine feeding.] *Biochem. Ztschr.*, 1925, v. 160, pp. 210–224. **310**

Application of 2 kilogrammes of potassium iodide per hectare did not affect the yield of fodder beet but increased the iodine content of the leaves nine times and doubled that of the roots.

1925. Fellenberg, Theodor von, and *Dr.* Schmidt. Joddüngung und Jodfütterung. [Iodine manuring and iodine feeding.] *Mitt. Geb. Lebensmitteluntersuch. Hyg.*, 1925, v. 16, pp. 100–113. **311**

See preceding entry.

1925. Iterson, *Dr.* C. van, and *Dr.* A. Wijnberg, *laboratory of the Köninklijke Beetwortelsuikercultuur Kuhn & Co., Naarden, Netherlands*. Proeven over den invloed van jodiumbemesting op beetwortelen. [Investigations on the effect of iodine manuring on sugar beet.] *Tijdschr. Algem. Techn. Vereenig. Beetwortelsuikerfabr.*, 1925, no. 7, pp. 139–141. **312**

No confirmation was obtained of Stoklasa's finding (see entry **309**) that the application of 1·72 kilogrammes of potassium iodide per hectare favourably affected the yield of sugar beet.

1925. [Lafon, A. J., and Ch. Quillard.] Le mirage de l'iode. Par L.-M. Bernard. [The iodine mirage. By L.-M. Bernard.] Paris: *Société d'Éditions Géographiques, Maritimes et Coloniales*, 1939, xi+169 pp. **313**

On pp. 78–79 it is recorded that in a series of investigations carried out by Lafon and Quillard, manuring with potassium iodide at an average rate of two kilogrammes per hectare increased the yield of sugar beet. These investigations were the subject of an unpublished report submitted to *Établissements Poulenc Frères*, Paris, in February, 1925.

1925. LIPMAN, C. B., and A. GORDON, *University of California*. Further studies on new methods in the physiology and pathology of plants. *J. Gen. Physiol.*, 1925, v. 7, pp. 615–623. **314**

Injection into the trunks of pear and apricot trees of solutions containing 1 to 5 grammes of potassium iodide in about 2½ litres of distilled water produced injurious effects on the leaves and branches.

1925. NADSON, G. A., and A. J. ŽOLKEVIČ, *State Institute for Rontgenology and Radiology, Leningrad*. Kalium als Antagonist der Röntgenstrahlen und des Radiums. [Potassium as an antagonist to X-rays and to radium.] *Biochem. Ztschr.*, 1925, v. 163, pp. 457–463. **315**

White mustard seeds which were previously treated with solutions of potassium iodide grew much better on exposure to radium than untreated seeds.

1925. UNGERER, *Dr.* E., *Institute of Agricultural Chemistry, Breslau University*. Ueber die Wirkung einer Jodkali-Beigabe zu Zuckerrüben. [The effect of potassium iodide on sugar beet.] *Ztschr. Pflanzenernähr. Düng.* [B], 1925, v. 4, pp. 369–374. **316**

Potassium iodide, applied in pot experiments at rates of 1 and 2 kilogrammes per hectare, significantly decreased the yield of sugar beet although the weight of beet-tops was slightly increased. The sugar content of the beets was also significantly reduced by both treatments.

1925. WERBA, *Dr.* KARL, *Jablonica, Czechoslovakia*. Vergleichende Kunstdüngungsversuche zu Zuckerrübe. [Comparative trials with artificial fertilizers on sugar beet.] *Landwirtsch. Fachpresse Tschechoslowakei*, 1925, v. 3, p. 325. **317**

Application of potassium iodide solution, at the rate of 2 kilogrammes of iodine per hectare, during the early stages of growth increased the yield of roots and leaves by 84 and 106 metric quintals, respectively, per hectare.

1926. AMADORI, LEONIDA, *Pisa*. L'azione dell'jodio metallico sulle piante. (Nota preliminare.) [The action of metallic iodine on plants. Preliminary note.] *Atti Soc. Toscana Sci. Nat. Pisa, Processi Verbali*, 1926, v. 35, pp. 35–39. **318**

A 0·06 per cent solution of iodine in water was applied to the soil before, and several days after, germination of seeds of tomato, garden nasturtium, French beans, *Convolvulus tricolor*, soya bean, and basil. Treatment at time of planting either slightly accelerated or retarded germination. Seedlings several days old had less resistance than seed and died rather quickly after treatment. Some plants persisted in a stunted condition for a month.

1926. DENNY, F. E., *Boyce Thompson Institute for Plant Research, Inc., Yonkers, New York*. Second report on the use of chemicals for hastening the sprouting of dormant potato tubers. *Amer. J. Botany*, 1926, v. 13, pp. 386–396. **319**

Exposure of cut tubers to low concentrations of ethyl iodide vapour for 24 hours accelerated sprouting.

1926. LOEW, *Prof.* OSCAR, *biochemical department, Botanical Institute, Munich University*. Notiz über Stimulierung der Pflanzenentwicklung durch Jodkalium. [Stimulating the development of plants with potassium iodide.] *Ztschr. Pflanzenernähr. Düng.* [A], 1926, v. 7, pp. 233–234. **320**

See entry 306.

1926. STOKLASA, JULIUS, *director, State Experiment Station, Prague*. Die physiologische Funktion des Jods beim Bau- und Betriebsstoffwechsel in der chlorophyllhaltigen und chlorophyllosen Zelle. [The physiological function of iodine in the anabolism and metabolism of chlorophyll-containing and chlorophyll-free cells.] *Biochem. Ztschr.*, 1926, v. 176, pp. 38–61. **321**

Iodine is assimilated by soil organisms and plays a part as an iodine-oxidase in bacteria. Seedling plants develop poorly in media devoid of iodine, but quite small additions produce favourable growth, iodine having a beneficial effect on the development of new living tissue. Phanerogams assimilate iodine by their roots and leaves but to differing extents. Other aspects of the effect of iodine on plant physiology are discussed.

1926. STOKLASA, JULIUS. Das Jod als biogenes Element im Organismus der Zuckerrübe. [Iodine as a biogenic element in the organism of the sugar beet.] *Fortschr. Landwirtsch.*, 1926, v. 1, pp. 597–601. **322**

Author quotes his own and other results which show that treatment of iodine-deficient soils with ordinary fertilizers containing added potassium iodide produces a marked increase in the yield of leaves and roots of sugar beet and in their iodine content. The respiration activity of the plant is also increased.

1926. EGYPT. UNION DES AGRICULTEURS. L'iode en agriculture et en physiologie. [Iodine in agriculture and physiology.] *Bull. Union Agric. Égypte*, 1926, v. 24, pp. 55–58. **323**

A review (without references) of contemporary work on the effect of iodine on sugar beet culture.

1927. AMADORI, LEONIDA, *Pisa*. Secondo contributo alla conoscenza dell'azione sulle piante delle sostanze chiamate acceleratrici. L'azione dell'jodio metallico. [Second contribution to the knowledge of the action of so-called stimulants on plants. The action of metallic iodine.] *Atti. Soc. Toscana Sci. Nat. Pisa, Processi Verbali*, 1927, v. 36, pp. 62–64. **324**

Seeds of seven species of plants were treated before and after germination with a solution containing 0·3 milligramme of iodine per millilitre of water. No stimulating effect on the germination process was noted but the percentage germination was increased. Subsequent growth of the seedlings was impaired.

1927. BEAR, FIRMAN E., *professor of agricultural chemistry and soils, Ohio State University*. Medicated fertilizers. *Amer. Fertil.*, 1927, v. 66, no. 9, pp. 23–25. **325**

Author reviews the more important results of adding iodine to soils as fertilizer and questions the value of such addition.

1927. ENGELS, *Dr.* O., *Agricultural Experiment Station, Speyer-on-Rhine.* Die Joddüngung vom wissenschaftlichen und praktischen Standpunkt aus betrachtet. [Iodine manuring from the scientific and practical points of view.] *Landwirtsch. Blätter*, Speyer, 1927, v. 71, pp. 669–671; 685–686. **326**

A brief discussion of some contemporary work.

1927. FELLENBERG, THEODOR VON, *chemist, Public Health Laboratory, Berne.* Über das Verhalten saurer und alkalischer Böden im Joddüngungsversuch. [The behaviour of acid and alkaline soils in iodine manuring experiments.] *Mitt. Geb. Lebensmitteluntersuch. Hyg.*, 1927, v. 18, pp. 253–264. Also in *Biochem. Ztschr.*, 1927, v. 188, pp. 326–338. **327**

Addition of 0·0157 gramme of potassium iodide to 6 kilogrammes of two very acid and two slightly alkaline soils had no significant effect on the yield of carrots grown in pots with and without added farmyard manure. The assimilation of iodine was greater from the acid soils. It is thought that the plant assimilates iodine in the elementary form.

1927. HAAS, A. R. C., and H. S. REED, *Citrus Experiment Station, Riverside, California.* Significance of traces of elements not ordinarily added to culture solutions, for growth of young orange trees. *Botan. Gaz.*, 1927, v. 83, pp. 77–84. **328**

Deficiency symptoms in orange trees growing in sand disappeared a few weeks after the addition of a trace element mixture, containing iodine, to the culture solution.

1927. SCHÖNE, *Dr.* ALBERT, *Magdeburg.* Ueber die Verbreitung des Jodes in der Natur und seine physiologische Bedeutung im pflanzlichen und tierischen Organismus. [The distribution of iodine in nature and its physiological significance in plant and animal organisms.] *Deutsche Zuckerindust.*, 1927, v. 52, pp. 190–191. **329**

A brief review, particularly of the work of Stoklasa and his collaborators.

1927. STOKLASA, JULIUS, *director, State Experiment Station, Prague.* Über die Verbreitung des Jodes in der Natur und seine physiologische Bedeutung im pflanzlichen und tierischen Organismus. [The distribution of iodine in nature and its physiological significance in plant and animal organisms.] *Ztschr. angewandte Chem.*, 1927, v. 40, pp. 20–27. **330**

A review. Iodine promotes growth of nitrifying bacteria, intensifies the assimilation of nitrogen and gives greater plant growth, larger yield of seed and improved development of the germ.

1927. STROBEL, A., and K. SCHARRER, *Institute of Agricultural Chemistry, College of Agriculture and Brewing, Weihenstephan, Munich.* Das Jod als Pflanzennährstoff. [Iodine as a plant nutrient.] *Naturwissenschaften*, 1927, v. 15, p. 539. **331**

Results of earlier experiments (see entries 235 and 236) are not considered sufficient evidence that iodine is essential to plants.

1927. WRANGELL, M. VON, *Agricultural College, Hohenheim, Germany.* Das Jod als Pflanzennährstoff. [Iodine as a plant nutrient.] *Naturwissenschaften*, 1927, v. 15, pp. 70–73. **332**

Pot and field experiments with various plants showed that potassium iodide applied at rates up to 6 kilogrammes per hectare did not increase plant yields; indeed in cucumbers and beans iodine decreased yields. The effects on the iodine content of the crops were very variable, but the value was never more than doubled.

1928. BESSER, W. Zur Frage der Joddüngung. [The question of iodine manuring.] *Metallbörse*, 1928, v. 18, pp. 2749–2750. **333**

A brief discussion of the results of some experiments reported in the literature.

1928. DENNY, F. E., and ERNEST N. STANTON, *Boyce Thompson Institute for Plant Research, Inc., Yonkers, New York.* Localization of response of woody tissues to chemical treatments that break the rest period. *Amer. J. Botany*, 1928, v. 15, pp. 337–344. **334**

Individual twigs of dormant lilac plants growing in pots and exposed to the vapour of ethyl iodide (1 drop in 28 millilitres of water) started to grow while untreated controls remained dormant.

1928. DOERELL, *Dr.* E. G., *Prague.* Beiträge zur Joddüngungsfrage. [Contributions to the question of iodine manuring.] *Ztschr. angewandte Chem.*, 1928, v. 41, p. 1117. **335**

A summary of results of experiments reported in the following entry.

1928. DOERELL, *Dr.* E. G. Beiträge zur Joddüngungsfrage. [Contributions to the question of iodine manuring.] *Ztschr. Pflanzenernahr. Dung.* [A], 1928, v. 12, pp. 344–349. **336**

Application of potassium iodide to the soil at rates of 3·2 and 4·3 kilogrammes per hectare increased the yield of hops. A dressing of 5·4 kilogrammes per hectare caused a decrease. Iodide improved the colour of the hops but decreased the tannin content. The author states that the iodine present in Chilean nitrate of soda is sufficient to increase crop yield slightly.

1928. MÜNTER, *Dr.* F., *director, Agricultural Chemistry Experiment Station, Halle-on-Saale.* Jod als Rübendünger. [Iodine as fertilizer for sugar beet.] *Fortschr. Landwirtsch.*, 1928, v. 3, pp. 407–408. **337**

Application of potassium iodide or sodium iodate at rates of 1 and 2 kilogrammes per hectare had no beneficial effect on the yield of tops or roots of sugar beet. No significant superiority of Chilean nitrate of soda over synthetic sodium nitrate was observed.

1928. MÜNTER, F. Arbeiten der agrikultur-chemischen Versuchsstation Halle a.d.S. [Researches at the Agricultural Chemistry Experiment Station, Halle-on-Saale.] *Landwirtsch. Jahrb.*, 1928, v. 67, pp. 1–102. **338**

On pp. 88–90 results are given of iodine manurial trials with sugar beet over three successive years. Application of up to 2 kilogrammes of iodine, as potassium iodide or sodium iodate, per hectare had no beneficial effect on growth or on yield of dry matter or sugar.

1929. ENGELS, *Dr.* O., *Agricultural Experiment Station, Speyer-on-Rhine*. Die Bedeutung des Jodes für den pflanzlichen, sowie menschlichen und tierischen Organismus. [The importance of iodine for plant, human and animal organisms.] *Kunstdünger u. Leim*, 1929, v. 26, pp. 364–366. **339**

A general discussion.

1929. GAUS, W., and R. GRIESSBACH, *I. G. Farbenindustrie A.-G., Ludwigshafen-on-Rhine*. Jodfrage und Landwirtschaft. [The iodine question and agriculture.] *Ztschr. Pflanzenernähr. Düng.* [A], 1929, v. 13, pp. 321–425. **340**

Authors deny that iodine acts as a stimulant to plants and increases their yield. They admit that iodine manuring may increase the iodine content of plants. The increase varies widely between species, and the iodine is often stored in organs of the plant which are waste products from the point of view of agriculture, *e.g.* leaves of sugar beet. They, therefore, contend that there is no advantage in the use of iodized fertilizers.

1929. GUM, ROBERT, *Munich*. Ein Beitrag zur Frage der Joddüngung. [A contribution to the question of iodine manuring.] *Thesis, Munich Technical College*, 1929, 67 pp. **341**

Rape, garden cress and mustard were all injured by 0·1 per cent solutions of potassium or calcium iodide in pot experiments. Lower concentrations varied in their effects. In field experiments 5·0 and 0·5 kilogrammes of potassium or calcium iodide per hectare had injurious effects on dwarf beans, but not on carrots or garden cress. Celery was stimulated by these amounts, and the yield increased. Plants manured with iodine have a higher iodine content, especially in the leaves.

1929. SCHMITZ, EMIL, *Institute for Soil and Plant Science, Agricultural College, Bonn-Poppelsdorf*. Über den Einfluss von Chlorat, Jodat, Perchlorat und Perjodat auf die Keimung und erste Jugendentwicklung von Kulturgewächsen. [The effect of chlorate, iodate, perchlorate and periodate on the germination and early development of cultivated plants.] *Inaugural Dissertation, Agricultural College, Bonn-Poppelsdorf*, 1929, 56 pp. **342**

In tests on sand and loam cultures, in which seeds of various species were used, sodium iodate and periodate were applied singly in amounts equivalent to those in a normal dressing of Chilean nitrate of soda and in five and ten times these amounts. Neither salt had any effect on the germination and iodate had no effect on the growth of the seedlings. Periodate at the normal level slightly checked the growth of wheat and oat seedlings and had a transitory effect on winter barley. At levels five and ten times normal it had a small to marked injurious effect on the seedlings of wheat, horse beans, vetches, maize, oats and winter barley.

1929. STOKLASA, JULIUS, *director, State Experiment Station, Prague*. Über den Einfluss des Jodions auf das Wachstum und die Zellvermehrung der Halophyten. [The effect of the iodine ion on the growth and cell multiplication of halophytes.] *Biochem. Ztschr.*, 1929, v. 211, pp. 213–228. **343**

Pot culture trials with sand as the medium showed that when 0·005 gramme of iodine as potassium iodide and iodate was added to each litre of nutrient solution the rate of germination of sugar beet was increased, the seedlings were larger and the subsequent growth of the plants was more vigorous. The iodine content of the leaves, stems and roots was increased.

1929. STRÖBELE, *Dr.* F., *director, Limburgerhof Agricultural Experiment Station, I.G. Farbenindustrie A.-G., Ludwigshafen-on-Rhine*. Das Jod bei der Pflanzenernährung. [Iodine in plant nutrition.] *Ergebn. Agrikulturchem.*, 1929, v. 1, pp. 53–84. **344**

From a survey of the literature and taking into account some of his own experiments the author cannot confirm Stoklasa's finding of increased crop yield from iodine manuring. Small dressings of iodine, such as occur in Chilean nitrate, have no effect; medium dressings produce results within the limits of experimental error; large dressings may depress yield and produce other harmful effects on the plant.

1930. COTTON, MARJORIE, *Columbia University, New York*. Toxic effects of iodine and nickel on buckwheat grown in solution cultures. *Bull. Torrey Botan. Club*, 1930, v. 57, pp. 127–140. **345**

Potassium iodide at a concentration equivalent to 40·1 parts of iodine per million killed almost all the plants within 3 weeks of application. Growth was depressed at concentrations as low as 1·27 parts per million. Weaker concentrations than this had a toxic effect on the leaves. No stimulating effect was observed.

1930. WENDT, *Dr.* G. VON, *Helsingfors*, and A. ANDERSEN, *agronomist, Lindingö*. Stimulationsversuche mit Jod. [Stimulation experiments with iodine.] *Gartenflora*, 1930, v. 79, pp. 181–183; 213–219. **346**

Dilute solutions of iodine, amounting to not more than 500 microgrammes of pure iodine per square metre of soil, applied weekly, stimulated the development of beans, peas, strawberries, lettuce, spinach, rhubarb. Iodine application to the soil also improved the colour of lobelia blooms.

1931. MALHOTRA, R. C., *professor of biology, St. Mary's College, Kansas*. Periodic permeability of iodine solution and water in the protoplasm of *Zea mays* seeds. *Protoplasma*, 1931, v. 13, pp. 374–388. **347**

Maize seeds were placed in 0·05 per cent iodine solution and incubated at temperatures varying between 25° and 60° C. Rate of intake of iodine solution increased with time of contact and with rise of temperature. Iodine appeared to stimulate germination at 25–30° C but retarded it at higher temperatures.

1931. MEYER, A. H., *associate professor of soil research, Louisiana Agricultural Experiment Station, Baton Rouge*. Some neglected soil factors in plant growth. *J. Amer. Soc. Agron.*, 1931, v. 23, pp. 606–625. **348**

When small quantities of boron, zinc, aluminium, manganese and copper (as suitable salts) were added to the basal nutrient solution, the further addition of iodine (0·25 milligramme per culture) as potassium iodide gave much more luxuriant growth and a higher yield of dry matter in both the tops and roots of buckwheat grown in quartz sand cultures.

1931. PICADO T., C., *San José, Costa Rica*. El yodo cofermento del metabolismo de los azúcares en las plantas y animales. [Iodine as co-enzyme in carbohydrate metabolism of plants and animals.] *Arch. Soc. Biol. Montevideo*, 1931, Suppl. 3, pp. 737–739. **349**

Irrigation with weak aqueous potassium iodide (1:20,000 and 1:100,000 solutions were used) increased the carbohydrate reserves in cabbage, radish, beet and sugar cane.

1931. SCHARRER, K., and W. SCHROPP, *Institute of Agricultural Chemistry, College of Agriculture and Brewing, Weihenstephan, Munich.* Mitteilung zur Kenntnis des Jods als biogenes Element. 24. Untersuchungen über den Einfluss steigender Gaben von Jodid-, Jodat- und Perjodation auf die Keimung und die erste Jugendentwicklung einiger Kulturpflanzen. [Iodine as a biogenic element. 24. The effect of increasing doses of iodide, iodate and periodate on the germination and early development of some cultivated plants.] *Biochem. Ztschr.*, 1931, v. 236, pp. 187–204. **350**

Application of increasing amounts of potassium iodide, iodate and periodate to the soil showed that the higher amounts adversely affected germination and early development of four cereals. The iodide had the greatest effect and the periodate the least. The sensitivity of the plants was in decreasing order: oats, wheat, rye, barley.

1931. SCHARRER, K., and W. SCHROPP. Mitteilung zur Kenntnis des Jods als biogenes Element. 25. Weitere Untersuchungen über die Wirkung steigender Jodmengen in Form von Jodid-, Jodat-, und Perjodation sowie elementarem Jod auf die Keimung und die erste Jugendentwicklung verschiedener Kulturpflanzen. [Iodine as a biogenic element. 25. Further investigations into the effect of increasing doses of iodine in the form of iodide, iodate, periodate and elementary iodine on the germination and early development of various cultivated plants.] *Biochem. Ztschr.*, 1931, v. 239, pp. 74–93. **351**

Potassium salts had a more detrimental effect on germination than sodium salts, and iodides than periodates. The injurious effect on subsequent growth decreased in the order iodides, elementary iodine, iodates, periodates. Sensitivity of the plants tested was in decreasing order: oats, summer barley, wheat, winter barley, rye.

1932. HARRIES, RACHEL, *University College of Wales, Aberystwyth.* An investigation by cultural methods of some of the factors influencing the development of the gametophytes and the early stages of the sporophytes of *Laminaria digitata, L. saccharina*, and *L. Cloustoni*. *Ann. Botany*, 1932, v. 46, pp. 893–928. **352**

In seawater cultures of *Laminaria* the amount of iodine present in the initial supply of water was sufficient for sexual growth and reproduction, and production of small plantlets. Periodic addition of 0·05 milligramme of potassium iodide per litre accelerated development but larger quantities were ineffectual or had an inhibitory effect.

1932. NEHRING, K., W. ZIELSTORFF and W. SCHMIDT, *Institute of Agricultural Chemistry, University of Königsberg, East Prussia.* Über die Einwirkung verschiedener Jodgaben auf die Erträge, Zusammensetzung und Verdaulichkeit von Wiesengras. [The effect of different amounts of iodine on the yield, composition and digestibility of meadow grasses.] *Landwirtsch. Jahrb.*, 1932, v. 76, pp. 505–523. **353**

Manuring with potassium iodide had no effect on yield, but increased to some extent the iodine content of grasses. Spraying with a solution of potassium iodide, however, increased iodine content of plants to a very marked extent; iodine uptake amounted to 20 per cent of the total applied, while with potassium iodide manuring it was under 1 per cent.

1932. SCHMIDT, *Dr.* E. W., *director, Research Institute, Klein-Wanzleben, Germany.* Über Jodnekrose an Zuckerrübenkeimlingen. [Necrosis produced by iodine in sugar beet seedlings.] *Angewandte Botanik*, 1932, v. 14, pp. 229–232. **354**

Characteristic necrotic symptoms appeared in the leaves 12 to 14 days after the seedlings had been sprayed with dilute aqueous potassium iodide solution. A solution containing 0·001 per cent of iodide was required to produce these symptoms in sand-grown seedlings, and one ten times stronger (0·01 per cent) was required for seedlings grown in earth. No symptoms appeared in either sand- or earth-grown seedlings with an iodide concentration of 0·0001 per cent.

1933. KAHO, HUGO, *plant physiology laboratory, University of Tartu.* Das Verhalten der Pflanzenzelle gegen Schwermetallsalze. [The behaviour of plant cells in the presence of heavy metal salts.] *Planta*, 1933, v. 18, pp. 664–682. **355**

A 0·2 *M* solution of cadmium iodide had an exceptionally toxic effect on the plasma of the epidermal cells of red cabbage leaves.

1933. [KHALIZEV, A. A., and S. A. REMIZOV.] ХАЛИЗЕВ, А. А., and С. А. РЕМИЗОВ. Значение микроэлементов для агрохимической методики. [The importance of trace elements in agrochemical technique.] *Khimizatsiya Sotsialist. Zemledel.*, 1933, no. 3, pp. 206–214. **356**

A mixture of very small quantities of trace elements (including iodine at a rate of 0·125 milligramme per litre of the culture solution) had a favourable effect on growth and yield of ten kinds of legumes and vegetables in pot experiments.

1933. KRENGEL, W. Ist die Joddüngung im Gemüsebau zweckmässig und wirtschaftlich? [Is iodine manuring effective and economic in vegetable growing?] *Obst- u. Gemüsebau*, 1933, v. 79, pp. 87–88. **357**

A popular review of earlier work. The conclusion is that iodine manuring is not a practical proposition for the vegetable grower, and that if extra iodine is required in the human diet recourse should be had to vegetables which are naturally rich in iodine.

1933. [SHKOLNIK, M. YA.] Школьник, М. Я. Влияние бора и других дополнительных элементов на развитие льна. [The effect of boron and other additional elements on the development of flax.] *Izvestiya Akad. Nauk SSSR*, 7 *Ser.*, *Otdelenie Mat. Estestv. Nauk*, 1933, no. 8, pp. 1163–1188. **358**

Flax seedlings grew normally in a nutrient solution to which small quantities of some trace elements, including iodine as potassium iodide at the rate of 0·00025 gramme per litre, were added.

1933. [VLASYUK, *Prof.* P. A.] Власюк, Проф. П. А., *Ukrainian Sugar Industry Research Institute, and agrochemical laboratory, Verkhnyachka Selection Station.* Химическая стимуляция как элемент повышения урожайности с.-х. растений. [Chemical stimulation as a factor tending to increase the productivity of farm crops.] *Nauk. Zapiski Tsukr. Prom.*, 1933, v. 10, no. 27, pp. 181–197; English summary pp. 197–198. **359**

Soaking seeds before sowing in an aqueous solution (1:10,000) of potassium iodide increased, in some cases very markedly, crop yield of vegetable marrows, carrots, sugar beet (roots, tops and sugar) and mangolds (roots and tops).

1933. [VLASYUK, *Prof.* P. A.] Власюк, Проф. П. А., Новые приемы химизации в социалистическом земледелии. (Химическая стимуляция и каталитические удобрения.) [New methods of chemization in socialistic agriculture. (Chemical stimulation and catalytic fertilization.)] *Nauk. Zapiski Tsukr. Prom.*, 1933, v. 10, no. 28, pp. 113–131; English summary p. 132. **360**

Treatment of soil at sowing time with an aqueous solution of potassium iodide at the rate of 5 kilogrammes of iodine per hectare slightly decreased crop yield in sugar beet and markedly increased it in mangolds, carrots and vegetable marrows. The treatment effectively controlled weeds and insect pests in the sugar beet plots.

1934. BEAUMONT, A. B., and E. B. HOLLAND. The absorption by food plants of chemical elements of importance in human nutrition. *Massachusetts Agric. Exp. Stat.*, Bulletin No. 315 (Annual Report for 1933–34), 1935, pp. 14–15. **361**

Potassium iodide at 16 kilogrammes per hectare increased the yield of turnips, but not of spinach, more than any other treatment.

1934. LEHMAN, BEATRICE, and F. M. ANDREWS, *Indiana University*. Nuclear division in *Tradescantia virginiana*. *Plant Physiol.*, 1934, v. 9, pp. 845–849. **362**

Vapour from a 5 per cent solution of iodine had no effect on cell division in the staminal hairs of the common spiderwort. Cell division ceased, however, when the hairs were immersed in a 1 in 833 aqueous solution of iodine.

1934. SCHOLZ, *Dr.* WERNER, *Institute of Agricultural Chemistry and Bacteriology, Breslau University*. Pflanzennährstoffe welche der Landwirt seinen Pflanzen in der Düngung nur unbewusst oder überhaupt nicht gibt. [Plant nutrients which the farmer supplies to his plants in fertilizers unknowingly or not at all.] *Ztschr. Pflanzenernähr. Düng.* [B], 1934, v. 13, pp. 12–22. **363**

A review of the literature on elements essential for plant growth. The opinion is expressed that iodine is not a plant nutrient and that iodine manuring is not necessary in agricultural practice.

1934. [SUKHOV, K. S., and M. N. LANSHINA.] Сухов, К. С., and М. Н. Ланшина. Патологические изменения в растительных клетках при действии иодистого калия. (В связи с вопросом о природе Х-тел.) Предварительное сообщение. [Pathological changes in plant cells caused by the action of potassium iodide, with reference to the problem of the nature of the X-bodies. Preliminary communication.] In: *Вирусные болезни растений в Крыму і на Украине.* [Virus diseases of plants in the Crimea and the Ukraine.] Simferopol: *Госуд. Издат. Крым.*, 1934, pp. 122–124. **364**

Intracellular inclusions, closely resembling the X-bodies found by other workers in the cells of plants affected with virus disease, were observed in the growing point of beet seedlings watered with a 0·01 per cent potassium iodide solution, which is stated to cause a necrosis of the seedlings (see entry 354). Inclusions were absent from the cells of untreated beet seedlings.

1934. VOGEL, *Dr.* F., *Weihenstephan*. Die Wirkung des Jods auf verschiedene Gemüsearten. [The effect of iodine on different vegetables.] *Obst- u. Gemüsebau*, 1934, v. 80, pp. 19–21; 41–42. **365**

An extensive series of pot and field experiments was carried out on 16 different vegetables. With the exception of radishes little or no increase in yield resulted from iodine manuring. Lettuce, endive, spinach, mangolds, carrots and beetroot absorbed iodine well; savoys, kohl-rabi and tomatoes did so fairly well, but cauliflower, cabbage, celery, beans and cucumbers absorbed only very small amounts. Iodization of vegetables is considered a practical proposition and is best done by a single moderate dose.

1934. WEBER, H. J., *Alfter, near Bonn*. Meine Versuche mit Jodkali. [My experiments with potassium iodide.] *Rhein. Monatsschr. Obst-, Garten- u. Gemüsebau*, 1934, pp. 32–33. **366**

Plot trials confirm the value of small applications of potassium iodide to the soil for the culture of lettuce, cauliflower, early potatoes and tomatoes. The lettuce and cauliflower were ready to cut 8 days earlier as a result of the treatment and photographs of the plots with and without potassium iodide leave no doubt as to its value for early potatoes.

1934. WYND, F. LYLE, *Henry Shaw School of Botany, Washington University*. The effects of increasing the iodine content of the tomato plant on respiration and enzymatic activity. *Ann. Missouri Botan. Garden*, 1934, v. 21, pp. 367–432. **367**

Addition of 1 to 20 parts of potassium iodide per million to a basal nutrient solution had a depressing effect on growth of tomatoes in water cultures. Respiration, and peroxidase and invertase activity were decreased by the lowest concentration but greatly increased by the higher concentrations.

1935. ENGELS, *Dr.* O., *Agricultural Experiment Station, Speyer-on-Rhine*. Die künstlichen Düngemittel (Handelsdünger) als Träger von Pflanzennährstoffen, und sonstigen notwendigen Bestandteilen, welche der Landwirt meist unbewusst den Pflanzen verabreicht. [Artificial fertilizers (commercial fertilizers) as a source of plant nutrients and of other necessary constituents usually supplied unknowingly by the farmer.] *Kunstdünger u. Leim*, 1935, v. 32, pp. 195–199; 227–231. **368**

Manuring with iodine is considered unnecessary as enough iodine is present in the soil and in the usual fertilizers to ensure sufficient uptake by plants.

1935. FREY-WYSSLING, A., *Zurich*. Die unentbehrlichen Elemente der Pflanzennahrung. [Elements essential for plant nutrition.] *Naturwissenschaften*, 1935, v. 23, pp. 767–769. **369**

Iodine is included among those elements which, while not essential to plant life, exert a stimulating effect on growth in small amounts, but may be poisonous at higher levels.

1935. KENTUCKY AGRICULTURAL EXPERIMENT STATION. [Studies on iodine.] *Kentucky Agric. Exp. Stat.*, 48th Annual Report, for 1935 (1936), part 1, pp. 17–19. **370**

Short notes are given on: (*a*) the effect of potassium iodide on maize; (*b*) the effect of iodine on plant and animal life; (*c*) iodine in vegetables. It is stated that iodine manuring prevented the occurrence of potato scab.

1935. [KHALIZEV, A. A., and M. V. KATALIMOV.] Хализев, А. А., and М. В. Каталымов. Ueber Mikroelemente. [Trace elements.] In: Доклады Научного Института по Удобрениям и Инсектофунгисидам к 3 Международному Конгрессу Почвоведов в Оксфорде (1935). [*Reports of the Scientific Institute for Fertilizers and Insectofungicides for the 3rd International Congress of Soil Science at Oxford* (1935).] Leningrad: *ОНТИ*, pp. 51–65. In German. **371**

Small-scale pot experiments with mixtures of trace elements, some of which included potassium iodide at a rate of 2 milligrammes per kilogramme of soil, showed that trace elements cause a significant increase in yield of such plants as flax, mustard and oats.

1935. SCHMIDT, *Dr.* E. W., *director, Research Institute, Klein-Wanzleben, Germany.* Beiträge zur Keimungsphysiologie der Zuckerrübe. 4. Über die Wirkung von Giften auf Rübenkeimlinge. [The physiology of germination of sugar beet. 4. The effect of poisons on beet seedlings.] *Ztschr. Wirtschaftsgr. Zuckerindust.*, 1935, v. 85, technical part, pp. 303–315. **372**

Potassium iodide applied in solution at rates of 1 part of iodide to 10,000 and 25,000 parts of soil injured the leaves and roots of sugar beet seedlings.

1935. [SHCHERBAKOV, A. P.] Щербаков, А. П., *Scientific Institute for Fertilizers and Insectofungicides, Academy of Sciences of the U.S.S.R., Moscow.* Влияние микроэлементов на распределение кальция, магния и фосфорной кислоты в растении. [The effect of trace elements on the distribution of calcium, magnesium and phosphoric acid in plants.] *Khimizatsiya Sotsialist. Zemledel.*, 1935, no. 7, pp. 34–41. **373**

A mixture of trace elements (including iodine at a rate of 0·1 milligramme per 4 kilogrammes of culture medium) increased the growth and yield of flax in pot experiments.

1935. [SHCHERBAKOV, A. P.] Щербаков, А. П. Einfluss von Mikroelementen auf die Verteilung des Kalkes, der Magnesia und der Phosphorsäure in den Pflanzen. [The effect of trace elements on the distribution of calcium, magnesium and phosphoric acid in plants.] *Ztschr. Pflanzenernähr. Düng.*, 1935, v. 39, pp. 129–140. **374**

A German translation of the Russian paper noted in the preceding entry.

1935. YOUNG, R. S. Certain rarer elements in soils and fertilizers, and their role in plant growth. *Cornell Univ. Agric. Exp. Stat.*, Memoir No. 174, 1935, 70 pp. **375**

The growth of timothy in coarse sandy loam was stimulated by 10 parts of iodine per million of soil. A low concentration of iodine was necessary before growth in three types of algae became equal to or greater than controls. A literature review with 15 pages of references is included.

1936. BRENCHLEY, WINIFRED E., *Rothamsted Experimental Station, Harpenden, Herts.* The essential nature of certain minor elements for plant nutrition. *Botan. Rev.*, 1936, v. 2, pp. 173–196. **376**

"While it is generally recognized that iodine is toxic in stronger concentrations, opinions differ as to its action in great dilution. Whereas Meyer (1931) claimed that iodine is essential for the best growth of buckwheat, Cotton (1930) states that it exerts no beneficial action on that species even in great dilution. Potassium iodide has been found to improve lettuce, cucumber and tomatoes, causing quicker growth and preventing crimping in lettuces and stem-rotting in tomatoes."

1936. KENTUCKY AGRICULTURAL EXPERIMENT STATION. [Studies on iodine.] *Kentucky Agric. Exp. Stat.*, 49th Annual Report, for 1936 (1937), part 1, pp. 22–24. **377**

Short notes are given on: (*a*) iodine content of plant materials; (*b*) iodine in soils, fertilizers and limestone; (*c*) iodine in milk; (*d*) effect of iodine on the growth of tomatoes; (*e*) effect of iodine on growth of buckwheat in water cultures; (*f*) effect of iodine on growth of tobacco.

1936. MUCKENHIRN, R. J., *department of soils, University of Wisconsin.* Response of plants to boron, copper and manganese. *J. Amer. Soc. Agron.*, 1936, v. 28, pp. 824–842. **378**

Growth of lettuce in sand cultures was unaffected by the application of sodium iodide, at the rate of 2·0 milligrammes per 13 kilogrammes of sand, along with the basal nutrient solution. In pot trials potassium iodide at the rate of 6·5 lb. per acre increased the yield of onions on one peat soil and decreased it on another.

1937. MCHARGUE, J. S., and R. K. CALFEE, *Kentucky Agricultural Experiment Station, Lexington.* The necessity of minor elements for the growth of tomatoes in a poor soil. *J. Amer. Soc. Agron.*, 1937, v. 29, pp. 385–391. **379**

Very marked beneficial effects on growth and yield and quality of fruit were obtained by the addition of 2·5 parts of iodine per million, along with small quantities of other minor elements, to soil cultures containing adequate amounts of the major elements.

1937. VEGESACK, R. VON. Jod als Düngemittel. [Iodine as a manure.] *Deutsche landwirtsch. Presse*, 1937, v. 64, pp. 541–542. **380**

Small-scale experiments with lupins, sugar beet and mangolds showed that iodine applied at a rate of 480 grammes per quarter hectare increased the yield. Iodine at a rate of 8 kilogrammes per hectare produced toxic symptoms.

1938. ARNON, D. I., *division of truck crops, University of California.* Micro-elements in culture-solution experiments with higher plants. *Amer. J. Botany*, 1938, v. 25, pp. 322–325. **381**

Addition of a number of trace elements to a basal

culture solution had a marked beneficial effect on the growth of asparagus and lettuce. The further addition of a number of other trace elements, added together and including iodine as iodide, had little or no effect.

1938. BOBKO, E. V., and V. V. ZERLING, *Institute of Forage Crops, Moscow.* Influence du bore sur le développement reproductif des plantes. [Effect of boron on the reproductive development of plants.] *Ann. Agron.*, Paris, 1938, v. 8, pp. 174–184. **382**

Among the trace elements studied, iodine was found to have a beneficial effect on the germination of pollen grains and the length of pollen tubes in several species of plants.

1938. ENGELS, *Dr.* O., *Agricultural Experiment Station, Speyer-on-Rhine.* Spurenelemente und ihre Bedeutung für das Pflanzenwachstum. [Trace elements and their significance in plant growth.] *Chemikerzeitung*, 1938, v. 62, pp. 165–167. **383**

It is proved that certain plants can be enriched in iodine by iodine manuring, but not that crop yields can also be increased in this way.

1938. [KASPAROVA, S. A.] Каспарова, С. А., *Institute of Biochemistry, Academy of Sciences of the U.S.S.R., Moscow.* О роли некоторых элементов минерального питания в определении устойчивости цикория при хранении. [The role of certain mineral elements in determining the resistance of chicory against infection during storage.] *Izvestiya Akad. Nauk SSSR, Otdelenie Mat. Estestv. Nauk, Ser. Biol.*, 1938, no. 2, pp. 381–397. English summary pp. 397–398. **384**

In pot trials, addition of potassium iodide to the soil at the rate of 1 to 3 milligrammes per kilogramme had no beneficial effect on the yield of chicory but increased the resistance of the roots against *Sclerotinia* infection during storage.

1938. MCMURTREY, Jr., J. E., *senior physiologist, division of tobacco and plant nutrition, Bureau of Plant Industry*, and W. O. ROBINSON, *soil chemistry and physics research division, Bureau of Chemistry and Soils.* Neglected soil constituents that affect plant and animal development. *U.S. Department of Agriculture*, Yearbook for 1938, pp. 807–829. **385**

The importance of trace elements for plant and animal development is discussed. Since iodine is so easily leached from soil, large, infrequent applications are not as desirable as small applications made to a particular crop.

1938. OREGON AGRICULTURAL EXPERIMENT STATION. Minor elements in relation to soil fertility. *Oregon Agric. Exp. Stat.*, Bulletin No. 359 (Biennial Report for 1936–1938), 1938, p. 106. **386**

Briefly reports that evidence has been obtained indicating that the effect of iodine on plant growth is indirect. An accompanying illustration shows iodine-treated alfalfa and other plants in healthier condition than plants not so treated. Stated that iodine is one of the essential minor elements.

1938. POWERS, W. L., *soil scientist, Oregon Agricultural Experiment Station, Corvallis.* The minor elements in soil fertility and plant nutrition. *Oregon Agric. Exp. Stat.*, Information Circular No. 192, 1938, 5+[3] pp. **387**

Brief reference is made to the author's work on the value of iodine for increasing crop yield.

1938. [SHCHERBAKOV, A. P.] Щербаков, А. П., *Scientific Institute for Fertilizers and Insectofungicides, Academy of Sciences of the U.S.S.R., Moscow.* Concerning physiological rôle of elements indispensable for plants in minute amounts. *C. R. Acad. Sci.*, Moscow, 1938, v. 21, pp. 189–193. In English. **388**

Buckwheat in sand grew better, gave a bigger crop, and assimilated more nitrogen and phosphorus from a basal nutrient solution when small quantities of trace-element salts, including potassium iodide at the rate of 0·125 milligramme of iodine per kilogramme, were added to the sand.

1938. SINGH, B. N., and S. PRASAD, *Institute of Agricultural Research, Benares Hindu University.* The tolerance of wheat plants for chlorides of certain non-essential elements. *Indian J. Agric. Sci.*, 1938, v. 6, pp. 720–745. **389**

Iodine chloride added to Knop's nutrient solution in four concentrations varying from 0·0001 to 0·01 *M* was slightly toxic at the lowest concentration and highly toxic at the highest to wheat seedlings grown in this solution.

1938. WHITE, PHILIP R., *department of animal and plant pathology, Rockefeller Institute for Medical Research, Princeton, New Jersey.* Accessory salts in the nutrition of excised tomato roots. *Plant Physiol.*, 1938, v. 13, pp. 391–398. **390**

Of twelve accessory salts included in a nutrient solution, potassium iodide appeared to be one of four essential for the growth of isolated tomato roots under the experimental conditions reported.

1939. DENNY, F. E., *Boyce Thompson Institute for Plant Research, Inc., Yonkers, New York.* Leaf-epinasty tests with chemical vapors. *Contrib. Boyce Thompson Inst. Plant Research*, 1939, v. 10, pp. 191–195. **391**

Of 77 volatile compounds tested only three, including ethyl iodide, induced stronger growth on the upper than on the under side of potato leaves.

1939. [FAVORSKI, M. V.] Фаворский, М. В., *cytological laboratory, All-Union Institute of Plant Industry, Leningrad.* New polyploidy-inducing chemicals. *C. R. Acad. Sci.*, Moscow, 1939, v. 25, pp. 71–74. In English. **392**

Barley seedlings produced swollen root tips when treated with iodoform (0·01 gramme in 200 millilitres of air), and growth was delayed.

1939. POWERS, W. L., *Oregon State Agricultural College, Corvallis.* Will iodine come to be considered an essential plant nutrient? *Science*, 1939, v. 89, pp. 434–435. **393**

The following tentative results from 10 years of water and soil culture experiments are briefly reported. Mathematically significant increases in yield have been obtained, especially with alfalfa, clover and lettuce, while germination has been stimulated with maize. Iodine seems to promote development of chlorophyll; and soil micro-organisms appear to be affected, particularly nitrogen-fixing legume root bacteria.

1940. LEROUX, DÉSIRÉ, *director, agricultural chemistry laboratory, Conservatoire National des Arts et Métiers, Paris.* Influence de quelques "oligo-éléments" sur le développement d'une légumineuse. [Influence of some trace elements on the development of a legume.] *C. R. Acad. Agric. France*, 1940, v. 26, pp. 481–487. **394**

Sodium iodide applied in solution at rates of 2 and 5 milligrammes of iodine per kilogramme of soil increased the yield of stems, leaves, pods and seeds of peas grown in pots.

1940. SINOTÔ, YOSITO, and AKIRA YUASA, *Botanical Institute, Tokyo Imperial University.* The cytomorphological effects of halogens and halogen salts on plant cells. *Botan. Mag.*, Tokyo, 1940, v. 54, pp. 205–214. **395**

Dilute aqueous solutions of iodine or iodides induce cytomorphological effects, such as irregular mitoses, vacuolization of the nucleus and destruction of nuclear contents, in the root tip cells of *Vicia faba* seedlings placed in them.

1940. SUTOH, H. Studies on the value of chemicals as manure for *Juncus effusus* L. var. *decipiens* Buch. Report 2. On the effect of different kinds of potash salts. *J. Agric. Chem. Soc. Japan*, 1940, v. 16, pp. 687–695. In Japanese: English summary in *Bull. Agric. Chem. Soc. Japan* [bound in with the *Journal*], pp. 121–122. **396**

Potassium iodide was highly toxic. No details given. (From English summary.)

1940. [VERNER, R. R.] ВЕРНЕР, Р. Р., *Pedagogic Institute, Syktyvkar.* Die Veränderung der Ölbildung unter Einwirkung von Jod. [Change in oil formation caused by iodine.] *C. R. Acad. Sci.*, Moscow, 1940, v. 27, pp. 853–856. In German. **397**

Injection of 1 to 5 milligrammes of potassium iodide in 300 millilitres of water into the stems of sunflower plants over a period of 16 days at the time of flowering stimulated oil formation in the seed in the early stages of maturity. The oil at these stages had a higher iodine value.

1941. GREENFIELD, SYDNEY S., *department of botany, Columbia University, New York.* Differential inhibition of photochemical and dark reactions in photosynthesis by inorganic compounds. *Science*, 1941, v. 93, pp. 550–551. **398**

Treatment of cells of *Chlorella vulgaris* with an aqueous solution of potassium iodide inhibited photosynthesis over a wide range of light intensities.

1941. LEROUX, DÉSIRÉ, *director, agricultural chemistry laboratory, Conservatoire National des Arts et Métiers, Paris.* Oligo-éléments et teneur en azote des graines de pois. [Trace elements and nitrogen content of pea seeds.] *C. R. Acad. Agric. France*, 1941, v. 27, pp. 807–810. **399**

Addition of 2 milligrammes of iodine as sodium iodide per kilogramme of dry soil had no significant effect on the nitrogen content of peas in pots. A dressing of 5 milligrammes, on the other hand, increased the nitrogen content on a dry matter basis from 4·43 to 4·75 per cent.

1941. LEWIS, J. C., and W. L. POWERS, *Oregon Agricultural Experiment Station, Corvallis.* Iodine in relation to plant nutrition. *J. Agric. Research*, 1941, v. 63, pp. 623–637. **400**

The authors adopt a more cautious attitude than previously expressed (see entry **393**). Their results of additions of iodine to Oregon (goitrous) soils were largely negative. Well-replicated pot culture trials with legumes on Aiken clay loam, however, gave a small response to iodine treatment that seemed statistically significant. The few other cases where stimulative actions were found in preliminary trials must be tested more thoroughly. The largely negative results of iodine fertilization of soils in a region of endemic goitre support the conclusion, based on solution culture trials, that iodine is either not essential for plant nutrition or is required only in very small amounts.

1941. LEWIS, J. C., and W. L. POWERS. Antagonistic action of chlorides on the toxicity of iodides to corn. *Plant Physiol.*, 1941, v. 16, pp. 393–398. **401**

Addition of 20 parts of chloride per million parts of a basal nutrient solution partially prevented the toxic action to maize caused by the addition of 2 parts of potassium iodide per million.

1941. [RICHTER, A. A., and N. G. VASILEVA.] РИХТЕР, А. А., and Н. Г. ВАСИЛЬЕВА, *photosynthesis laboratory, Academy of Sciences of the U.S.S.R., Moscow.* Spraying with micro-elements as a method of increasing the rate of photosynthesis. *C. R. Acad. Sci.*, Moscow, 1941, v. 30, pp. 659–660. In English. **402**

Spraying the leaves of horse beans (*Vicia faba*) in the evening with a 0·02 per cent solution of potassium iodide resulted in a 30·5 per cent increase in the rate of photosynthesis the following day.

1941. [TSERLING, V. V.] ЦЕРЛИНГ, В. В. Influence of major and minor elements on pollen germination in plants. *C. R. Acad. Sci.*, Moscow, 1941, v. 32, pp. 439–442. In English. **403**

Low concentrations of potassium iodide decreased the germination of pollen grains in sucrose solution.

1942. GREENFIELD, SYDNEY S., *department of botany, Columbia University, New York.* Inhibitory effects of inorganic compounds on photosynthesis in *Chlorella. Amer. J. Botany*, 1942, v. 29, pp. 121–131. **404**

Studies at high light intensity showed that a strong solution of potassium iodide was required to retard the process of photosynthesis in *Chlorella vulgaris*.

1942. HAGEMAN, R. H., E. S. HODGE and J. S. MCHARGUE, *Kentucky Agricultural Experiment Station, Lexington.* Effect of potassium iodide on the ascorbic acid content and growth of tomato plants. *Plant Physiol.*, 1942, v. 17, pp. 465–472. **405**

Potassium iodide applied in a basal nutrient solution at the rate of 4 parts of iodine per million of sand had no beneficial effect on the growth of tomato plants in sand cultures. Higher concentrations had an injurious effect. Iodide caused a marked decrease in the ascorbic acid content of the green parts of the plants.

1942. LEROUX, DÉSIRÉ, *director, agricultural chemistry laboratory, Conservatoire National des Arts et Métiers, Paris*. Contribution à l'étude agronomique de divers "oligo-éléments." [Contribution to the study of some trace elements in agriculture.] Alençon: *Imprimerie Alençonnaise, Maison Poulet-Malassis*, 1942, [iii]+176 pp. **406**

The results of the author's own pot trials are recorded. Applications of 2 and 5 milligrammes of iodine as sodium iodide per kilogramme of soil increased the yields of pea leaves, stems, pods and seeds and, at the higher level, the nitrogen content of the seeds.

1943. SHERMAN, G. DONALD, J. S. MCHARGUE and R. H. HAGEMAN, *Kentucky Agricultural Experiment Station, Lexington*. The influence of halides on the oxidation of manganese in soil. *Soil Sci.*, 1943, v. 56, pp. 127–134. **407**

Sodium iodide retards the oxidation of added manganous manganese in alkaline but not in acid soils. The significance of this finding in relation to the availability of soil manganese for plant growth is discussed.

1945. LO, TENG-YI, and SHAN-MING CHEN, *department of agricultural chemistry, National Chekiang University, Meitan, Kweichow, China*. The effect of chemical treatment on ascorbic acid content of vegetables. *Proc. Inst. Food Technologists*, 1945, pp. 154–157. **408**

Treatment with highly dilute aqueous solutions of potassium iodide or sodium iodide reduced the ascorbic acid content of mung bean sprouts.

1946. BRENCHLEY, WINIFRED E., *D.Sc., Rothamsted Experimental Station, Harpenden, Herts*. The role of minor elements in the growth of plants. *Chem. Prod. Chem. News*, 1946, v. 9, pp. 61–67. **409**

Includes a brief review of Rothamsted work on iodine in relation to plant growth, with the conclusion: "It is still not possible to say definitely that an exceptionally small trace of iodine may not yet be proved to be a requisite for the growth of plants."

1946. BRENCHLEY, WINIFRED E. Trace elements in relation to plant growth. *South East Nat. Antiquary*, 1946, v. 50, pp. 22–27. **410**

Author emphasizes the difficulty of obtaining iodine-free conditions in carrying out experiments to test whether iodine is essential to plants.

1946. PICADO T., C., *San José, Costa Rica*. El yodo confermento del metabolismo de los azúcares en las plantas y animales. [Iodine as co-enzyme in carbohydrate metabolism of plants and animals.] *Rev. Inst. Defensa Café Costa Rica*, 1946, v. 16, pp. 135–136. **411**

A shorter version of an earlier paper (see entry **349**).

1946. PONTAILLER, S., *agricultural engineer*. Recherches sur le rôle agricole des oligo-éléments. [Investigations on the role of trace elements in agriculture.] *Potasse*, Mulhouse, 1946, v. 20, pp. 180–182. **412**

A trace element mixture containing sodium iodide increased the yield of beetroot on soils on which heart-rot had occurred.

1946. WARINGTON, KATHERINE, *Rothamsted Experimental Station, Harpenden, Herts*. Molybdenum as a factor in the nutrition of lettuce. *Ann. Appl. Biol.*, 1946, v. 33, pp. 249–254. **413**

Presence of iodine (as iodate) in culture solution had no influence on the beneficial effect of molybdenum. Added by itself, either in the presence or absence of boron, iodine did not exert any appreciable influence on growth of lettuce.

1947. BRENCHLEY, WINIFRED E., *Rothamsted Experimental Station, Harpenden, Herts*. The essential nature of certain minor elements for plant nutrition. 2. *Botan. Rev.*, 1947, v. 13, pp. 169–193. **414**

Supplement to an earlier paper (see entry **376**). On p. 185 very brief reference is made to the most recent work on iodine.

1947. JACOBSON, LOUIS, and ROY OVERSTREET, *division of plant nutrition, University of California*. A study of the mechanism of ion absorption by plant roots using radioactive elements. *Amer. J. Botany*, 1947, v. 34, pp. 415–420. **415**

Apical segments of barley roots were placed in an aqueous solution of potassium iodide containing radioactive iodine at 0° C for 30 minutes. Maximum absorption of radioactive iodide ion occurred within a few millimetres of the root apex.

1948. ÅBERG, BÖRJE, *Institute of Plant Physiology, Royal Agricultural College of Sweden*. On the mechanism of the toxic action of chlorates and some related substances upon young wheat plants. *Kungl. Lantbruks-Högskolans Ann.*, 1948, v. 15, pp. 37–107. In English. **416**

Iodates at relatively high concentrations appreciably retard growth of wheat seedlings in water culture but are much less toxic than bromates or chlorates.

1948. EKDAHL, IVAR, *Institute of Plant Physiology, Royal Agricultural College of Sweden*. The action of chlorate and some related substances upon roots and root hairs of young wheat plants. *Kungl. Lantbruks-Högskolans Ann.*, 1948, v. 15, pp. 113–172. In English. **417**

The "related substances" include iodide and iodate. Potassium iodide has a strong and specific inhibiting effect on the growth of root hairs but only a weak retarding effect on root growth of wheat seedlings in water culture. It often causes the root hairs to burst at the tip. Potassium iodate has a weaker effect on root hairs than potassium iodide.

1948. VAN DERLINDEN, LEE, *research director, Chas. H. Lilly Co., Seattle, Washington*. Soils, hops, minor element fertility. *Amer. Fertil.*, 1948, v. 108, no. 9, pp. 7–9; 28; 30. **418**

Use of iodized fertilizer to supply 2 lb. of potassium iodide per acre is recommended.

IODINE IN CHILEAN NITRATE OF SODA

419-460

1906. Grazia, S. de, *Faculty of Agriculture, University of Naples*. Azione dei sali inquinanti il nitrato sodico usato in agricoltura sulla vegetazione e sul prodotto della segala. [Effect of the impurities in the nitrate of soda used in agriculture on the growth and yield of rye.] *Staz. Sper. Agrarie Ital.*, 1906, v. 39, pp. 529–542. **419**

De Grazia was one of the first to appreciate the agricultural value of the "impurities" in Chilean nitrate of soda. He found that Chilean nitrate increased the growth and yield of rye and attributed this in part to the presence of ingredients, other than nitrogen, now known to be trace elements essential for plant nutrition.

1908. Grazia, S. de, *Research Station for Agricultural Chemistry, Rome*. Sulle impurità del nitro del Chilì e sulla possibile convenienza dell'uso di nitro poco raffinato. [The impurities of Chilean nitrate and the possible advantages of using nitrate not highly refined.] *Staz. Sper. Agrarie Ital.*, 1908, v. 41, pp. 258–269. **420**

In pot experiments the impurities of Chilean nitrate, especially sodium chloride and magnesium sulphate, had a favourable effect on yield of rye, barley and wheat. Potassium iodide had no effect.

1924. Feilitzen, *Dr*. Hj. von, and *Dr*. H. Egnér, *Central Agricultural Research Station, Stockholm*. Wird die Düngerwirkung des Chilesalpeters durch seinen Jodgehalt und durch eine etwaige Radioaktivität des Salpeters beeinflusst? Einige kritische Bemerkungen. [Is the fertilizing action of Chilean nitrate of soda affected by its iodine content and by a possible radioactivity of the nitrate? Some critical remarks.] *Chemikerzeitung*, 1924, v. 48, pp. 325–326. **421**

Authors consider that Stoklasa's statement (see entry 423) that the superiority of Chilean nitrate over synthetic sodium nitrate is due to its iodine content is groundless and has no facts to support it.

1924. Rahm, *Dr*.—. Ueber physiologische Funktionen des Jodes im Organismus der Zuckerrübe. [The physiological function of iodine in the organism of the sugar beet.] *Deutsche landwirtsch. Presse*, 1924, v. 51, p. 223. **422**

Mainly a defence of German synthetic nitrate of soda against Chilean nitrate. The value of the iodine content of Chilean nitrate is called in question.

1924. Stoklasa, Julius, *director, State Experiment Station, Prague*. Über den Ursprung des Salpeters in Chile. [The origin of nitrate in Chile.] *Chemikerzeitung*, 1924, v. 48, p. 4. **423**

On account of its iodine content, Chilean nitrate is a more effective fertilizer for sugar beet than synthetic sodium nitrate.

1925. Stoklasa, Julius, *director, State Experiment Station, Prague*. Lässt sich der Chilesalpeter durch andere stickstoffhaltige Düngemittel ersetzen? [Can Chilean nitrate be replaced by other nitrogenous fertilizers?] *Ztschr. Zuckerindust. Čechoslovakischen Republik*, 1925, v. 50, pp. 17–21; 25–29. **424**

In pot trials with oats and sugar beet, Chilean nitrate was compared with three nitrogenous fertilizers not containing iodine. The best results, as measured by yield or composition of crop, were obtained with Chilean nitrate.

1926. Biederbeck, *Dr*. A. Lässt sich Chilesalpeter durch andere stickstoffhaltige Düngemittel ersetzen? [Can Chilean nitrate be replaced by other nitrogenous fertilizers?] *Ztschr. Zuckerindust. Čechoslovakischen Republik*, 1926, v. 50, pp. 177–181. **425**

Author questions the validity of Stoklasa's claims for Chilean nitrate of soda (see preceding entry).

1926. Dafert, O., and H. Brichta, *Research Station for Agricultural Chemistry, Vienna*. Hat der Jodgehalt des Chilesalpeters praktische Bedeutung für die Landwirtschaft? [Has the iodine content of Chilean nitrate practical importance for agriculture?] *Fortschr. Landwirtsch.*, 1926, v. 1, pp. 531–534. **426**

Pot experiments with barley and mustard and field experiments with turnips showed no significant differences in crop yield when Chilean nitrate of soda and synthetic sodium nitrate were used alone or supplemented with sodium iodate to give an iodine content of 0·05 to 0·4 per cent.

1927. Braun, J., *agricultural assessor, Wegfurt-Rhön, Germany*. Der Natronsalpeter als Rübendünger. [Sodium nitrate as a fertilizer for beets.] *Fortschr. Landwirtsch.*, 1927, v. 2, pp. 776–777. **427**

Explanation of the superiority of Chilean nitrate of soda as a fertilizer is sought in its iodine content.

1927. Haselhoff, *Prof*. E., *director, Agricultural Experiment Station, Harleshausen, Germany*. Deutscher Natronsalpeter oder ausländischer Chilisalpeter? [German or Chilean nitrate of soda?] *Amtsbl. Landwirtschaftskammer Regierungsbez. Kassel*, 1927, v. 31, p. 370. **428**

In pot and field experiments on oats synthetic sodium nitrate containing 0·1 per cent of added potassium iodide showed no superiority over iodine-free nitrate.

1927. Remy, *Dr*. Th., *director, Institute for Soil and Plant Science, Agricultural College, Bonn-Poppelsdorf*. Die synthetisch hergestellten Stickstoffdünger im Vergleich zu den bisher gebräuchlichen Handelsdüngern, speziell zum Chilesalpeter. [The synthetic nitrogenous fertilizers in comparison with the commercial fertilizers hitherto used, especially Chilean nitrate of soda.] *Ztschr. Vereins deutschen Zuckerindust.*, 1927, v. 77, part 1, pp. 204–216; discussion pp. 216–228. Also in *Deutsche Zuckerindustrie*, 1927, v. 52, pp. 817–820; discussion pp. 820–824. **429**

The author considers that in comparing synthetic

sodium nitrate (pure or plus potassium iodide) with Chilean nitrate of soda, investigators have used amounts of iodine out of all proportion to the amount in Chilean nitrate, and that they have used iodide instead of iodate or periodate. The results are, therefore, inconclusive and further and better planned experiments are necessary.

1928. EDDELBÜTTEL, *Dr.* H., *Rostock*. Chilesalpeter oder synthetischer Natronsalpeter? [Chilean nitrate of soda or synthetic sodium nitrate?] *Ztschr. angewandte Chem.*, 1928, v. 41, pp. 309–314. **430**

Author states that Chilean nitrate of soda is superior to synthetic sodium nitrate on account of its iodine content. The literature on the subject is briefly discussed.

1928. EHLING, LADISLAUS, *Arad, Rumania*. Über die Quellen der pflanzlichen Jodversorgung. [The sources of the iodine supply of plants.] *Dissertation, Stuttgart Technical College*, 1928, 22 pp. **431**

In a series of field trials with various crops, in which Chilean nitrate of soda at 80 kilogrammes per hectare was compared with synthetic sodium nitrate alone and supplemented with varying amounts of potassium iodide, iodine had no effect on crop yield or behaviour of the plants. In sand cultures, potassium iodide or iodate, applied in a nutrient salt mixture at rates equivalent to 50–1000 grammes of iodine per hectare, stimulated plant growth and markedly increased the iodine content of the plants. Higher concentrations had an injurious effect, especially on oats. It was also shown that mustard was able to absorb iodine vapour through the leaves.

1928. ELLEDER, HUGO, *Carlsbad*. Beitrag zur Frage der ernährenden Wirkung des Jods im Chilesalpeter. [Contribution to the question of the nutrient effect of the iodine in Chilean nitrate.] *Ztschr. Pflanzenernähr. Düng.* [A], 1928, v. 12, pp. 97–101. **432**

Field trials with sugar beet in which Chilean nitrate of soda was compared with synthetic sodium nitrate, alone or with the addition of iodine as potassium iodide in amount equal to that in the Chilean nitrate, showed some increase in the yield of tops due to the iodine but no increase, and if anything a decrease, in the yield of roots. There was no specific change in the sugar content of the roots.

1928. ENGELS, *Dr.* O., *Agricultural Experiment Station, Speyer-on-Rhine*. Die physiologische Bedeutung des Jods für den pflanzlichen Organismus und die Einwirkung desselben auf den Ernteertag beim Feld- und Gartenbau. Ein Beitrag zum Kapitel der Joddüngungsfrage. [The physiological significance of iodine for the plant organism and its influence on crop yield in field and garden cultivation. A contribution to the question of iodine manuring.] *Gartenbauwissenschaft*, 1928, v. 1, pp. 71–80. **433**

From a literature review and the results of his own experiment in which Chilean nitrate of soda was compared with synthetic sodium nitrate, alone and supplemented with iodine, as a fertilizer for sugar and fodder beets, the author thinks there is as yet no conclusive evidence of any beneficial effect on yield or iodine content of crops following the use of iodine-containing fertilizers.

1928. MÜNTER, *Dr.* F., *director, Agricultural Chemistry Experiment Station, Halle-on-Saale*. Jod als Rübendünger. [Iodine as fertilizer for sugar beet.] *Fortschr. Landwirtsch.*, 1928, v. 3, pp. 407–408. **434**

See entry 337.

1928. OREGON AGRICULTURAL EXPERIMENT STATION. Value of iodine as a plant nutrient. *Oregon Agric. Exp. Stat.*, Report for July 1926–June 1928 (1928), p. 76. **435**

Brief note on an experiment to test the claim that Chilean nitrate, owing to its iodine content, is of greater value than fixed atmospheric nitrogen fertilizers. Growth of lettuce indicated that one part of iodine per million parts of soil will increase yields, while two parts or more is toxic.

1929. DENSCH, *Prof.* A., *Dr.* K. STEINFATT and *Dr.* E. GÜNTHER, *Institute for Soil Science and Plant Nutrition, Prussian Agricultural Experiment Station, Landsberg-on-Warthe*. Ein Düngungsversuch mit Natronsalpeter, Chilesalpeter und Jod zu Möhren. [Fertilizer trial with synthetic sodium nitrate, Chilean nitrate of soda and iodine on carrots.] *Ztschr. Pflanzenernähr. Düng.* [B], 1929, v. 8, pp. 205–211. **436**

Pot trials with carrots and cabbages on a loamy sand of hydrogen ion concentration 5·8, with and without the addition of chalk and in which potassium iodate at different levels was used to supplement sodium nitrate and Chilean nitrate, indicate that the amount of iodine present in Chilean nitrate has no economic significance in fertilizing under these conditions.

1929. GERLACH, *Prof.* M., *Prussian Experiment Station for Treatment of Cereals and Forage Crops, Berlin*. Versuche über die Wirkung verschiedener stickstoffhaltiger Düngemittel. [Experiments with various nitrogenous fertilizers.] *Ztschr. Pflanzenernähr. Düng.* [B], 1929, v. 8, pp. 89–91. **437**

The iodine in Chilean nitrate of soda is considered to have no fertilizing value.

1929. HASELHOFF, *Prof.* E., *director, Agricultural Experiment Station, Harleshausen, Germany*. Die Wirkung der Stickstoffdünger. [The effect of nitrogenous fertilizers.] *Ztschr. Pflanzenernähr. Düng.* [B], 1929, v. 8, pp. 136–142. **438**

Field and pot experiments on fodder beet, potatoes and oats in which sodium nitrate with and without added iodine was used, did not give any indication that the iodine in Chilean nitrate of soda has a fertilizing value.

1930. MCHARGUE, J. S., W. R. ROY and J. G. PELPHREY, *Kentucky Agricultural Experiment Station, Lexington*. Iodine in some fertilizer materials. *Amer. Fertil.*, 1930, v. 73, no. 10, pp. 40–42; 63. **439**

Chilean nitrate of soda, guano, rock phosphate, oyster shells and limestone are regarded as the principal sources of iodine in fertilizers. The authors increased the iodine content of red clover more than 16 times by moderate applications of Chilean nitrate to the soil.

1930. WEISKE, *Dr.* F., *Institute for Soil and Plant Science, Agricultural College, Bonn-Poppelsdorf*. Untersuchungen über den Einfluss einiger Chilesalpeternebenbestandteile auf die Pflanzen. [Studies on the effects of some minor constituents of Chilean nitrate of soda on plants.] *Wissench. Arch. Landwirtsch., Abt. A*, 1930, v. 4, pp. 366–382. **440**

Barley and spinach were favourably influenced by sodium iodate and sodium periodate in their early but not later stages of development. Large doses of the periodate were very injurious to oats. These compounds had very little effect on sugar beet and potatoes, their action being harmful rather than otherwise.

1932. AUDIDIER, L., *professor of agriculture.* De l'emploi du nitrate de soude dans les prairies naturelles. [The use of sodium nitrate on natural pasture.] *Bull. Assoc. Amicale Anciens Élèves Inst. Nat. Agron.*, 1932, v. 43, Supplement to No. 5 (May), 27 pp. **441**

Chilean nitrate of soda increased the protein and iodine contents of hay.

1932. BRIOUX, C., *director, Lower Seine Agricultural Station, Rouen.* Comparaison du nitrate de soude du Chili et du nitrate synthétique. [Comparison of Chilean nitrate of soda and synthetic nitrate.] *Rapport Inst. Recherches Agron.*, Paris (for 1932), 1933, pp. 96–97. **442**

In pot experiments with white mustard and maize, Chilean nitrate of soda gave a greater yield than synthetic nitrate. When iodates were added to the latter the yield was increased, but still remained less than that given by Chilean nitrate.

1933. FRANCE. INSTITUT DES RECHERCHES AGRONOMIQUES. Comparaison du nitrate de soude du Chili et du nitrate synthétique. [Comparison of Chilean nitrate of soda and synthetic nitrate.] *Rapport Inst. Recherches Agron.*, Paris (for 1933), 1934, pp. 48–49. **443**

A series of pot experiments carried out at various agricultural stations gave varying results, but it is suggested that certain substances (including iodates) present in Chilean nitrate give it a slight advantage as a fertilizer over synthetic nitrate.

1933. KLEIN, *Prof.* W., *director, Institute of Animal Physiology, Agricultural College, Bonn-Poppelsdorf.* Wirkung von Jodkali auf Gemüsepflanzen. [Effect of potassium iodide on vegetables.] *Rhein. Monatsschr. Obst-, Garten- u. Gemüsebau*, 1933, pp. 274–275. **444**

See entry 660.

1934. BRIOUX, C., *director, Lower Seine Agricultural Station, Rouen.* Comparaison du nitrate de soude du Chili et du nitrate de soude synthétique. [Comparison of Chilean nitrate of soda and synthetic nitrate.] *Recherches Fertilisation Stat. Agron.*, Douai (1934), 1935, p. 49. **445**

A brief note in which it is stated that plants receiving synthetic nitrate supplemented with the trace elements present in Chilean nitrate of soda contained more nitrogen than those receiving synthetic nitrate alone.

1934. DOPTER, P., *director, Nord Agricultural Station, Lille.* Action des éléments secondaires du nitrate chilien sur l'activité microbienne des sols. [Action of the secondary elements in Chilean nitrate on the microbial activity of soils.] *Recherches Fertilisation Stat. Agron.*, Douai, 1934 (1935), p. 50. **446**

See entry 555.

1934. GAROLA, J., *director, Eure-et-Loir Agricultural Station, Chartres.* Comparaison du nitrate de soude du Chili et du nitrate de soude synthétique. [Comparison of Chilean nitrate of soda and synthetic nitrate.] *Recherches Fertilisation Stat. Agron.*, Douai (1934), 1935, pp. 48–49. **447**

Results of pot experiments in which the effect of Chilean nitrate on plant growth was compared with that of synthetic sodium nitrate alone or supplemented with iodate showed no significant differences with turnips; but a slight superiority of the natural nitrate, attributed to its impurities, was observed with carrots.

1935. BRITISH SUGAR BEET REVIEW. Iodine and boron in the control of beet diseases. *Brit. Sugar Beet Rev.*, 1935, v. 8, p. 280. **448**

A brief discussion of the role of iodine in plant nutrition with special reference to the value of Chilean nitrate in promoting healthy growth of sugar beet.

1935. MCHARGUE, J. S., D. W. YOUNG and R. K. CALFEE, *Kentucky Agricultural Experiment Station, Lexington.* The effect of certain fertilizer materials on the iodine content of important foods. *J. Amer. Soc. Agron.*, 1935, v. 27, pp. 559–565. **449**

Chilean nitrate of soda contains enough iodine to influence the iodine content of forage crops and vegetables if applied in adequate amounts to soils deficient in iodine. The iodine content can also be increased by adding potassium iodide directly to the soil.

1935. SCHARRER, K., and W. SCHROPP, *Institute of Agricultural Chemistry, College of Agriculture and Brewing, Weihenstephan, Munich.* Gefäss- und Wasserkulturversuche über die Wirkung des Bors allein und in Kombination mit Jod in Düngemitteln. [Pot and water culture experiments on the effect of boron alone and in combination with iodine in fertilizers.] *Phytopath. Ztschr.*, 1935, v. 8, pp. 525–540. **450**

The effect of Chilean nitrate was compared with that of synthetic sodium nitrate alone and supplemented with boron or iodine or the two together. It was proved that boron and not iodine prevented the incidence of heart rot and dry rot in sugar beet.

1937. DERAMOND, JACQUES, *agronomist.* Rapport concernant les recherches scientifiques françaises sur la valeur fertilisante comparée des nitrates de soude naturels du Chili et des nitrates de soude synthétiques de divers origines. [French scientific research on the comparative value as fertilizers of Chilean natural nitrate of soda and synthetic nitrates of soda of various origins.] Paris: *Société Commerciale des Nitrates du Chili, Services Agronomiques*, Report, 1937, 263 pp. **451**

Deramond gives full details of 34 series of pot and field experiments to compare Chilean nitrate of soda (alone and plus iodide or iodate) with synthetic nitrate of soda (similarly fortified) undertaken between 1925 and 1936 by the following departmental agricultural authorities: C. Brioux at Rouen (*Seine Inférieure*), A. Demolon at Laon (*Aisne*), P. Andouard at Nantes (*Loire Inférieure*), G. Joret at Amiens (*Somme*), L. Audidier (*Landes*), and A. Sirot of the central agricultural laboratory, Paris. Sugar beet and potatoes were the principal crops investigated, but mustard, maize, buckwheat, tomatoes, lucerne, pasture, vines, lettuce, spinach and radish were also used. The nitrates were enriched with a mixture of equal parts of KI and NaI or a mixture of equal parts of KIO_3 and $NaIO_3$

sufficient to supply 2 kg. of iodides or 2·607 kg. of iodates per hectare, thus providing in each case 1·607 kg. of iodine per hectare.

In general the results were inconclusive, most of the investigators being unable to say that iodides or iodates had any effect. Sirot, however, concludes that Chilean nitrate definitely enriches plants in iodine, promotes early fruiting and ripening of tomatoes, and increases resistance to plant diseases.

Among several unconfirmed iodine effects were: improvement in the purity of beet juice; depressing effect of iodates in some cases; increased dry matter and starch content, but reduced nitrogen content, of potatoes; iron added with iodine enhanced the iodine effect; plants with iodine plus iron grew better and had a more intense green colour; absorption of nitrogen and phosphorus was uninfluenced but there was a slight positive effect in the case of potassium.

1937. Scharrer, K., and W. Schropp, *Institute of Agricultural Chemistry, College of Agriculture and Brewing, Weihenstephan, Munich.* Weitere Gefäss- und Wasserkulturversuche über die Wirkung des Bors allein und in Kombination mit Jod in Düngemitteln. [Further pot and water culture experiments on the effect of boron alone and in combination with iodine in fertilizers.] *Phytopath. Ztschr.*, 1937, v. 10, pp. 57–78. **452**

A continuation of earlier work (see entry 450). Water culture experiments with sugar beet showed that Chilean nitrate of soda produced greater yield of leaves but smaller yield of roots than did synthetic sodium nitrate supplemented with boron and iodine in amounts equivalent to those in the natural nitrate. Heart rot and dry rot were most prevalent with synthetic nitrate, with or without added iodine.

1938. Baeyens, J., and A. Deckterioff, *Institute of Pedology, University of Louvain.* Gefässversuche mit Zuckerrüben zur vergleichenden Prüfung steigender Gaben von Chilesalpeter und synthetischen Natronsalpeter. [Pot experiments with sugar beets to compare increasing applications of Chilean nitrate of soda and synthetic sodium nitrate.] *Bodenk. Pflanzenernähr.*, 1938, v. 9–10, pp. 611–624. **453**

Sugar beets given synthetic sodium nitrate developed heart rot and dry rot, but those given Chilean nitrate of soda were completely unaffected and gave a higher yield. This is partly due to the boron content of Chilean nitrate, though it is considered that other trace elements present may also play their part.

1938. Giesecke, F., K. Schmalfuss and W. Rathje, *Institute of Plant Nutrition and Soil Biology, Berlin University.* Versuche über die Spurenelementwirkung des Chilesalpeters in Gefässkulturen. [Pot experiments on the effect of the trace elements in Chilean nitrate of soda.] *Bodenk. Pflanzenernähr.*, 1938, v. 9–10, pp. 580–587. **454**

Chilean nitrate of soda gave a much higher yield of rye, sugar and fodder beets than synthetic sodium nitrate. This is considered due to the higher content of iodine and boron, especially the latter, and possibly of other trace elements in the Chilean product.

1938. Schropp, W., and B. Arenz, *Institute of Agricultural Chemistry, College of Agriculture and Brewing, Weihenstephan, Munich.* Gefässversuche zur Prüfung der Wirkung der Spurenelemente im Chilesalpeter auf das Wachstum von Zucker- und Futterrüben. [Pot experiments to determine the effect of the trace elements in Chilean nitrate of soda on the growth of sugar and fodder beets.] *Bodenk. Pflanzenernähr.*, 1938, v. 9–10, pp. 588–611. **455**

Chilean nitrate of soda prevented heart rot and dry rot and gave an increased yield. The iodine content of both roots and tops, particularly the latter, increased with increasing doses of Chilean nitrate. Sugar and fodder beets given synthetic sodium nitrate developed both heart rot and dry rot, and gave a much smaller yield.

1939. Rietsema, *Dr.* I., *director, Catholic School of Agriculture and Horticulture, Breda, Netherlands.* Jodiumgehalte van groente. [Iodine content of vegetables.] *R. K. Boeren- en Tuindersstand,* 1939, no. 47, pp. 1416–1417. **456**

Lettuce, tomatoes and endive fertilized with Chilean nitrate of soda contained a considerably higher percentage of iodine than those fertilized with an equal quantity of synthetic sodium nitrate.

1943. Brenchley, Winifred E., *D.Sc., Rothamsted Experimental Station, Harpenden, Herts.* Trace elements in Chilean nitrate. *Manufacturing Chem.*, 1943, v. 14, pp. 5–6. **457**

Contains a brief review of the author's experiments in which some thirty species of crops were grown with and without added iodine. The conclusion is that "the real advantage of Chilean nitrate for plant growth is derived from its contained boron, rather than its iodine."

1947. Lehr, *Dr.* J. J., *agricultural chemist,* with the co-operation of *Prof.* J. Hudig, *director, laboratory for agricultural chemistry, College of Agriculture, Wageningen, Netherlands.* Chilisalpeter. Een monografie over de oudste minerale meststof ter wereld. [Chilean nitrate of soda. A monograph on the oldest mineral fertilizer in the world.] The Hague: *Inlichtingenbureau voor Chilisalpeter*, 1947, 224 pp. **458**

See entry 16.

1948. Baeyens, J., *Institute of Pedology, University of Louvain.* Physiological effect of minor elements in Chilean nitrate. *Plant and Soil*, 1948, v. 1, pp. 135–144. **459**

From the results of several years' experimentation with sugar beet the author considers that Chilean nitrate is superior to synthetic nitrate, more especially at high rates of application, and that, besides boron, other trace elements present in the natural nitrate probably contribute to this superiority.

1948. Schmalfuss, K., *Institute of Plant Nutrition, Soil Chemistry and Soil Biology, Berlin University.* Über Versuche zur Spurenelementwirkung des Chilesalpeters in Zylinderversuchen aus den Jahren 1937 und 1938. [Pot experiments carried out in 1937 and 1938 on the effect of trace elements in Chilean nitrate.] *Ztschr. Pflanzenernähr. Düng.*, 1948, v. 85, pp. 35–39. **460**

Experiments with maize, rye, oats, wheat and barley to compare the manurial effects of Chilean nitrate and synthetic sodium nitrate gave inconclusive results in respect of crop yield and contents of total nitrogen and protein nitrogen of both straw and grain. Iodine content of the straw was always higher with Chilean nitrate but that of the grain varied.

THYROXINE AND THYROID PREPARATIONS

461–492

1919. BUDINGTON, ROBERT A., *professor of zoology, Oberlin College, Oberlin, Ohio.* The influence of certain ductless gland substances on the growth of plant tissues. *Biol. Bull.*, 1919, v. 37, pp. 188–193. **461**

Growth of root tips of *Allium* bulbs is retarded by the presence of a small quantity of desiccated thyroid in the nutrient solution.

1924. REBELLO, SILVIO, *Faculty of Medicine, University of Lisbon.* Action des glandes à sécrétion interne et de leurs extraits sur le développement des plantes. [The effect of glands of internal secretion and of their extracts on the development of plants.] *C. R. Soc. Biol.*, Paris, 1924, v. 90, pp. 1095–1097. **462**

Hyacinth bulbs treated with powdered thyroid and thyroprotein showed marked root and flower development. Fresh thyroid, however, inhibited root growth.

1925. BUDINGTON, ROBERT A., *professor of zoology, Oberlin College, Oberlin, Ohio.* A suggestion as to the effect of thyroid gland substances on protoplasm in general. *Biol. Bull.*, 1925, v. 48, pp. 83–91. **463**

Roots of narcissus bulbs grown in aqueous solution of thyroid extract greatly decreased in length and increased in thickness. The suggestion is made that thyroid substances are as essential to plants as they are to animals.

1927. NIETHAMMER, ANNELIESE, *Institute of Botany, German Technical College, Prague.* Der Einfluss von den Reizchemikalien auf die Samenkeimung. 2. Mitteilung. [The influence of chemical stimulants on seed germination. 2.] *Jahrb. wissensch. Botanik*, 1927, v. 67, pp. 223–239. **464**

Germination of various seeds is stimulated by thyroid hormone.

1927. NIETHAMMER, ANNELIESE. Stimulationswirkungen im Pflanzenreich. 3. Die Beeinflussung ruhender Knospen und der Zellteilung durch Thyreoidia und Zinksulfat. [The effects of stimulation on plants. 3. The influence of thyroid extract and zinc sulphate on dormant buds and on cell division.] *Protoplasma*, 1927, v. 2, pp. 392–400. **465**

Injection of dilute aqueous solutions of thyroid extract into dormant buds of lilac had a stimulating effect on cell division.

1927. SCAGLIA, *Dr.* GIUSEPPE, *Institute of Anatomy, University of Cagliari.* Effetti di estratti tiroidei e dello iodio sullo sviluppo e accrescimento di *Hyacinthus orientalis.* Primi risultati. [The effect of thyroid extracts and iodine on the development and growth of *Hyacinthus orientalis.* Preliminary results.] *Scritti Biol.*, 1927, v. 2, pp. 261–266. **466**

Preliminary results are given of experiments described in greater detail in a later paper (see entry **468**).

1928. MEYER, FRITZ, *Kaiser-Wilhelm Institute for Physiology of Energy, Dortmund-Münster.* Zur Frage der Beeinflussung des Energieumsatzes der Hefe durch Schilddrüsenpräparate. [The effect of thyroid preparations on the energy metabolism of yeast.] *Endokrinologie*, 1928, v. 2, pp. 337–346. **467**

See entry **589**.

1928. SCAGLIA, *Dr.* GIUSEPPE, *Institute of Anatomy, University of Cagliari.* Accrescimento di vegetali sottoposti all'azione di estratti tiroidei e di iodio. [The effect of thyroid extracts and iodine on the growth of plants.] *Scritti Biol.*, 1928, v. 3, pp. 255–280. **468**

Addition of small quantities of various thyroid preparations to the culture medium (Knop's nutrient solution or spring water) in which hyacinths were growing inhibited growth and accelerated the development of inflorescences. Similar results were obtained with cabbage, turnips and mustard.

1930. AGOSTINI, ANGELA. Azione di alcuni estratti endocrini su due felci acquatiche. [Effect of some endocrine extracts on two aquatic ferns.] *Scritti Biol.*, 1930, v. 5, pp. 333–353. **469**

Addition of thyroid extract to water cultures slightly stimulated branch formation in *Azolla caroliniana* W., and had deleterious effects on *Marsilia quadrifolia* L.

1932. NIETHAMMER, ANNELIESE, *Institute of Botany, German Technical College, Prague.* Die Pollenkeimung und chemische Reizwirkungen im Zusammenhange mit der Mikrochemie des Kornes. [Germination of pollen under the influence of chemical stimuli and its relation to the microchemistry of the seed.] *Biochem. Ztschr.*, 1932, v. 249, pp. 412–420. **470**

Of the substances studied, thyroid exerted the most marked stimulating effect on pollen with moderate germinating ability. Pollens which do not normally germinate could not be stimulated, except in one case in which thyroidin was effective.

1933. HYKES, O. V., *Brno.* De l'influence de quelques hormones sur la feuillaison et le développement des végétaux. [Influence of various hormones on foliation and development of plants.] *C. R. Soc. Biol.*, Paris, 1933, v. 113, pp. 629–632. **471**

Dilute solutions of thyroxine stimulated leaf formation in dormant tree twigs, but the effect disappeared after 3 to 4 weeks' continuous application. The effect on root formation was irregular.

1934. CHOUARD, PIERRE, *D. ès-Sc., lecturer, Faculty of Science, Bordeaux.* Action de la folliculine et de la thyroxine sur les reine-marguerite (*Callistephus sinensis* Nees=*Aster sinensis* L.). [Action of folliculin and of thyroxine on China asters (*Callistephus sinensis* Nees=*Aster sinensis* L.).] *C. R. Soc. Biol.*, Paris, 1934, v. 117, pp. 1180–1183. **472**

Plants treated once a week for nine weeks with 0·7 milligramme of synthetic thyroxine in 100 millilitres of water suffered at first from chlorosis. This condition was cured by application of plant nutrients, and the plants grew 25 per cent taller than the controls. The flowers were not affected. Similar results were obtained with chrysanthemums.

1934. DAVIS, ELIZABETH ELLEN, *University of Colorado*. Influence of thyroxin on the growth of plants. *Plant Physiol.*, 1934, v. 9, pp. 377–384. **473**

Injection of 1 to 5 millilitres of an aqueous solution of thyroxine (0·4 milligramme of sodium salt in 5 millilitres of water) into *Allium* bulbs hastens the time of flowering and increases the height and number of flower stalks.

1934. SELLEI, JOSEF, *Hungarian State Railways Hospital, Budapest*. Wirkung von Farbstoffen und Hormonen auf die Pflanzenproduktion. [The action of dyestuffs and hormones on plant production.] *Arch. Pharm.*, Berlin, 1934, v. 272, pp. 737–743. **474**

Application of a dilute solution of thyroid extract to the soil first retarded, then, after about 10 days, stimulated the germination of wheat grains.

1934. YUN, I. S., and W. L. HONG, *Severance Union Medical College, Seoul, Korea*. [The effect of various endocrine preparations on the growth of beans.] *J. Chosen Med. Assoc.*, 1934, v. 24, pp. 568–591. In Japanese: English summary in Abstract Section, pp. 51–52. **475**

Both 1 per cent and 5 per cent solutions of thyroxine inhibited the growth of beans.

1935. CHOUARD, PIERRE, *D. ès-Sc., lecturer, Faculty of Science, Bordeaux*. Action de la folliculine et de la thyroxine sur les reines-marguerites (*Callistephus sinensis* Nees=*Aster sinensis* L.). [Action of folliculin and of thyroxine on China asters (*Callistephus sinensis* Nees=*Aster sinensis* L.).] *Gynécologie*, 1935, v. 34, pp. 252–257. **476**

See entry 472.

1935. COTTE, G., P. MANCEAU and CLAIRE MEYER. Recherches sur l'action de quelques hormones sur les plantes. [Investigations on the action of some hormones on plants.] *Gynécologie*, 1935, v. 34, pp. 612–623. **477**

A strong solution of thyroxine (4 microgrammes in 120 millilitres of distilled water) produced a better growth of cress (*Lepidium sativum*) than a weak solution (1 microgramme in 120 millilitres of water), though even the latter compared favourably with the controls. In a further series of experiments, a solution containing 1 microgramme of thyroxine in 200 millilitres of water gave, after five days' growth, an average length for root plus stem of 72·4 mm., a solution containing 0·1 microgramme in 200 millilitres 88·5 mm. and controls 69·35 mm.

1935. FLORENTIN, P., and M. EHRENFELD, *Nancy*. Action de la thyroxine sur la croissance des racines d'*Allium cepa*. [Action of thyroxine on the growth of the roots of *Allium cepa*.] *C. R. Soc. Biol.*, Paris, 1935, v. 118, pp. 1003–1005. **478**

A concentration of 1 part of thyroxine in 100,000 parts of culture medium slightly retarded root growth for two weeks but later had a stimulating effect.

1935. HAVAS, LÁSZLÓ, and JOHN CALDWELL, *Rothamsted Experimental Station, Harpenden, Herts*. Some experiments on the effects of animal hormones on plants. *Ann. Botany*, 1935, v. 49, pp. 729–747. **479**

Even concentrated extracts of thyroid were not toxic and had no marked effect.

1936. ARATA, *Dr*. MARIA. L'azione di ormoni e altre sostanze animali sull'accrescimento delle piante. [The effect of hormones and other animal substances on plant growth.] *Reale Ist. Lombardo Sci. Lettere Rendiconti*, 1936, v. 69, pp. 349–363. **480**

Treatment of oat seedlings with a fairly concentrated aqueous solution of thyroidin had a pronounced inhibitory effect on their growth.

1936. MEYER, CLAIRE. Hormones et végétaux. [Hormones and plants.] *Bull. Soc. Linn. Lyon*, 1936, v. 5, pp. 56–57. **481**

Germination of seeds of garden cress and lentils on cottonwool was stimulated by soaking the latter in thyroxine solution (strength not stated).

1937. AMLINSKY, I. E., *general biological laboratory, Clinical Institute, Moscow*. De l'influence de la thyréocrine et de l'iode sur le développement des filaires. [Effect of thyreocrine and of iodine on the development of green algae.] *Bull. Biol. Méd. Exp. URSS*, 1937, v. 3, pp. 41–42. **482**

Weak solutions of thyreocrine (proprietary thyroid preparation) and of iodine stimulate growth in *Cladophora* and *Oedogonium* while strong solutions are toxic. Solutions of medium strength stimulate the reproductive processes.

1937. BRAIN, E. DOROTHY, *F.L.S., Reading, Berks*. Experiments on the influence of parathyroid and thyroid hormones upon the growth of seedlings. *Ann. Botany*, 1937, New Series, v. 1, pp. 615–621. **483**

Dilute solutions may in some cases stimulate growth; stronger ones may have a retarding effect.

1937. BRAIN, E. DOROTHY. The influence of animal hormones on plants: a review of experimental work. *Lancet*, 1937, v. 232, pp. 1241–1243. **484**

There are insufficient data from which to draw definite conclusions about the effects of animal hormones on plants. Uniformly consistent results with thyroid extract, however, indicate that it stimulates cell growth by division.

1937. DUNN, MARIN S., *Ph.D., biology laboratories, Philadelphia College of Pharmacy and Science*. Notes on the effects of certain glandular products upon plant growth. *Amer. J. Pharm.*, 1937, v. 109, pp. 9–17. **485**

Addition of thyroxine to the culture medium in which poplar twigs are grown slightly stimulates the growth of the buds.

1937. NICOL, HUGH, *Rothamsted Experimental Station, Harpenden, Herts*. Animal hormones and plants. *J. Soc. Chem. Indust.*, London, 1937, v. 56, pp. 526–527. **486**

A brief review.

1937. Weber, A. P., *biological chemistry laboratory, Pasteur Institute, Paris.* L'influence des hormones cristallisées sur la croissance de certaines espèces de levures. [The effect of crystalline hormones on the growth of certain species of yeasts.] *Ann. Ferment.*, 1937, v. 3, pp. 15–29; 65–86. **487**

See entry **598**.

1938. Lustig, B., and H. Wachtel, *chemical laboratory, Pearson Foundation, Vienna; and Radium Institute, Cracow.* Über biochemische Beeinflussung der Keimung und des Wachstums der Cardaminesamen. 2. Mitteilung. Wirkungen von Vitaminen und Hormonen auf die Pflanze. [Biochemical effects on germination and growth of cardamine seeds. 2. The effect of vitamins and hormones on plants.] *Biochem. Ztschr.*, 1938, v. 297, pp. 386–394. **488**

Thyroid and thyroxine had no effect on the germination and growth of cardamine seeds. Thyroxine decreased the concentration of sodium iodide required to inhibit growth.

1938. Zollikofer, Clara, *Institute of General Botany, Zurich University.* De l'influence des hormones animales sur les plantes. [The effect of animal hormones on plants.] *Scientia*, Bologna, 1938, v. 64, pp. 66–74. **489**

A review of the effect of thyroxine on plant growth.

1939. Havas, László J., *Brussels.* Effects of animal hormones and of vitamins on the incremental growth of "crown gall." *Proc. 3rd Internat. Congr. Microbiol.*, New York, 1939 (1940), pp. 549–550. **490**

The average weight of tumours induced by inoculating tomato plants with *Bacillus tumefaciens* was increased about 37 per cent by treating the plants with thyroid extract.

1940. Castan, R. Sur le rôle des hormones animales et végétales dans le développement et l'organogénèse des plantes vasculaires : les "organisateurs" végétaux. [The role of animal and vegetable hormones in the development and organ formation of vascular plants. The plant "organisers."] *Rev. Gén. Botan.*, 1940, v. 52, pp. 192–208; 234–255; 285–304; 333–352; 413–430. **491**

In concentrations of 1, 5, 20, and 40 milligrammes per litre, thyroxine increased the growth of roots of garden cress (*Lepidium sativum*). The greater the concentration the greater was the growth of roots. These results are on pp. 235–238.

1942. Kotsovsky, *Dr.* D., *Institute for Study of Ageing, Kishinev, Rumania.* Über die Hormonwirkung auf die Altersentwicklung der Pflanzen. [The effect of hormones on the age-development of plants.] *Biologe*, 1942, v. 11, pp. 276–278. **492**

Growth and development of soya beans in a nutrient solution were accelerated by the addition of small quantities of thyroidin.

GROWTH REGULATING SUBSTANCES

493-523

1940. Howard, Fred H., and Leslie McClintock, *Harvard University, Cambridge, and Clark University, Worcester, Mass.* Notes on the effect of monoiodoacetamide on the growth of *Avena* coleoptiles. *J. Cell. Comp. Physiol.*, 1940, v. 15, pp. 249–251. **493**

Iodoacetamide at a concentration of 0·002 *M* had an inhibiting effect on the growth of the coleoptiles.

1941. Albaum, Harry G., and Barry Commoner, *department of biology, Brooklyn College; and marine biological laboratory, Woods Hole, Mass.* The relation between the four-carbon acids and the growth of oat seedlings. *Biol. Bull.*, 1941, v. 80, pp. 314–323. **494**

Iodoacetate inhibited the effect of auxin on the growth of oat seedlings. The authors think that the 4-carbon acids participate directly in the growth processes in the plant.

1941. Commoner, Barry, and Kenneth V. Thimann, *biological laboratories, Harvard University.* On the relation between growth and respiration in the *Avena* coleoptile. *J. Gen. Physiol.*, 1941, v. 24, pp. 279–296. **495**

Iodoacetate at a concentration of 5×10^{-5} *M* inhibits completely the growth and slightly the oxygen uptake of *Avena* coleoptile sections in sucrose and auxin solutions.

1942. Hitchcock, A. E., and P. W. Zimmerman, *Boyce Thompson Institute for Plant Research, Inc., Yonkers, New York.* Root-inducing activity of phenoxy compounds in relation to their structure. *Contrib. Boyce Thompson Inst. Plant Research*, 1942, v. 12, pp. 497–507. **496**

Halogen substituted phenoxy compounds were effective when used alone or in a mixture with either or both β-indolebutyric acid and α-naphthaleneacetic acid.

1942. Zimmerman, P. W., and A. E. Hitchcock, *Boyce Thompson Institute for Plant Research, Inc., Yonkers, New York.* Substituted phenoxy and benzoic acid growth substances and the relation of structure to physiological activity. *Contrib. Boyce Thompson Inst. Plant Research*, 1942, v. 12, pp. 321–343. **497**

2:3:5-Triiodobenzoic acid induced morphogenetic effects on plants when applied to the leaves and stems in the form of a lanolin preparation containing 0·1 to 2·0 per cent.

1942. Zimmerman, P. W., and A. E. Hitchcock. Flowering habit and correlation of organs modified by triiodobenzoic acid. *Contrib. Boyce Thompson Inst. Plant Research*, 1942, v. 12, pp. 491–496. **498**

Treatment of tomato plants or the soil on which they

are growing with an aqueous solution of 2:3:5-triiodobenzoic acid affects flowering, growth habit and correlation of organs in the plants. Axillary buds which normally produce leafy shoots are induced to grow flower clusters.

1943. ZIMMERMAN, P. W., *Boyce Thompson Institute for Plant Research, Inc., Yonkers, New York*. Present status of plant hormones. *Indust. Engin. Chem.*, 1943, v. 35, pp. 596–601. **499**
2:3:5-Triiodobenzoic acid is stated to be very active as a plant hormone.

1945. SYNERHOLM, MARTIN E., and P. W. ZIMMERMAN. A note on the preparation of 2-chloro-3, 5-diiodobenzoic acid and 2-chloro-3,5-dibromobenzoic acid and their effects on tomato plants. *Contrib. Boyce Thompson Inst. Plant Research*, 1945, v. 14, pp. 39–42. **500**
Growth effects of these compounds are illustrated and the position of the substituents in relation to their activity is briefly discussed.

1946. BAWDEN, R. F., *Rahr Malting Co., Manitowoc, Wisconsin*. Plant hormone-like substances as related to barley germination. *Amer. Soc. Brewing Chem. Proc.*, 1946, v. 11, pp. 10–13. **501**
Highly dilute aqueous solutions of 2:3:5-triiodobenzoic acid have no stimulating effect on the germination of barley.

1946. CLEMENTS, RICHARD, *B.Sc., F.L.S.* Chemical stimulants for crops. Practical applications of growth-regulating substances. *Discovery*, 1946, v. 7, pp. 332–335. **502**
A general article in which brief reference is made to the value of iodoacetate as a retarder of bud development, and of 2:3:5-triiodobenzoic acid as a weed killer.

1946. ENNIS, Jr., W. B., C. P. SWANSON, R. W. ALLARD and F. T. BOYD, *special projects division, Chemical Warfare Service, Camp Detrick, Frederick, Maryland*. Effects of certain growth-regulating compounds on Irish potatoes. *Botan. Gaz.*, 1946, v. 107, pp. 568–574. **503**
After two months' treatment, plants sprayed with a solution of the ammonium salt of 2:3:5-triiodobenzoic acid (0·1 gramme in 50 millilitres of water for every square yard) yielded tubers with a mean fresh weight about 10 per cent higher than those from untreated plants.

1946. FISHER, E. H., A. J. RIKER and T. C. ALLEN, *department of economic entomology and plant pathology, University of Wisconsin*. Bud, blossom, and pod drop of canning string beans reduced by plant hormones. *Phytopathology*, 1946, v. 36, pp. 504–523. **504**
See entry **806**.

1946. OWEN, O., *M.Sc.* The use of 2, 3, 5-triiodobenzoic acid to induce flowering in tomatoes. *Exp. and Research Stat., Cheshunt, Herts.*, Annual Report for 1946 (1947), p. 65. **505**
Application of 2:3:5-triiodobenzoic acid at rates of 0·3 to 3 milligrammes per 100 grammes of soil had no effect. Rates of 30 milligrammes and over invariably caused acute and permanent distortion of the plants. In no case, however, were flower shoots produced instead of vegetable shoots.

1946. SWARBRICK, T., *M.A., Ph.D., Shell Petroleum Co., Ltd., London*. Growth-regulating substances. Their chemistry and development. *Chem. Age*, London, 1946, v. 55, pp. 559-561. **506**
Brief reference is made to the flower-forming properties of 2:3:5-triiodobenzoic acid.

1946. SWARBRICK, T. Harnessing the hormone. The use of growth-regulating substances in gardens, fields and orchards. London: *Grower Publications Ltd.*, 1946, 52 pp. **507**
The growth-promoting and weed-killing effects of triiodobenzoic acid are discussed on pp. 43–49.

1946. THOMPSON, H. E., CARL P. SWANSON and A. G. NORMAN, *special projects division, Chemical Warfare Service, Camp Detrick, Frederick, Maryland*. New growth-regulating compounds. 1. Summary of growth-inhibitory activities of some organic compounds as determined by three tests. *Botan. Gaz.*, 1946, v. 107, pp. 476–507. **508**
Of 1060 compounds tested, 14 contained the iodo group. Only one of these, namely 2-iodo-4-chlorophenoxyacetic acid, came in the group having 80 per cent or more of the activity of the reference substance, 2:4-dichlorophenoxyacetic acid, as measured by the maize germination test.

1946. [TUMANOV, I. I., and A. A. LIZANDR.] ТУМАНОВ, И. И., and А. А. ЛИЗАНДР, *Timiryazev Institute of Plant Physiology, Academy of Sciences of the U.S.S.R., Moscow*. О физиологическом действии на растения трииодбензойной кислоты. [Physiological effect of triiodobenzoic acid on plants.] *Botan. Zhurnal SSSR*, 1946, v. 31, no. 3, pp. 13–20; English summary pp. 20–21. **509**
Spraying with a 0·025 to 0·005 per cent solution of triiodobenzoic acid markedly retarded the growth of *Perilla nankinensis*. Similar treatment produced formative changes in alfalfa. A 0·001 per cent solution used at the beginning of flowering increased the yield of alfalfa seed. Treatment of seeds with 0·01 to 0·00001 per cent solutions before sowing retarded the early growth of spring wheat and peas but had no effect on flax and sunflower.

1947. GALSTON, ARTHUR W., *department of botany, Yale University*. The effect of 2, 3, 5-triiodobenzoic acid on the growth and flowering of soybeans. *Amer. J. Botany*, 1947, v. 34, pp. 356–360. **510**
2:3:5-Triiodobenzoic acid does not induce vegetative soya beans to flower but greatly increases the flowering response due to photoperiodic induction.

1947. KRAUS, E. J., *department of botany, University of Chicago*, and J. W. MITCHELL, *Bureau of Plant Industry, Soils and Agricultural Engineering, Beltsville, Maryland*. Growth-regulating substances as herbicides. *Botan. Gaz.*, 1947, v. 108, pp. 301–350. **511**
2:3:5-Triiodobenzoic acid was applied, as an emulsion spray, in concentrations varying from 0·13 to 1 per cent in lanolin. The treated plants were smaller in overall size than the controls.

1947. MITCHELL, J. W., JOHN W. WOOD, W. C. WOLFE and GEORGE W. IRVING, Jr., *Bureau of Plant Industry, Soils and Agricultural Engineering, and Bureau of Agricultural and Industrial Chemistry, Beltsville, Maryland.* Relative growth rates of bean and oat plants containing known amounts of a labelled plant-growth regulator (2-iodo^{131}-3-nitrobenzoic acid). *Science*, 1947, v. 106, pp. 395–397. **512**

Application of 2-iodo-3-nitrobenzoic acid, containing radioactive iodine, in increasing small doses to the outside of the primary leaves inhibited the growth of bean seedlings but had no significant effect on that of oats and maize seedlings.

1947. NEWMAN, MELVIN S., WILLIAM FONES and MARY RENOLL, *department of chemistry, Ohio State University.* New compounds as plant growth regulators. *J. Amer. Chem. Soc.*, 1947, v. 69, pp. 718–723. **513**

Methods are given for the preparation of a large number of phenoxyacetic acid derivatives, including 2-iodo-4-chloro-, 2-chloro-4-iodo- and 2:4-diiodophenoxyacetic acids.

1947. UNITED STATES. BUREAU OF AGRICULTURAL AND INDUSTRIAL CHEMISTRY. Path of synthetic growth regulator in growing plants indicated by radioactive iodine in molecules. *U.S. Department of Agriculture*, Report of Chief of Bureau of Agricultural and Industrial Chemistry, 1947, p. 39. **514**

See entries **512** and **515**.

1947. WOOD, JOHN W., J. W. MITCHELL and GEORGE W. IRVING, Jr., *Bureau of Agricultural and Industrial Chemistry, and Bureau of Plant Industry, Soils and Agricultural Engineering, Beltsville, Maryland.* Translocation of a radioactive plant-growth regulator in bean and barley plants. *Science*, 1947, v. 105, pp. 337–339. **515**

Application of 2-iodo-3-nitrobenzoic acid containing radioactive iodine to the primary leaves of bean plants inhibited the growth of the various parts of the plants growing above ground, especially the bud. The substance was apparently absorbed by the leaves and translocated and accumulated mainly in the terminal buds and hypocotyls. Although the substance was also absorbed by barley leaves there was no significant decrease in growth rate. The greatest accumulation was in the second leaf. The technique used in these experiments is illustrated in *Chem. Engin. News*, 1948, v. 26, pp. 42–43.

1948. BOND, LORA, *department of botany, Wellesley College, Wellesley, Mass.* Responses of pea roots to application of certain growth-regulating substances. *Botan. Gaz.*, 1948, v. 109, pp. 435–447. **516**

Application of 2:3:5-triiodobenzoic acid (1 per cent in lanolin) to cut pea roots induced only a very slight morphological response.

1948. THIMANN, KENNETH V., and WALTER D. BONNER, Jr., *biological laboratories, Harvard University.* Experiments on the growth and inhibition of isolated plant parts. 1. The action of iodoacetate and organic acids on the *Avena* coleoptile. *Amer. J. Botany*, 1948, v. 35, pp. 271–281. **517**

Growth of isolated sections of the *Avena* coleoptile in auxin solution was inhibited by iodoacetate in low concentrations.

1948. THIMANN, KENNETH V., and WALTER D. BONNER, Jr. The action of triiodobenzoic acid on growth. *Plant Physiol.*, 1948, v. 23, pp. 158–161. **518**

Experiments described show primarily that triiodobenzoic acid enables a small quantity of auxin to promote a disproportionately large amount of growth.

1948. WAARD, JEANNE DE, and P. A. FLORSCHÜTZ, *botanical laboratory, University of Utrecht.* On the interaction of 2.3.5.-triiodobenzoic acid and indole-3-acetic acid in growth processes. *Koninkl. Nederlandsche Akad. Wetensch. Proc.*, 1948, v. 51, pp. 1317–1321. In English. **519**

Presence of triiodobenzoic acid (5 to 50 milligrammes per litre) in a solution of indole-acetic acid (0·05 milligramme per litre) inhibited the growth promoting activity of the latter. The standard *Avena* coleoptile test was used.

1948. WAARD, JEANNE DE, and J. W. M. ROODENBURG, *botanical laboratory, University of Utrecht; and division of horticulture, Netherlands Ministry of Agriculture.* Premature flower-bud initiation in tomato seedlings caused by 2, 3, 5-triiodobenzoic acid. (Preliminary communication.) *Koninkl. Nederlandsche Akad. Wetensch. Proc.*, 1948, v. 51, pp. 248–251. In English. **520**

Spraying young tomato seedlings with a solution containing 200 milligrammes of 2:3:5-triiodobenzoic acid per litre of water induced flower-bud formation a long time before this stage is normally reached.

1948. WALKER, RUTH DONOVAN, *M.Sc., Wye College, Ashford, Kent.* Studies on some plant growth regulating substances. *Thesis, University of London*, 1948, 176 pp. **521**

On pp. 157–161 it is reported that treatment of a small number of young tomato plants or the soil in which they were growing with triiodobenzoic acid had variable effects on flower formation. In hops, similar treatment usually had an injurious effect on growth.

1948. WHITING, A. GERALDINE, and MARY AILEEN MURRAY, *department of botany, University of Chicago.* Abscission and other responses induced by 2, 3, 5-triiodobenzoic acid in bean plants. *Botan. Gaz.*, 1948, v. 109, pp. 447–473. **522**

Treatment of young plants with triiodobenzoic acid (2 per cent in lanolin) or its ammonium salt (0·1 to 1·0 per cent in aqueous and emulsion sprays) considerably modifies vegetative growth. The most significant telemorphic response is the abscission of leaves and buds on later growth.

1949. SNYDER, WILLIAM E., *department of floriculture and ornamental horticulture, Cornell University, New York.* Some responses of plants to 2, 3, 5-triiodobenzoic acid. *Plant Physiol.*, 1949, v. 24, pp. 195–206. **523**

Soaking of *Coleus* cuttings for 24 hours in solutions containing 5 to 250 parts per million of triiodobenzoic acid inhibited subsequent rooting. Treatment of kidney bean and California privet plants with lanolin containing 2 per cent of triiodobenzoic acid stimulated axillary bud development, provided the applications were made above the bud.

OTHER BIOCHEMICAL ASPECTS

ABSORPTION OF IODINE BY SEEDS AND FRUITS

524-529

1909. Atkins, W. R. Gelston, *B.A., School of Botany, Trinity College, Dublin.* The absorption of water by seeds. *Sci. Proc. Roy. Dublin Soc.*, 1909, New Series, v. 12, pp. 35–46. **524**

Bean seeds placed in decinormal iodine did not concentrate the solution but decolorized it by the formation of starch iodide. All parts of the seed were penetrated by the iodine.

1924. Braun, Harry, *laboratory of plant pathology, Bureau of Plant Industry, U.S. Department of Agriculture.* A gradient of permeability to iodin in wheat seed coats. (A preliminary note.) *J. Agric. Research*, 1924, v. 28, pp. 225–226. **525**

Iodine permeates the whole surface of the grain radially but not uniformly. An apparent lateral and distal spread from the embryo end is caused by the existence of a gradient of permeability to iodine in the seed coats.

1927. Kahlenberg, Louis, and Ralph Traxler, *department of chemistry, University of Wisconsin.* On the passage of boric acid and certain salts into fruits and vegetables. *Plant Physiol.*, 1927, v. 2, pp. 39–54. **526**

Potassium iodide (in a 0·1 *M* solution) entered red plums, California grapes, tomatoes, cucumbers, carrots, peaches, and some varieties of apple. Wisconsin grapes, crab apples, and some other varieties of apple were found to be impermeable. Fruits and vegetables used in the experiments were perfectly sound, and were suspended in the solution.

1931. Malhotra, R. C., *professor of biology, St. Mary's College, Kansas.* Periodic permeability of iodine solution and water in the protoplasm of *Zea mays* seeds. *Protoplasma*, 1931, v. 13, pp. 374–388. **527**

See entry **347**.

1932. Brown, R., *botanical department, Seale-Hayne Agricultural College, Newton Abbot, Devon.* Absorption of the solute from aqueous solutions by the grain of wheat. *Ann. Botany*, 1932, v. 46, pp. 571–582. **528**

Data on the rate of absorption of iodine are given.

1943. Piettre, Lisette. Perméabilité des grains de blé après épuisement par les solvants organiques: phénomènes de sorption et de désorption. [Permeability of wheat grains after treatment with organic solvents: phenomena of sorption and desorption.] *C. R. Acad. Agric. France*, 1943, v. 29, pp. 260–266. **529**

The permeability of wheat grains soaked in solutions of potassium iodide, and potassium iodide plus iodine, was studied.

ENZYME ACTION : PHOTOSYNTHESIS : RESPIRATION

530-546

1903. Asō, K., *assistant professor, Tokyo Imperial University.* Which compound in certain plant-juices can liberate iodine from potassium iodide? *Beihefte botan. Zentralbl.*, 1903, v. 15, pp. 208–214. In English. **530**

There is no decisive proof that an organic peroxide is responsible for the liberation of iodine from potassium iodide by certain plant juices; nor can ordinary oxidase liberate iodine.

1926. Kaho, Hugo, *School of Botany, University of Tartu, Estonia.* Über den Einfluss der Temperatur auf die koagulierende Wirkung einiger Alkalisalze auf das Pflanzenplasma. [The effect of temperature on the coagulating action of some alkali salts on plant plasma.] *Biochem. Ztschr.*, 1926, v. 167, pp. 182–194. **531**

Coagulating action of potassium iodide was most effective at 0° C and 36° C, and least effective between 9° C and 13° C.

1935. Kohn, Henry I., *biological laboratories, Harvard University.* Inhibition of photosynthesis in *Chlorella pyrenoidosa* by the iodoacetyl radical. *J. Gen. Physiol.*, 1935, v. 19, pp. 23–34. **532**

Iodoacetic acid and iodoacetamide inhibit photosynthesis in the green alga *Chlorella pyrenoidosa.*

1936. [Prokoshev, S. M., and I. A. Babichev.] Прокошев, С. М., and И. А. Бабичев, *enzyme laboratory, All-Union Institute of Plant Industry, Leningrad.* Специфичность протеаз в семенах и проростках ряда культур. [The specificity of protease in the seeds and sprouts of various cultures.] *Trudi Priklad. Botan. Genetike i Selektsi*, 1936, 3rd Series, no. 14, pp. 79–95; English summary pp. 95–96. **533**

Iodoacetic acid strongly inhibits proteolysis of dormant seeds of wheat and soya bean, and of soya bean sprouts. The inhibiting action on sprouting wheat was much less marked.

1937. Caldwell, John, and Jane Meiklejohn, *Rothamsted Experimental Station, Harpenden, Herts.* Observations on the oxygen uptake of isolated plant tissue. 2. The effect of inhibitors. *Ann. Botany*, 1937, New Series, v. 1, pp. 487–498. **534**

Iodoacetic acid has an irreversible inhibiting action on the oxygen uptake of tomato stem slices.

1937. RABINOWITCH, E., and J. WEISS, *Sir William Ramsay Laboratories of Inorganic and Physical Chemistry, University College, London.* Reversible oxidation of chlorophyll. *Proc. Roy. Soc.* [A], 1937, v. 162, pp. 251–267. **535**

A yellow oxidized solution of chlorophyll regains its original green colour on addition of potassium iodide.

1938. BALLS, A. K., and W. S. HALE, *Bureau of Chemistry and Soils, U.S. Department of Agriculture, Washington, D.C.* Preparation and properties of wheat proteinase. *Cereal Chem.*, 1938, v. 15, pp. 622–628. **536**

Iodoacetic acid at a concentration of 0·01 *M* inhibits the activity of wheat proteinase.

1938. TURNER, JOHN STEWART, *Botany School, Cambridge University.* The respiratory metabolism of carrot tissue. 2. The effect of sodium iodoacetate on the respiration and fermentation. *New Phytol.*, 1938, v. 37, pp. 289–311. **537**

Dilute aqueous solutions of sodium iodoacetate inhibit fermentation of carrot tissue in an atmosphere of nitrogen. Iodoacetate also inhibits respiration if sufficient time is allowed for its action.

1939. BODNÁR, J., and BÉLA TANKÓ, *Medical-Chemical Institute, University of Debrecen, Hungary.* Die Rolle des Phosphats bei der alkoholischen Gärung höherer Pflanzen. [The role of phosphate in alcoholic fermentation in higher plants.] *Ztschr. physiol. Chem.*, 1939, v. 257, pp. 255–267. **538**

Iodoacetic acid completely inhibits the reduction of methylene blue in pea meal which takes place on the addition of hexose diphosphate.

1939. WOLF, JOHANNES, *Botanical Institute, Leipzig University.* Beiträge zur Kenntnis des Säurestoffwechsels sukkulenter Crassulaceen. 5. Mikrorespiratorische Untersuchungen an Blattgewebe von *Bryophyllum calycinum.* [Oxygen metabolism in the succulent *Crassulaceae.* 5. Microrespiration investigations on leaf tissues of *Bryophyllum calycinum.*] *Planta*, 1939, v. 29, pp. 450–467. **539**

Iodoacetate restricts the extra oxygen intake associated with increased carbon dioxide output.

1940. [KRYUKOVA, N.] КРЮКОВА, Н., *Institute of Biochemistry, Academy of Sciences of the U.S.S.R., Moscow.* Синтез и гидролиз сахарозы в тканях высших растений при исключении реакции фосфорилирования. [Synthesis and hydrolysis of saccharose in the tissues of higher plants under conditions of inhibited phosphorylation. *Biokhimiya*, 1940, v. 5, pp. 574–582. English summary p. 583. **540**

Inhibition of phosphorylation in plant tissues by iodoacetate (0·005 *M*) also inhibits the synthesis of saccharose but has no appreciable effect on the rate of saccharose hydrolysis.

1940. MICHLIN, D. M., and O. J. BORODINA, *Institute of Biochemistry, Academy of Sciences of the U.S.S.R., Moscow.* Pflanzliche Aldehyd-Mutase. [Plant aldehyde mutase.] *Enzymologia*, 1940, v. 9, pp. 28–33. **541**

Iodoacetic acid at a concentration of 0·02 *M* completely inhibits the activity of aldehyde mutase prepared from pea seeds.

1941. GREENFIELD, SYDNEY S., *department of botany, Columbia University, New York.* Differential inhibition of photochemical and dark reactions in photosynthesis by inorganic compounds. *Science*, 1941, v. 93, pp. 550–551. **542**

See entry **398**.

1941. [RICHTER, A. A., and N. G. VASILEVA.] РИХТЕР, А. А., and Н. Г. ВАСИЛЬЕВА, *photosynthesis laboratory, Academy of Sciences of the U.S.S.R., Moscow.* Spraying with micro-elements as a method of increasing the rate of photosynthesis. *C. R. Acad. Sci.*, Moscow, 1941, v. 30, pp. 659–660. In English. **543**

See entry **402**.

1942. GREENFIELD, SYDNEY S., *department of botany, Columbia University, New York.* Inhibitory effects of inorganic compounds on photosynthesis in *Chlorella. Amer. J. Botany*, 1942, v. 29, pp. 121–131. **544**

See entry **404**.

1943. HARTT, CONSTANCE E. The synthesis of sucrose in the sugar-cane plant. 3. The effects of specific inhibitors upon the interconversion of glucose and fructose and the formation of sucrose in detached blades of the sugar-cane plant. *Hawaiian Planters' Rec.*, 1943, v. 47, pp. 223–255. **545**

Iodoacetic acid (0·0001 *M*) did not inhibit either interconversion or synthesis; but a strong concentration (0·01 *M*) completely inhibited both processes.

1944. BERGER, JULIUS, and GEORGE S. AVERY, Jr., *department of botany, Connecticut College, New London.* Glutamic and isocitric acid dehydrogenases in the *Avena* coleoptile and the effect of auxins on these enzymes. *Amer. J. Botany*, 1944, v. 31, pp. 11–19. **546**

Iodoacetate at concentrations of 0·001 *M* to 0·01 *M* does not markedly inhibit crude *iso*citric dehydrogenase preparations, whereas at a concentration of 0·05 *M* it strongly inhibits both glutamic and *iso*citric dehydrogenases.

HYDROPONICS 547–548

1939. MATLIN, D. R., *M.A., professor of plant chemiculture, Belmont Evening High School, Los Angeles, and plant technologist, Palos Verdes Hydroponic Gardens, California.* Growing plants without soil. The A.B.C. of plant chemiculture, soilless agriculture, water culture, hydroponics, tank farming, sand culture, including plant growth hormones and their use. London: *E. & F. N. Spon Ltd.*, 1939, viii+139 pp. **547**

Formulae given for plant nutrient solutions (pp. 21–22) are identical with those in Matlin, 1943 (see following entry).

1943. MATLIN, D. R., *Ph.D.* Chemical gardening: latest developments in soilless culture of plants. London: *E. & F. N. Spon Ltd.*, 1943, vi+159 pp. **548**

Solution B of Matlin's complete formula for experimental purposes includes 2 ounces of potassium iodide dissolved in 1 gallon of distilled water and added to a 500 gallon tank (p. 26). Solution B of Matlin's formula for commercial production includes 0·04 ounce (= 1·13 grammes) of potassium iodide dissolved in a quart of tap water and added to a 25 gallon tank (p. 27).

MICRO-ORGANISMS

EFFECT OF IODINE ON BACTERIA AND FUNGI

549–646

SOIL MICROFLORA : NITROGEN CYCLE 549–562

1926. STOKLASA, JULIUS, *director, State Experiment Station, Prague.* Die physiologische Funktion des Jods beim Bau- und Betriebsstoffwechsel in der chlorophyllhaltigen und chlorophyllosen Zelle. [The physiological function of iodine in the anabolism and metabolism of chlorophyll-containing and chlorophyll-free cells.] *Biochem. Ztschr.*, 1926, v. 176, pp. 38–61. **549**

See entry 321.

1927. STOKLASA, JULIUS, *director, State Experiment Station, Prague.* Über die Verbreitung des Jodes in der Natur und seine physiologische Bedeutung im pflanzlichen und tierischen Organismus. [The distribution of iodine in nature and its physiological significance in plant and animal organisms.] *Ztschr. angewandte Chem.*, 1927, v. 40, pp. 20–27. **550**

Iodine promotes growth of nitrifying bacteria and intensifies the assimilation of nitrogen.

1931. KARNAHL, HELMUT, *Institute for Agricultural Bacteriology and Soil Science, Leipzig University.* Der Einfluss von anorganischen Jodverbindungen auf Vorkommen und Lebenstätigkeit einiger wichtiger Bodenbakterien. [The influence of inorganic iodine compounds on the occurrence and metabolism of some important soil bacteria.] *Zentralbl. Bakteriol.*, *2. Abt.*, 1931, v. 82, pp. 494–518. **551**

Addition of 1 gramme of potassium iodide, potassium iodate, sodium iodide or sodium iodate per kilogramme of soil reduced normal CO_2 production by about 50 per cent. With lower concentrations the reduction in CO_2 production gradually decreased until at a concentration of 0·01 milligramme per kilogramme CO_2 production was almost normal. All four salts added at concentrations of 1 or more grammes per litre to the nutrient solution inhibited denitrification. Smaller amounts had no effect. Under similar conditions nitrogen fixation and urea decomposition were checked by addition to the nutrient solution of 1 gramme of any one of the four salts per litre.

1931. VERONA, O., and C. FERRETTI, *laboratories of plant pathology and agricultural bacteriology, Royal Higher Agricultural Institute, Pisa.* L'azione oligodinamica dello jodio e dello joduro potassico nella nutrizione dei microrganismi del terreno agrario. [The oligodynamic action of iodine and potassium iodide in the nutrition of soil micro-organisms.] *Atti Soc. Toscana Sci. Nat. Pisa, Memorie*, 1931, v. 41, pp. 62–93. **552**

Authors investigated the effect of the addition of 0·01 to 5 grammes of iodine or potassium iodide per litre of culture medium on the nutrition of soil bacteria, fungi (including species of *Penicillium*, *Macrosporium*, *Rhizopus*, *Fusarium*, *Cladosporium* and *Actinomyces*) and the freshwater alga *Spirogyra*, as well as on the processes of ammonification, nitrification, denitrification, and nitrogen fixation in the soil. From the results obtained it is concluded that at the lower concentrations both substances had generally a beneficial effect on the metabolism of the micro-organisms tested and on the biochemical activities of the soil.

1933. GREAVES, J. E., *Utah Agricultural Experiment Station, Logan.* Some factors influencing nitrogen fixation. *Soil Sci.*, 1933, v. 36, pp. 267–280. **553**

Manganese, iron and iodine greatly stimulate nitrogen fixation by *Azotobacter chroococcum* when added in small amounts to liquid culture media. It is suggested that these elements are essential to the growth and metabolism of this micro-organism.

1933. ITANO, ARAO, and AKIRA MATSUURA. Influence of iodine on physiological activities of micro-organisms. *Ber. Ōhara Inst. landwirtsch. Forsch. Kurashiki*, 1933, v. 6, pp. 73–81. In English. **554**

The optimum amount of iodine for stimulating the physiological activities of *Azotobacter chroococcum*, *Bacillus subtilis* and *Saccharomyces cerevisiae* is about 0·007 per cent of the culture medium. For *A. chroococcum* and *B. subtilis* 2 per cent is lethal, and for *S. cerevisiae* 0·5 per cent.

1934. DOPTER, P., *director, Nord Agricultural Station, Lille.* Action des éléments secondaires du nitrate chilien sur l'activité microbienne des sols. [Action of the secondary elements in Chilean nitrate on the microbial activity of soils.] *Recherches Fertilisation Stat. Agron.*, Douai, 1934 (1935), p. 50. **555**

A simple (unspecified) salt of iodine added to a sample of soil had no effect on its microbial activity.

1939. GREAVES, *Dr.* J. E., *chemist and bacteriologist, Utah Agricultural Experiment Station, Logan.* Some factors influencing nitrogen fixation by *Azotobacter chroococcum*. *Soil Sci. Soc. Amer. Proc.*, 1939, v. 4, pp. 250–251. Also in *Proc. 3rd Internat. Congr. Microbiol.*, New York, 1939 (1940), p. 698. **556**

Addition of sodium iodide (40 parts per million), together with minute amounts of manganous carbonate and ferrous sulphate, to Ashby's basal solution increased nitrogen fixation by *Azotobacter chroococcum* cultures by about 200 per cent.

1939. Powers, W. L., *Oregon State Agricultural College, Corvallis*. Will iodine come to be considered an essential plant nutrient? *Science*, 1939, v. 89, pp. 434–435. **557**

Iodine seems to affect soil micro-organisms, particularly nitrogen-fixing legume root bacteria.

1940. Leroux, Désiré, *director, agricultural chemistry laboratory, Conservatoire National des Arts et Métiers, Paris*. Influence de quelques *oligo-éléments* sur la combustion de la matière organique et la nitrification dans le sol. [The influence of some trace elements on the oxidation of organic matter and on nitrification in the soil.] *C. R. Acad. Sci.*, Paris, 1940, v. 210, pp. 770–772. **558**

Addition of 2, 5 or 10 milligrammes of iodine per kilogramme of dry soil increased the production of carbon dioxide and formation of nitrate nitrogen.

1941. Leroux, Désiré, *director, agricultural chemistry laboratory, Conservatoire National des Arts et Métiers, Paris*. Influence de quelques *oligo-éléments* sur la fixation de l'azote atmosphérique au cours de la végétation d'une *Légumineuse*. [Influence of some trace elements on the fixation of atmospheric nitrogen during the growth of a legume.] *C. R. Acad. Sci.*, Paris, 1941, v. 212, pp. 504–507. **559**

When 2 or 5 milligrammes of any one of the trace elements, iodine included, are added to each kilogramme of the soil in which peas are grown the amount of atmospheric nitrogen fixed is increased.

1942. Carlson, W. E., *Montana State College, Bozeman*. Biological experiments with iodine. *J. Amer. Soc. Agron.*, 1942, v. 34, pp. 861–862. **560**

Experiments with iodine in the nutrition of alfalfa led to a further enquiry on the effect of iodine on the reactions of soil bacteria. The author concludes: "Yield increase of a crop as evidence that an element is essential or as indicating a deficiency of any element added in small amounts to the soil, may be misleading. The effect of the element on the soil's microflora should also be evaluated."

1942. Lewis, J. C., *Western Regional Research Laboratory, Albany, California*. The influence of copper and iodine on the growth of *Azotobacter agile*. *Amer. J. Botany*, 1942, v. 29, pp. 207–210. **561**

An interaction between copper and iodine is demonstrated in the early growth stages of *Azotobacter agile*. The manner of interaction is unknown, but the period during which there is no growth due to the presence of 1 part of copper per million parts of culture medium is reduced by the addition of iodine.

1947. Fedorov, M. V., *Timiryazev Agricultural Academy, Moscow*. Fixation of atmosphere nitrogen by *Azotobacter* as affected by substances inhibiting the processes of glycolysis. *C. R. Acad. Sci.*, Moscow, 1947, v. 55, pp. 259–262. In English. **562**

Presence of iodoacetic acid at concentrations of 0·0001 to 0·001 *M* in the nutrient solution increases nitrogen fixation by *Azotobacter agile* by as much as 25 per cent.

BACTERIA

563–579

1928. Ishikawa, Mitsuteru, *North-western University Medical School, Chicago, and Washington University School of Medicine, St. Louis*. Influence of iodide on bacterial decomposition of nitrogenous substances. *J. Infect. Dis.*, 1928, v. 43, pp. 321–326. **563**

Potassium iodide and potassium iodate inhibit the formation of ammonia by cultures of proteolytic organisms, and also the production of amino-acids by the proteolytic bacteria-free enzyme. Iodide suppresses the liberation of ammonia from urea by urea-splitting bacteria. This is apparently due to an inhibitory effect of iodide on enzyme activity.

1931. Kushima, B. [The effect of various neutral salts on the growth of bacteria.] *Jap. Ztschr. Mikrobiol. Path.*, 1931, v. 25, pp. 1–22. Cited from *Chem. Abstr.*, 1932, v. 26, p. 5603. **564**

Effects of potassium iodide and sodium iodide on the growth of *Staphylococcus albus*, *Eberthella typhosa*, *Vibrio cholerae* and *Bacillus anthracis* were studied.

1932. Field, Jr., John, and Sally M. Field, *laboratory of physiology, Stanford University, California*. Effect of sodiummonoiodoacetate upon metabolism of *Streptobacterium casei*. *Proc. Soc. Exp. Biol. Med.*, 1932, v. 29, pp. 357–358. **565**

Iodoacetate at a concentration of 0·008 per cent had little effect on the rate or extent of lactic acid production by suspensions of the streptobacteria. At concentrations of 0·08 and 0·16 per cent inhibition was noted after 65 and 35 minutes, respectively.

1932. Field, Jr., John, and Sally M. Field. On the kinetics of monoiodoacetate poisoning in *Streptobacterium casei*. *Proc. Soc. Exp. Biol. Med.*, 1932, v. 29, pp. 733–735. **566**

Over the concentration range 0·0004 to 4·0 per cent of iodoacetate, the rate of poisoning was found to be a constant power of the concentration.

1932. Meyer, Kurt, *department of bacteriology, Rudolf Virchow Hospital, Berlin*. Über den Einfluss der Monojodessigsäure auf die bakterielle Milchsäurebildung. [The effect of iodoacetic acid on bacterial lactic acid production.] *Biochem. Ztschr.*, 1932, v. 256, pp. 105–114. **567**

Iodoacetic acid at a concentration of 0·0002 *M* inhibits completely lactic acid production from glucose by bacteria, but a concentration of 0·1 *M* is necessary to effect total destruction of the bacteria.

1933. MEYER, KURT. Über den Einfluss der Monojodessigsäure auf die bakterielle enzymatische Glucosidspaltung. [The effect of iodoacetic acid on bacterial and enzymic decomposition of glucosides.] *Biochem. Ztschr.*, 1933, v. 262, pp. 329–331. **568**

Iodoacetic acid inhibits the hydrolysis of β-glucosides (aesculin, amygdalin, arbutin, salicin) by the β-glucosidase from lactic acid streptococci and by emulsin. The inhibiting action in the former is about 500 times stronger than in the latter.

1936. CHODAT, F., and G. CARRISSON, *Institute of General Botany, University of Geneva.* Effet du monojodacétate de sodium sur la respiration du *staphylocoque doré.* [Effect of sodium iodoacetate on the respiration of *Staphylococcus aureus.*] *Arch. Sci. Phys. Nat.*, 1936, v. 18, Suppl. pp. 139–141. **569**

Respiration of *Staphylococcus aureus* is reduced by 46 and 5·7 per cent in the presence of iodoacetate at concentrations of 0·001 and 0·00002 *M*, respectively.

1936. MANDILLON, G., and ESPIL, L. Étude du pouvoir empêchant sur le développement de différents microbes saprophytes et pathogènes de l'acide monoiodoacétique cultivés en milieu liquide organique. [The inhibitive effect of monoiodoacetic acid on the development of saprophytic and pathogenic micro-organisms cultivated in a liquid organic medium.] *Bull. Mém. Soc. Méd. Chirurg. Bordeaux*, 1936 (1937), pp. 95–99. **570**

Tables show the inhibiting effects of varying concentrations of iodoacetic acid on the growth of various bacilli and staphylococci.

1937. MASCHMANN, ERNST, *biochemistry department, Georg Speyer-Haus, Frankfort-on-Main.* Über Bakterienproteasen. 2. [Bacterial proteinases. 2.] *Biochem. Ztschr.*, 1937, v. 295, pp. 1–10. **571**

Iodoacetic acid (0·01 *M*) had no effect on the capacity of culture filtrates of *Bacillus perfringens* to hydrolyze gelatin.

1937. MICHAELIS, MORITZ, *Biochemical Institute, Foundation for Chemical Research, Helsinki.* Einige Beobachtungen über den Einfluss von Halogenessigsäuren auf den Hexosenabbau durch *Bacterium coli.* [Some observations on the effect of halogenated acetic acids on the decomposition of hexoses by *Bacterium coli.*] *Suomen Kemistilehti* [B], 1937, v. 10, pp. 10–12. **572**

Concentrations of chloro-, bromo- and iodo-acetic acids required to inhibit the development of *Bacterium coli* in glucose media were, respectively, 0·005, 0·0005 and 0·00002 *M*.

1937. WRIGHT, HEDLEY D., *department of bacteriology, University of Liverpool.* The effect of iodoacetic acid, fluoride, phloridzin and phenol on bacterial fermentation: a further consideration of the fermentation of disaccharides. *J. Path. Bacteriol.*, 1937, v. 45, pp. 117–129. **573**

Iodoacetic acid (1:16,000) completely inhibited fermentation of sucrose and glucose by certain streptococci, *Bacterium coli* and *Proteus* X19.

1938. KOSER, STEWART A., R. D. FINKLE, A. DORFMAN and FELIX SAUNDERS, *departments of bacteriology and parasitology, and of biochemistry, University of Chicago.* Studies on bacterial nutrition. The possible role of inorganic salts and of alterations in the culture medium in providing growth-promoting effects. *J. Infect. Dis.*, 1938, v. 62, pp. 202–208. **574**

Addition of 0·02 to 0·002 milligramme of potassium iodide per millilitre of synthetic medium had no effect on the growth of *Staphylococcus albus, Streptococcus haemolyticus, Shiga's bacillus, Brucella abortus, Corynebacterium diphtheriae,* and *Saccharomyces cerevisiae.*

1938. WRIGHT, HEDLEY D., *department of bacteriology, University of Liverpool.* The fermentation of glucosides by streptococci. *J. Path. Bacteriol.*, 1938, v. 46, pp. 261–269. **575**

Iodoacetic acid at a concentration as low as 1:100,000 had an inhibiting effect on the hydrolysis and fermentation of salicin, aesculin and arbutin by streptococci.

1939. CHAIX, PAULETTE, and CLAUDE FROMAGEOT, *Institute of Chemistry, University of Lyons.* Influence du fluorure de sodium et de l'acide monoiodacétique sur les dégradations anaérobie et aérobie de quelques substrats par *Propionibacterium pentosaceum.* [Effect of sodium fluoride and iodoacetic acid on the anaerobic and aerobic degradation of some substrates by *Propionibacterium pentosaceum.*] *Enzymologia*, 1939, v. 7, pp. 353–361. **576**

Iodoacetic acid at a concentration of 0·0004 *M* completely inhibits the fermentation but has only a slight effect on the oxidation of glucose by the bacterium.

1940. PENNSYLVANIA AGRICULTURAL EXPERIMENT STATION. Bacterial estimates accurate. *Pennsylvania Agric. Exp. Stat.*, Bulletin No. 399 (53rd Annual Report), 1940, p. 14. **577**

Potassium iodide, in the concentrations used (not stated), had no stimulating effect on the growth of Gram-positive and Gram-negative organisms.

1941. BARRON, E. S. GUZMAN, and THEODORE E. FRIEDEMANN, *Lasker Foundation for Medical Research and Department of Medicine, University of Chicago.* Studies on biological oxidations. 14. Oxidations by micro-organisms which do not ferment glucose. *J. Biol. Chem.*, 1941, v. 137, pp. 593–610. **578**

Iodoacetic acid (0·005 *M*) had no effect on the rate of oxidation of glucose by *Micrococcus piltonensis* and inhibited by less than 50 per cent the rate of oxidation by *Sarcina lutea, Phytomonas campestris* and *Pseudomonas aeruginosa.* The inhibiting effect is complete in bacteria (gonococci, haemolytic streptococci, pneumococci) which ferment glucose.

1948. ÅBERG, BÖRJE, *Institute of Plant Physiology, Royal Agricultural College of Sweden.* On the mechanism of the toxic action of chlorates and some related substances upon young wheat plants. *Kungl. Lantbruks-Högskolans Ann.*, 1948, v. 15, pp. 37–107. In English. **579**

The literature on the effect of iodates on bacteria and fungi is briefly reviewed.

YEASTS 580–631

INORGANIC IODINE 580–599

1888. SCHULZ, *Prof.* HUGO, *Greifswald, Germany.* Ueber Hefegifte. [Yeast poisons.] *Pflügers Arch. ges. Physiol.*, 1888, v. 42, pp. 517–541. **580**

Iodine at a suitable dilution had a beneficial effect on the fermentation of yeast. In one series of experiments the optimum dilution was 1 in 600,000 and in another series 1 in 100,000.

1913. KOSSOWICZ, ALEXANDER, and WALTER LOEW. Vorlaüfige Mitteilung über das Verhalten von Bakterien, Hefen und Schimmelpilzen zu Jodverbindungen. [Preliminary note on the behaviour of bacteria, yeasts and moulds to iodine compounds.] *Ztschr. Gärungsphysiol.*, 1913, v. 2, p. 158. **581**

Pure yeasts grown in mineral-sugar solutions containing potassium iodide liberated little or no iodine. Similar results were obtained with most of the moulds tested. With cultures of *Penicillium glaucum* and *Aspergillus niger*, however, there was considerable liberation of iodine.

1923. STEPPUHN, O., and L. UTKIN-LJUBOWZOFF, *State Chemical-Pharmaceutical Research Institute, Moscow.* Über das Wesen der Autolyse. 1. Über die Einwirkung von Jod auf Hefeautolyse. [The mechanism of autolysis. 1. The effect of iodine on the autolysis of yeast.] *Biochem. Ztschr.*, 1923, v. 140, pp. 17–27. **582**

Low concentrations of iodine promote the autolysis of yeast. High concentrations have an inhibitory effect.

1925. LIEBEN, FRITZ, and DANIEL LÁSZLO, *Institute of Physiology, Vienna University.* Über den Einfluss einiger Ionen auf die Zuckerassimilation durch sauerstoffgeschüttelte Hefe. [The influence of certain ions on sugar assimilation by oxygenated yeast.] *Biochem. Ztschr.*, 1925, v. 162, pp. 278–288. **583**

Iodide ion increases sugar assimilation in oxygenated yeast suspensions.

1926. ZELLER, HEINRICH, *Medical Clinic, Königsberg University.* Wirkung von Arzneimitteln und Strahlen auf Hefe. 1. Versuche über die Grundlage des Arndt-Schulzschen Gesetzes. [The effect of drugs and radiation upon yeast. 1. Basis for the Arndt-Schulz law.] *Biochem. Ztschr.*, 1926, v. 171, pp. 45–75. **584**

Deals with the effect of varying quantities of potassium iodide and thyroxine on the rate of evolution of carbon dioxide by yeast. Of the substances classified by Schulz as cell stimulants (see entry **580**) only three, including potassium iodide, are truly stimulant.

1926. ZELLER, HEINRICH. Wirkung von Arzneimitteln und Strahlen auf Hefe. 2. Nachweis der Wirkung von Röntgenstrahlen auf Substanzen durch Hefe. [Effect of drugs and radiation on yeast. 2. Demonstration of the effect of Röntgen rays on substances by means of yeast.] *Biochem Ztschr.*, 1926, v. 172, pp. 105–125. **585**

Irradiation of a 1 per cent solution of potassium iodide had no effect on its behaviour towards the fermentative action of yeast. Irradiation of a 10 per cent solution of sodium iodide and of 1 to 5 per cent solutions of thyroidin, however, increased their respective inhibiting effects on yeast fermentation.

1927. SCHARRER, K., and W. SCHWARTZ, *Institute of Agricultural Chemistry, College of Agriculture and Brewing, Weihenstephan, Munich.* Zur Kenntnis des Jods als biogenes Element. 11. Die Wirkung des Jods auf Hefe. 1. [Iodine as a biogenic element. 11. The effect of iodine on yeast. 1.] *Biochem. Ztschr.*, 1927, v. 187, pp. 159–179. **586**

Inorganic iodides in the nutrient solution had a stimulating effect on yeast production at low concentrations and a toxic effect at high concentrations. (See also entry **594**.)

1927. SCHARRER, K., and W. SCHWARTZ. Die Wirkung von Jod auf Hefe. [The effect of iodine on yeast.] *Wochenschr. Brauerei*, 1927, v. 44, pp. 516–517. **587**

A summary of the paper annotated in the preceding entry.

1928. GREAVES, J. E., C. E. ZOBELL and J. DUDLEY GREAVES, *Utah Agricultural College Experiment Station, Logan.* The influence of iodine on the growth and metabolism of yeasts. *J. Bacteriol.*, 1928, v. 16, pp. 409–430. **588**

Small quantities of iodine (elementary, or as salts of sodium, potassium or calcium) accelerate yeast growth. It is suggested that iodine-cultured yeast may be a means of furnishing iodine to man. The results indicate that iodine is essential to yeast growth and metabolism.

1928. MEYER, FRITZ, *Kaiser-Wilhelm Institute for Physiology of Energy, Dortmund-Münster.* Zur Frage der Beeinflussung des Energieumsatzes der Hefe durch Schilddrüsenpräparate. [The effect of thyroid preparations on the energy metabolism of yeast.] *Endokrinologie*, 1928, v. 2, pp. 337–346. **589**

Aqueous extracts of desiccated thyroid increase the energy metabolism but not the respiratory quotient of yeast cells.

1929. BOAS, FRIEDRICH, *Institute of Botany, College of Agriculture and Brewing, Weihenstephan, Munich.* Ionenwirkung und Leistung der Zelle. [Ion action and cellular activity.] *Biochem. Ztschr.*, 1929, v. 215, pp. 257–266. **590**

Sodium iodide, at a concentration of 0·3 to 0·5 *M* in a neutral or faintly alkaline nutrient solution (sucrose at a concentration of 0·1 *M* in yeast water) containing mixed cultures, destroyed bacteria but had no effect on the development of moulds. At a concentration of 0·033 *M* it increased the yeast-cell count by 60 per cent.

1929. BRANHAM, SARA E., *University of Rochester, Rochester, N.Y.* The effects of certain chemical compounds upon the course of gas production by baker's yeast. *J. Bacteriol.*, 1929, v. 18, pp. 247–264. **591**

Tincture of iodine at concentrations of 1:500 to

1:1000 stimulated yeast fermentation in sucrose solution after 3 to 5 hours. Higher concentrations inhibited fermentation.

1930. KOOIJMANS, J., *microbiology laboratory, Technical College, Delft*. Einfluss des Jods auf die Reproduktion der Hefe. [Effect of iodine on the reproduction of yeast.] *Zentralbl. Bakteriol.*, 2. *Abt.*, 1930, v. 82, pp. 347–353. **592**

Addition of minute amounts of potassium iodide to a basal nutrient solution slightly stimulated growth in some strains of yeast. Best results were obtained at a concentration of about one part in ten million.

1930. SCHARRER, K., and G. CLAUS, *Institute of Agricultural Chemistry, and Institute of Botany, Weihenstephan, Munich*. Der Einfluss des Jodes auf die Kohlensäureproduktion gärender Hefe. [Effect of iodine on the carbon dioxide production of fermentation yeasts.] *Arch. Mikrobiol.*, 1930, v. 1, pp. 343–364. **593**

Activity of yeast in sugar solution was stimulated by the addition of 0·006 to 0·01 per cent of iodine as potassium or sodium iodide and reduced by higher concentrations. No stimulation occurred with potassium iodate. Potassium periodate at a level of 0·0001 to 0·0005 per cent caused slight stimulation.

1932. SCHARRER, K., and W. SCHWARTZ, *Institute of Agricultural Chemistry, Weihenstephan, Munich, and Institute of Botany, Technical College, Karlsruhe*. Die Wirkung des Jods auf Hefe. 2. [The effect of iodine on yeast. 2.] *Biochem. Ztschr.*, 1932, v. 245, pp. 218–233. **594**

Iodides and iodates stimulated growth and budding of yeast, but free iodine in aqueous or alcoholic solution was toxic. A number of organic iodine compounds were also tested and found to have a stimulating effect at low concentrations but to be toxic at higher concentrations.

1933. ITANO, ARAO, and AKIRA MATSUURA. Influence of iodine on physiological activities of microorganisms. *Ber. Ōhara Inst. landwirtsch. Forsch. Kurashiki*, 1933, v. 6, pp. 73–81. In English. **595**

See entry 554.

1936. BERTRAND, GABRIEL, and ANTON PHILIP WEBER. Action conjugée de la folliculine et de certains catalyseurs minéraux sur le développement d'une levure. [Joint action of folliculin and some mineral catalysts on the development of yeast.] *C. R. Acad. Sci.*, Paris, 1936, v. 202, pp. 1629–1632. **596**

Addition of small quantities of some trace elements, including iodine at the rate of 1 milligramme per litre, to Reader's solution did not markedly increase the amount of dry matter produced by two species of *Rhodotorula*. Further addition of small quantities of folliculin, however, increased the dry matter yield by 178 per cent compared with that of controls.

1937. BLAGOVESCHENSKY, A. V., and T. A. SOROKINA, *enzyme laboratory of the chemical section, All-Union Institute of Experimental Medicine, Moscow*. The effect of oxidants on the yeast proteinase. *Bull. Biol. Méd. Exp. USSR*, 1937, v. 4, pp. 176–179. In English. **597**

Activity of yeast proteinase is inhibited by iodine.

1937. WEBER, A. P., *biological chemistry laboratory, Pasteur Institute, Paris*. L'influence des hormones cristallisées sur la croissance de certaines espèces de levures. [The effect of crystalline hormones on the growth of certain species of yeasts.] *Ann. Ferment.*, 1937, v. 3, pp. 15–29; 65–86. **598**

Thyroxine at a concentration of 0·0001 per cent appreciably stimulated the growth of *Rhodotorula suganii* and slightly that of *R. glutinis* var. *saitoi* in Reader's solution supplemented with small quantities of some trace elements, including iodine at the rate of 1 milligramme per litre.

1938. KOSER, STEWART A., R. D. FINKLE, A. DORFMAN and FELIX SAUNDERS, *departments of bacteriology and parasitology, and of biochemistry, University of Chicago*. Studies on bacterial nutrition. The possible role of inorganic salts and of alterations in the culture medium in providing growth-promoting effects. *J. Infect. Dis.*, 1938, v. 62, pp. 202–208. **599**

See entry 574.

IODOACETIC ACID 600-631

1930. LUNDSGAARD, EINAR, *Medical-Physiological Institute, Copenhagen University*. Die Monojodessigsäurewirkung auf die enzymatische Kohlenhydratspaltung. [The influence of monoiodoacetic acid on the enzymic hydrolysis of carbohydrate.] *Biochem. Ztschr.*, 1930, v. 220, pp. 1–7. **600**

Alcoholic fermentation produced by live yeast or by a zymase preparation from dried brewers' yeast was completely inhibited by iodoacetic acid at a concentration of 1:5000. Under such conditions the formation of hexose-phosphate could not be detected. Invertase, ptyalin and catalase were much more resistant, their activity not being affected by a concentration of 1:300.

1930. LUNDSGAARD, EINAR. Über die Einwirkung der Monojodessigsäure auf den Spaltungs- und Oxydationsstoffwechsel. [The influence of monoiodoacetic acid on hydrolytic and oxidative metabolism.] *Biochem. Ztschr.*, 1930, v. 220, pp. 8–18. **601**

Although iodoacetic acid inhibited the glycolytic action of yeast, the oxidative processes were able to proceed in its presence.

1931. MACFARLANE, MARJORIE GIFFEN, *biochemical department, Lister Institute, London*. Fermentation by yeast preparations. 1. The effect of monoiodoacetate on the fermentation of hexosediphosphate. *Biochem. J.*, 1931, v. 25, pp. 822–826. **602**

Iodoacetate inhibited the fermentation of hexosediphosphate by hexosephosphatase.

1932. EHRENFEST, ELLEN, *laboratory of biological chemistry, School of Medicine, Washington University*. The influence of monoiodoacetate on oxidation and fermentation by yeast. *J. Biol. Chem.*, 1932, v. 97, Sci. Proc., pp. lxxvi–lxxviii. **603**

Iodoacetate in a dilution of 1:56,000 completely inhibits the fermentation and oxidation of glucose by yeast at a hydrogen ion concentration of 4·6.

1932. LUNDSGAARD, EINAR, *Medical-Physiological Institute, Copenhagen University*. Weitere Untersuchungen über die Einwirkung der Halogenessigsäuren auf den Spaltungs- und Oxydationsstoffwechsel. [Further investigations on the influence of halogenated acetic acids on hydrolytic and oxidative metabolism.] *Biochem. Ztschr.*, 1932, v. 250, pp. 61–88. **604**

Iodoacetic acid (0·001 *M*) at a hydrogen ion concentration of 4·5 to 5·0 inhibited almost completely fermentation by yeast, but had no effect on respiration. Iodopropionic acid had no appreciable effect on fermentation.

1932. Zuckerkandl, Fritz, and Luise Messiner-Klebermass, *Medical-Chemical Institute, Vienna University*. Die Umwandlung von Acetaldehyd durch Hefe. Beitrag zur Kenntnis der Co-Zymasewirkung. 2 Mitteilung. [The conversion of acetaldehyde by yeast. Contribution to the knowledge of co-zymase action. 2.] *Biochem. Ztschr.*, 1932, v. 255, pp. 330–343. **605**

Yeast poisoned with iodoacetic acid is unable to form ethyl alcohol from acetaldehyde by reduction in the presence of glucose or glycogen.

1933. Cayrol, P. Recherches sur l'action des acides halogénés et de leurs esters sur les cellules de levures. [The effect of halogen acids and their esters on yeast cells.] *Ann. Physiol. Physicochim. Biol.*, 1933, v. 9, pp. 999–1102. **606**

Inhibiting action on yeast is, in general, a function of the CH_2XCOOR group, where X is either Br or I.

1933. Ehrenfest, Ellen, *laboratory of biological chemistry, School of Medicine, Washington University*. The removal of iodoacetate inhibition of yeast fermentation. *J. Biol. Chem.*, 1933, v. 100, Sci. Proc., pp. xxxviii–xxxix. **607**

Author disagrees with the findings of Lundsgaard (see entry **604**) and states her reasons.

1933. Kluyver, A. J., and J. C. Hoogerheide. On the influence of monoiodoacetic acid on the respiration and fermentation of yeast. *Koninkl. Nederlandsche Akad. Wetensch. Proc.*, 1933, v. 36, pp. 596–605. In English. **608**

Oxygen consumption and CO_2 output by yeast in the presence of 0·001 to 0·014 per cent of iodoacetic acid were studied. At a concentration of 0·0025 per cent aerobic and anaerobic fermentation ceased but respiration was almost unaffected. The latter, however, steadily decreased with increasing concentrations of acid.

1933. Schroeder, E. F., Gladys E. Woodward and Muriel E. Platt, *University of Pennsylvania Graduate School of Medicine, Philadelphia*. The effect of amines on yeast poisoned by iodoacetic acid. *J. Biol. Chem.*, 1933, v. 100, pp. 525–535. **609**

Yeast poisoned with sodium iodoacetate was not reactivated by the addition of certain amines.

1933. Schroeder, E. F., Gladys E. Woodward and Muriel E. Platt. The relation of sulfhydryl to inhibition of yeast fermentation by iodoacetic acid. *J. Biol. Chem.*, 1933, v. 101, pp. 133–144. **610**

Inhibitory action of iodoacetic acid on yeast fermentation cannot be attributed entirely to its action in destroying glutathione.

1933. Sturm, Alexander, and Johannes Schulz, *Medical Clinic, Jena University*. Beeinflussung glykolytischer Stoffwechselvorgänge durch Jod unter besonderer Berücksichtigung der Hefegärung, zugleich ein Beitrag zur Monojodessigsäurewirkung auf die Hefegärung. [Influence of iodine on glycolysis with special reference to yeast fermentation, and the influence of monoiodoacetic acid on yeast fermentation.] *Biochem. Ztschr.*, 1933, v. 263, pp. 198–218. **611**

An iodide (NaI) concentration of 0·01 to 0·0001 *M* increases the fermentation of yeast, the optimum effect being obtained at a concentration of 0·001 *M*. Iodoacetic acid has an inhibiting effect on the action of the iodide ion, but this becomes progressively less marked as the hydrogen ion concentration increases to 6·9 when the acid may actually have a stimulating effect.

1936. Schäffner, Anton, and Fritz Krumey, *Biochemical Institute, German Technical College, Prague*. Über die dephosphorylierenden Enzyme der Hefe. (6. Mitteilung über die Enzyme der Gärung.) [The enzymes of fermentation. 6. The dephosphorylating enzymes of yeast.] *Ztschr. physiol. Chem.*, 1936, v. 243, pp. 149–165. **612**

Iodoacetic acid, which has no corresponding effect of its own, destroys the accelerating effect of arsenate on the dephosphorylation of hexose diphosphate by yeast maceration juice.

1936. Smythe, C. V., *Rockefeller Institute for Medical Research, New York*. The reaction of iodoacetate and of iodoacetamide with various sulphydryl groups, with urease, and with yeast preparations. *J. Biol. Chem.*, 1936, v. 114, pp. 601–612. **613**

Iodoacetate inhibits fermentation by living yeast cells and by cell-free yeast extracts more rapidly than does iodoacetamide.

1937. Bilger, F., W. Halden, E. Mayer-Pitsch and M. Pestemer, *Medical Chemistry Institute and Institute for Theoretical and Physical Chemistry, Graz University*. Zur Kenntnis des Fett- und Lipoidstoffwechsels der Hefen. 5. Quantitative Beziehungen bei der biologischen Ergosterin-Bildung. [Fat and lipoid metabolism in yeast. 5. Quantitative relations with the biological formation of ergosterol.] *Monatsh. Chem.*, 1937, v. 70, pp. 259–272. **614**

Iodoacetic acid inhibits the biological synthesis of total sterols and of ergosterol in yeast.

1937. Dixon, Malcolm, *Biochemical Laboratory, Cambridge University*. Action of iodoacetate on dehydrogenases and alcoholic fermentation. *Nature*, London, 1937, v. 140, p. 806. **615**

The specific poisoning of the alcohol dehydrogenase by low concentrations of iodoacetate provides a possible explanation of the inhibition by iodoacetate of alcoholic fermentation in yeast.

1937. Machlis, Samuel, and Kenneth C. Blanchard, *department of biology, Washington Square College, New York University*. The role of glutathione in the metabolism of yeast. *J. Cell. Comp. Physiol.*, 1937, v. 9, pp. 207–216. **616**

Ratio of reduced to total glutathione in yeast was not

appreciably altered by the destruction of a considerable part of the reduced glutathione by iodoacetic acid or by iodine.

1937. RAPKINE, LOUIS, *Institute of Physico-Chemical Biology, Paris.* Sur les processus chimiques au cours de la division cellulaire. 3. Inhibition et rétablissement de la division cellulaire. [Chemical processes during the course of cellular division. 3. Inhibition and re-establishment of cellular division.] *J. Chim. Phys.*, 1937, v. 34, pp. 416–427. **617**

Iodoacetic acid and iodine completely inhibited cell division in a special strain of yeast (*Schizosaccharomyces pombe*).

1937. RUNNSTRÖM, J., and F. ALM, *department of experimental zoology, Stockholm University.* Über die Gärungshemmung durch Monojodacetat bei Trockenhefe. [Inhibition of fermentation of dry yeast by monoiodoacetate.] *Naturwissenschaften*, 1937, v. 25, p. 74. **618**

Inhibition of fermentation by iodoacetate increases with increasing acidity. The iodoacetate reacts with the protein of the enzyme and not with the co-enzyme.

1937. TURNER, JOHN STEWART, *Botany School, Cambridge University.* On the relation between respiration and fermentation in yeast and the higher plants. *New Phytol.*, 1937, v. 36, pp. 142–169. **619**

A critical review of the literature on the effect of iodoacetate on the metabolism of plants.

1938. ADLER, ERICH, HANS VON EULER and GUNNAR GÜNTHER, *Biochemical Institute, Stockholm University.* Dehydrasen und Jodessigsäure. [Dehydrogenases and iodoacetic acid.] *Skand. Arch. Physiol.*, 1938, v. 80, pp. 1–15. **620**

Alcohol dehydrogenase was inhibited by low concentrations of iodoacetic acid. Dehydrogenases of lactic, malic and glutamic acids, glycerophosphate and hexosemonophosphate were not affected by relatively high concentrations.

1938. ADLER, ERICH, and GUNNAR GÜNTHER. Über die Komponenten der Dehydrasesysteme. 20. Zur Kenntnis der enzymatischen Triosephosphorsäure-Dehydrierung. [The components of dehydrogenase systems. 20. The enzymic dehydrogenation by triosephosphoric acid.] *Ztschr. physiol. Chem.*, 1938, v. 253, pp. 143–158. **621**

In enzyme preparations from yeast, iodoacetic acid in low concentrations inhibited dehydrogenation by triosephosphoric acid.

1938. OSTERN, P., T. BARANOWSKI and J. TERSZAKOWEĆ, *Institute for Medical Chemistry, University of Lwów.* Über die Phosphorylierung des Adenosins durch Hefe und die Bedeutung dieses Vorgangs für die alkoholische Gärung. 2. [The phosphorylation of adenosine by yeast and the significance of this process in alcoholic fermentation. 2.] *Ztschr. physiol. Chem.*, 1938, v. 251, pp. 258–284. **622**

Iodoacetate inhibits completely the formation of muscle adenosine-phosphoric acids from adenosine, phosphate and fructose diphosphate.

1938. SMYTHE, C. V., *Rockefeller Institute for Medical Research, New York.* The utilization of pyruvic acid by bakers' yeast. *J. Biol. Chem.*, 1938, v. 125, pp. 635–651. **623**

Low concentrations of iodoacetate decreased the amount of pyruvic acid used under aerobic conditions at a hydrogen ion concentration of 2·5 to that used under anaerobic conditions. Iodoacetamide was less effective.

1939. HAAG, E., and P. BOLOMEY, *fermentation laboratory, Pasteur Institute, Paris.* Relations entre le glutathion et l'action inhibitrice de l'acide monoiodacétique dans la fermentation alcoolique. [Relation between glutathione and the inhibiting action of iodoacetic acid on alcoholic fermentation.] *C. R. Soc. Biol.*, Paris, 1939, v. 130, pp. 217–218. **624**

In a slightly acid medium iodoacetic acid at a concentration of 0·0007 *M* completely inhibited alcoholic fermentation by zymase prepared by Lebedev's method. There was no relation between the fermenting power and the glutathione content of the zymase preparation.

1939. HAAG, E., and P. BOLOMEY. Acide monoiodacétique, glutathion et fermentation du glucose au moyen du suc de Lebedew. [Iodoacetic acid, glutathione and glucose fermentation by Lebedev's maceration juice.] *Ann. Ferment.*, 1939, v. 5, pp. 45–56. **625**

A detailed account of the work described in an earlier paper (see preceding entry).

1940. PULVER, R., and F. VERZÁR, *Physiological Institute, Basle University.* Connection between carbohydrate and potassium metabolism in the yeast cell. *Nature*, London, 1940, v. 145, pp. 823–824. **626**

Iodoacetic acid at a concentration of 0·0005 *M* inhibits simultaneously the uptake of glucose and of potassium in a 20 per cent suspension of yeast.

1941. RUNNSTRÖM, JOHN, and KNUT BRANDT, *Wenner-Gren Institute for Experimental Biology, Stockholm University.* Über den Einfluss von Kohlenmonoxyd, Cystein, Glutathion, Jodessigsäure und Fluorid auf den Umsatz der Brenztraubensäure durch Bäckerhefe. [Effect of carbon monoxide, cysteine, glutathione, iodoacetic acid and fluoride on the transformation of pyruvic acid by bakers' yeast.] *Ark. Kemi Mineral. Geol.*, 1941, v. 15A, no. 6, 29 pp. **627**

Iodoacetic acid inhibits not only the oxidation but also to some extent the decarboxylation of pyruvic acid.

1943. PICKETT, M. J., and C. E. CLIFTON, *department of bacteriology and experimental pathology, Stanford University, California.* The effect of selective poisons on the utilization of glucose and intermediate compounds by micro-organisms. *J. Cell. Comp. Physiol.*, 1943, v. 22, pp. 147–165. **628**

Iodoacetate at concentrations higher than 0·00025 *M* inhibits both the oxidation and fermentation of glucose by yeast.

1944. MASSART, L., and C. VAN DEN NOORTGAETE, *University of Ghent.* De invloed van natriumfluoride en monojoodacetaat op de ademhaling van bakkersgist. [The effect of sodium fluoride and mono-iodoacetate on the respiration of bakers' yeast.] *Natuurwetensch. Tijdschr.*, 1944, v. 26, pp. 67–72. English summary p. 72. **629**

Monoiodoacetate at a concentration of 0·001 *M* inhibits not only the oxido-reduction of triosephosphates but also another enzymatic reaction of the chain.

1947. KINSEY, V. EVERETT, and W. MORTON GRANT, *Howe Laboratory of Ophthalmology, Harvard Medical School, Boston, Mass.* Action of mustard gas and other poisons on yeast cells. 6. Study of the relationship between inhibition of carbohydrate metabolism and inhibition of growth by various poisons, and effects of other toxic agents on yeast. *J. Cell. Comp. Physiol.*, 1947, v. 30, pp. 31–42. **630**

Iodoacetic acid at concentrations up to 0·0008 *M* decreased carbon dioxide output in proportion to the effect on the rate of cell division, but had no effect on oxygen consumption.

1948. ALDOUS, J. G., *department of pharmacology, Dalhousie University, Halifax, N.S.* The effect of *p*H upon the toxicity of iodoacetic acid to yeast cells. *J. Biol. Chem.*, 1948, v. 176, pp. 83–88. **631**

At a hydrogen ion concentration of 3·5 to 5·0 the toxic action of iodoacetic acid on yeast cells is irreversible while at 5·0 to 5·5 the action is reversible.

FUNGI IMPERFECTI 632–646

1913. GAIN, EDMOND, and BROCQ-ROUSSEU, —, *Faculty of Science, University of Nancy.* Résistance à l'iodure de potassium de l'*Acremonium Potronii* Vuill. [The resistance of *Acremonium potronii* Vuill. to potassium iodide.] *C.R. Soc. Biol.*, Paris, 1913, v. 74, p. 46. **632**

Maximum dose tolerated by this fungus in peptone bouillon cultures was 0·02 gramme of potassium iodide per 5 millilitres of bouillon.

1931. MÜLLER, D., *Institute of Plant Physiology, Copenhagen University.* Glykoseoxydase. 4. Mitteilung. Glykoseoxydase aus *Aspergillus niger*. Verhalten gegen Disaccharide (Maltoxydase), Glykuronsäure und Äthylalkohol; Versuche mit Methylenblau und Monojodessigsäure. [Glucose-oxidase. 4. Glucose-oxidase from *Aspergillus niger*. Behaviour towards disaccharides (maltose-oxidase), glucuronic acid and ethyl alcohol; experiments with methylene blue and monoiodoacetic acid.] *Biochem. Ztschr.*, 1931, v. 232, pp. 423–434. **633**

Iodoacetic acid in citrate buffer solution at a concentration of 1 part in 2500 had little effect on the activity of glucose-oxidase, but at a concentration of 1 part in 5000 it inhibited alcoholic fermentation by zymase.

1933. YAMAMOTO, ATUSI, *Botanical Institute, Tokyo Imperial Institute.* Über den Einfluss einiger Gifte und der Temperatur auf den Ausnutzungsgrad der Atmungsenergie beim Wachstum des Schimmelpilzes. [The effect of some poisons and of temperature on the efficiency of respiration during the growth of moulds.] *Acta Phytochim.*, 1933, v. 7, pp. 65–92. **634**

Iodoacetic acid, even at a concentration as low as 0·00005 *M*, has an inhibiting effect on both respiration and growth of *Aspergillus niger*.

1934. BERNHAUER, KONRAD, and FRANZ SLANINA, *department of biochemistry of the chemical laboratory, German University, Prague.* Chemismus und Enzymchemie der Säurebildungs- und Säureumwandlungsvorgänge bei Schimmelpilzen. 11. Mitteilung. Die Oxalsäurebildung aus Ameisensäure, Glykolsäure, Bernsteinsäure und anderen Säuren durch *Aspergillus niger*. [Chemistry and enzyme chemistry of acid formation and transformation in moulds. 11. Formation of oxalic acid from formic, glycollic, succinic and other acids by *Aspergillus niger*.] *Biochem. Ztschr.*, 1934, v. 274, pp. 97–111. **635**

Addition of 0·001 *M* iodoacetic acid to the nutrient solution markedly inhibited the growth of mycelia.

1936. [BARINOVA, S. A., and V. S. BUTKEVICH.] БАРИНОВА, С. А., and В. С. БУТКЕВИЧ, *Institute of Plant Physiology, Academy of Sciences of the U.S.S.R., Moscow.* Влияние монойодуксусной кислоты на спиртовое брожение и образование кислот у *Aspergillus niger*. [The action of iodoacetic acid on alcoholic fermentation and acid formation by *Aspergillus niger*.] *Mikrobiologiya*, 1936, v. 5, pp. 768–776; English summary p. 776. **636**

Iodoacetic acid at concentrations of 0·0001 to 0·0004 *M* inhibits completely alcoholic fermentation but has no effect on the formation of citric and oxalic acids in *Aspergillus niger* cultures. At a concentration of 0·001 *M*, it also inhibits completely acid formation.

1937. JOHNSON, ETHEL MURIEL, EDWIN COULTHARD KNIGHT and THOMAS KENNEDY WALKER, *College of Technology, Manchester University.* The mechanism of the formation of organic acids by mould fungi. 2. The action of *Aspergillus niger* on glucose in the presence of sodium iodoacetate. *Biochem. J.*, 1937, v. 31, pp. 903–908. **637**

Presence of sodium iodoacetate at concentrations between 0·0013 *M* and 0·001 *M* in glucose solutions in contact with fully developed *Aspergillus niger* increased both the quantity of glucose consumed and the degree of acidity produced in a given time.

1939. CAPPELLETTI, *Prof.* CARLO. Sulla resistenza di alcuni funghi in coltura a forti dosi di ioduro potassico. [The resistance of certain fungi in culture to large doses of potassium iodide.] *Nuovo Giorn. Botan. Ital.*, 1939, v. 46, pp. 380–386. **638**

Penicillium digitatum and *Stachylidium griseum* grew normally in a 10 per cent glucose medium containing from 2 to 12 per cent of added potassium iodide, although at the higher concentrations production of conidia in *Stachylidium* was inhibited.

1939. JOHNSON, ETHEL MURIEL, EDWIN COULTHARD KNIGHT and THOMAS KENNEDY WALKER, *College of Technology, Manchester University.* The mechanism of the formation of organic acids by mould fungi.

3. The influence of iodoacetate and of fluoride on the formation of acids. *Biochem. J.*, 1939, v. 33, pp. 357–365. **639**

Sodium iodoacetate at a concentration of 0·0025 *M* in 10 per cent sucrose solution in contact with fully developed *Aspergillus niger* decreased the total acid formation, the amount of sugar metabolized and the yield of citric acid, and increased the yield of gluconic acid. At concentrations of 0·001 *M* and 0·002 *M* it decreased the total acid formation and the yield of gluconic acid, and increased the yield of citric acid.

1940. MOREAU, FERNAND, and *Madame* FERNAND MOREAU. Recherches sur les Saprolégniées. [Investigations on the *Saprolegniaceae*.] *Ann. Sci. Nat. Botan. Biol. Vég.*, 1940, 11th Series, v. 1, pp. 221–358. **640**

Of various potassium salts tested at concentrations varying from 0·01 to 0·06 *M*, potassium iodide had the most toxic effect on *Achlya colorata* Pringsh.

1940. PEARCE, A. A., *Molteno Institute, University of Cambridge*. On the so-called "iodide oxidase." Mechanism of iodide oxidation by *Aspergillus*. *Biochem. J.*, 1940, v. 34, pp. 1493–1500. **641**

The culture medium of *Aspergillus niger* oxidizes iodide to free iodine. This oxidation is not, however, catalyzed by a specific iodide oxidase but by hydrogen peroxide formed in the medium.

1941. BLANK, LESTER M., *associate pathologist, Division of Cotton and other Fiber Crops and Diseases, U.S. Bureau of Plant Industry*. Response of *Phymatotrichum omnivorum* to certain trace elements. *J. Agric. Research*, 1941, v. 62, pp. 129–159. **642**

See entry 678.

1942. THOM, *Dr.* CHARLES C., *United States Department of Agriculture, Washington, D.C.* Chemical induction of genetic changes in *Aspergilli*. *J. Franklin Inst.*, 1942, v. 233, pp. 284–286. **643**

Briefly mentions that potassium iodide induces variation in *Aspergillus niger*.

1943. REILLY, D., and T. P. CURTIN, *University College, Cork*. The influence of halide concentration on the metabolism of *Penicillium sclerotiorum* van Beyma. *Biochem. J.*, 1943, v. 37, pp. 36–39. **644**

Growth of *Penicillium sclerotiorum* on media containing potassium iodide in place of the usual potassium chloride did not yield the halide derivative analogous to sclerotiorine.

1945. STEINBERG, ROBERT A., *United States Department of Agriculture, Washington, D.C.* Use of microorganisms to determine essentiality of minor elements. *Soil Sci.*, 1945, v. 60, pp. 185–189. **645**

Aspergillus niger is a useful test organism in minor element studies when accuracy, speed and precision are necessary. Iodine does *not* appear to be one of its essential nutritional requirements.

1949. CAVILL, G. W. K., J. N. PHILLIPS and J. M. VINCENT, *department of organic chemistry, University of Liverpool; and school of agriculture, University of Sydney*. Relationship between fungistatic activity and structure in a series of simple aromatic compounds. *J. Soc. Chem. Indust.*, London, 1949, v. 68, pp. 12–16. **646**

Of 127 compounds tested against *Aspergillus niger*, methyl 3:5-diiodo-4-hydroxybenzoate showed the highest activity.

PLANT PROTECTION 647–818

GENERAL 647–652

1942. CHESTER, K. STARR, *Oklahoma Agricultural Experiment Station, Stillwater*. The nature and prevention of plant diseases. Philadelphia: *Blakiston Co.*, 1942, xii+584 pp. **647**

"Although relatively unexploited, iodine in various compounds or mixtures is of considerable value as a disinfectant of seeds, tubers and tools, *e.g.*, the potato cutting knife" (p. 521).

1942. MCCALLAN, S. E. A., and R. H. WELLMAN. Fungicidal versus fungistatic. *Contrib. Boyce Thompson Inst. Plant Research*, 1942, v. 12, pp. 451–463. **648**

Fungicidal means the property of killing fungi and fungistatic the property of inhibiting their growth. Iodine possesses both high fungicidal and high fungistatic activity.

1944. BOWEN, C. VERNE, *Bureau of Entomology and Plant Quarantine, Agricultural Research Administration, U.S. Department of Agriculture, Washington, D.C.* Organic iodine compounds tested against insects, fungi, and bacteria. A review of the literature. New York: *Iodine Educational Bureau, Inc.*, 1944, 20 pp. **649**

Of 294 compounds listed, 112 were tested for fungicidal or insecticidal action and the remainder for bactericidal action. There is an extensive bibliography.

1945. RAUCOURT, M., *director*, and H. BÉGUÉ, *associate director, phytopharmaceutical laboratory, Centre for Agronomic Research, Versailles*. Formulaire phytopharmaceutique. [Phytopharmaceutical formulary.] Paris: *Imprimerie Nationale*, 1945, 205 pp. **650**

French decrees relating to the agricultural use of certain chemicals, including the iodides of lead and mercury, iodine, and tincture of iodine.

1947. FREAR, DONALD E. H., *Ph.D., professor of agricultural and biological chemistry, Pennsylvania State College, State College*. A catalogue of insecticides and fungicides. Volume 1. Chemical insecticides. Waltham, Mass: *Chronica Botanica Company*, 1947, xii+203 pp. **651**

Many iodine compounds are mentioned in this catalogue.

1948. FREAR, DONALD E. H., *Ph.D.* A catalogue of insecticides and fungicides. Volume 2. Chemical fungicides and plant insecticides. Waltham, Mass.: *Chronica Botanica Company*, 1948, xii+153 pp. **652**

Includes several iodine compounds.

VARIOUS SOIL AND PLANT TREATMENTS

653–694

1853. Rivet, —. Note sur l'influence des engrais iodurés (engrais marins) pour préserver la vigne de l'attaque de l'*Oïdium Tuckeri*, et sur les qualités particulières du vin provenant des vignes ainsi traitées. [Note on the influence of manures containing iodine (marine manures) in preserving vines from attack of *Oïdium tuckeri*, and on the particular qualities of the wine from vines so treated.] *C. R. Acad. Sci.*, Paris, 1853, v. 37, pp. 724–725. **653**

Manure produced by the fermentation of marine plants has been applied to vines in some parts of Spain since 1835. The soil, as a result, contains up to 1 part of iodine per 600,000. The vines which grow there have never been attacked by *Oïdium* and the resulting wine contains 1 part of iodine in 50,000 and possesses special properties.

1893. Lodeman, E. G., *Cornell University Agricultural Experiment Station, Ithaca.* The spraying of orchards. *Cornell Univ. Agric. Exp. Stat.*, Bulletin No. 60, 1893, pp. 263–302. **654**

On pp. 296–297 brief report is made of unsuccessful attempts to use iodine as a fungicide. "A watery solution of the iodide of potassium was used for dissolving the iodine crystals, and this solution was so diluted with water that it resembled weak black tea in color. The proportions used were: iodine solution, 1 pint; water, 2 gallons. All the plants to which this solution was applied were injured by it."

1924. Brenchley, Winifred E., *D.Sc., Rothamsted Experimental Station, Harpenden, Herts.* The effect of iodine on soils and plants. *Ann. Appl. Biol.*, 1924, v. 11, pp. 86–111. **655**

Bacterial counts gave no evidence that iodine applied as sodium iodide at various levels to different soils produced any partial sterilization. There was some indication, however, that iodoform, given appropriate conditions, might prove beneficial.

1925. Owen, O., *M.Sc., chemist.* The action of some chemical agents on Colletotrichum tabificum. *Exp. and Research Stat., Cheshunt, Herts.*, Eleventh Annual Report, for 1925 (1926), pp. 116–118. **656**

Sclerotia of the fungus *Colletotrichum tabificum*, which causes a root disease in tomatoes, were killed by immersion for 17 hours in 0·1 to 0·45 per cent solutions of iodine.

1929. Goodwin, W., E. S. Salmon and W. M. Ware, *South Eastern Agricultural College, Wye, Kent.* The action of certain chemical substances on the zoospores of *Pseudoperonospora Humuli* (Miy. et Takah.) Wils. *J. Agric. Sci.*, 1929, v. 19, pp. 185–200. **657**

Exposure to iodine vapour rapidly kills the zoospores of hop downy mildew and potato blight (*Phytophthora infestans*).

1929. Lipp, J. William, *research laboratories, U.S. Bureau of Entomology, Moorestown, N.J.* Studies of substitutes for arsenate of lead as a soil insecticide. *J. Econ. Entomol.*, 1929, v. 22, pp. 600–601. **658**

See entry 767.

1933. Gleisberg, Johannes, *Bonn.* Massnahmen zur Erreichung gesunder Treibgemüse- und Tomaten-Kulturen. [Measures for attaining healthy forced vegetables and tomato cultures.] *Rhein. Monatsschr. Obst-, Garten- u. Gemüsebau*, 1933, pp. 301–303. **659**

Application of potassium iodide to the soil, as advised by Klein (see following entry), is confirmed as a valuable means of preventing stem disease in tomatoes and of preventing the onset of brown speck and other fungus diseases.

1933. Klein, *Prof.* W., *director, Institute of Animal Physiology, Agricultural College, Bonn-Poppelsdorf.* Wirkung von Jodkali auf Gemüsepflanzen. [Effect of potassium iodide on vegetables.] *Rhein. Monatsschr. Obst-, Garten- u. Gemüsebau*, 1933, pp. 274–275. **660**

After the application of iodized chalk and Chilean nitrate of soda to the soil of a greenhouse where in previous years tomato stem disease had been rife, there was no evidence of the disease in the succeeding tomato crop and the yield of fruit was greatly increased.

1933. Newton, W., R. J. Hastings and J. E. Bosher, *Dominion Laboratory of Plant Pathology, Saanichton, British Columbia.* Nematode infestation symptoms on barley as a means of determining the efficiency of chemicals as lethal agents against *Tylenchus dipsaci* Kuhn. *Canad. J. Research*, 1933, v. 9, pp. 37–42. **661**

Potassium iodide and potassium iodate were among 100 chemicals tested for lethal effect on *Tylenchus dipsaci*. In 2 per cent concentration both were toxic to the barley used as a detector crop, and the results on the nematode itself were indefinite.

1933. Poate, Hugh R. G., *M.B., F.R.H.S., president of Horticultural Council and Royal Horticultural Society of New South Wales.* Eelworm in daffodils. *Australian Garden Lover*, 1933, October 1, pp. 261–263; 265; 267. **662**

Dr. Poate, an Australian authority on the cultivation of daffodils, found that iodine was the only substance which would kill eelworms immediately. An aqueous solution (1:4000) was used.

1933. Rademacher, Bernhard, and Otto Schmidt, *Plant Breeding Institute, Halle University.* Die bisherigen Erfahrungen in der Bekämpfung des Rübennematoden (*Heterodera schachtii* Schm.) auf dem Wege der Reizbeeinflussung. [The control of the sugar-beet nematode (*Heterodera schachtii*) by chemical stimulation of hatching.] *Wissensch. Arch. Landwirtsch., Abt. A*, 1933, v. 10, pp. 237–296. **663**

Among 321 chemicals tested in preliminary experiments were: water-soluble traces of iodine, iodine green, potassium iodide. None was considered worthy of further trial.

1933. RALEIGH, W. P. Fungicidal efficiency of a solution of mercuric chloride and potassium iodide. *Phytopathology*, 1933, v. 23, pp. 28–29. **664**

Potassium iodide added to a 1 : 1200 mercury bichloride solution (in the proportion of 0·25 gramme iodide per 100 millilitres of solution) increased the efficacy of the latter as a dip for seed potatoes in the control of *Rhizoctonia solani*. A 2 per cent solution of potassium iodide used alone did not control this fungus.

1934. STEINER, *Dr.* RUDOLF, *patentee*, *Budapest*. Verfahren zur Herstellung von Pflanzenschutzmitteln. [Process for preparing protective agents for plants.] *Austrian Patent No.* 139,130, October 25, 1934. **665**

Salts of iodohydroxyquinolinesulphonic acid are used.

1937. REICHERT, I., *Ph.D.*, and F. LITTAUER, *Ph.D.*, *division of plant pathology*, *Agricultural Research Station*, *Rehovot*, *Palestine*. A new method of control of wastage in oranges. *Hadar*, 1937, v. 10, pp. 141–145. **666**

An alcoholic iodine solution was successfully applied for the control of *Diplodia natalensis* on oranges.

1937. TAUBENHAUS, J. J., W. N. EZEKIEL and J. F. FUDGE, *Texas Agricultural Experiment Station*, *College Station*. Relation of soil acidity to cotton root rot. *Texas Agric. Exp. Stat.*, Bulletin No. 545, 1937, 39 pp. **667**

The application of manganese sulphate, potassium iodide, iron sulphate, nickel sulphate, copper sulphate and borax to the soil had no effect on the incidence or prevalence of root rot.

1938. SEALE-HAYNE AGRICULTURAL COLLEGE, *Newton Abbot*, *Devonshire*. The use of chemicals in the hot treatment of narcissus bulbs. *Seale-Hayne Agric. College*, 15th Report of the Department of Plant Pathology, for 1937–38 (1939), pp. 22–28. **668**

Iodine added to the hot-water bath used to kill eelworms in bulbs before storage prevents the development of fungous infection (from species of *Fusarium*) which commonly causes rotting of the bulbs during storage. The iodine bath (1 gramme of iodine and 1½ grammes of potassium iodide in 8,000 millilitres of water) is effective against both the eelworm and the *Fusarium* bulb rot, and does no harm to the subsequent growth of the bulb.

1939. FRANKLIN, MARY T., *B.Sc.*, *Institute of Agricultural Parasitology*, *St. Albans*, *Herts*. The treatment of seed potatoes for the destruction of adherent *Heterodera schachtii* cysts. *J. Helminthol.*, 1939, v. 17, pp. 113–126. **669**

Soaking the dry cysts in a solution of decinormal iodine diluted twenty times for up to 6 hours had apparently no lethal effect on the contents.

1940. IVERSON, V. E., and H. C. KELLY, *Montana Agricultural Experiment Station*, *Bozeman*. Control of bacterial ring rot of potatoes with special reference to the ultraviolet-light method for selecting disease-free seed stock. *Montana Agric. Exp. Stat.*, Bulletin No. 386, 1940, 15 pp. **670**

One of the most effective knife disinfectants used in measures for preventing the spread of bacterial ring rot of potatoes is the following: 37·8 grammes of iodine and 75·6 grammes of potassium iodide in 1 pint of glycerine and 2 gallons of water. These same amounts of iodine and potassium iodide in 1 gallon of water and no glycerine make a very effective solution for disinfecting seed pieces of potato. Immersion for 3 minutes suffices.

1940. KRÜGER, EBERHARD. Untersuchungen über den Einfluss von Elektrolyten und Nicht-elektrolyten auf die Sporangienkeimung und die Differenzierung der Zoosporen bei *Phytophthora infestans*. [Investigations on the effect of electrolytes and non-electrolytes on the germination of spores and the differentiation of zoospores in *Phytophthora infestans* (potato blight).] *Arb. biol. Reichsanst. Land- u. Forstwirtsch.*, 1940, v. 23, pp. 51–95. **671**

Of the anions examined, iodide, as potassium iodide, had the greatest effect. A concentration of 0·000975 *M* had a pronounced effect on the differentiation of zoospores; a 0·0156 *M* solution inhibited formation of zoospores, which was completely stopped at 0·0625 *M*. In the isosmotic solution of 0·70 *M*, 48·08 per cent of sporangia showed plasma syneresis.

1940. LAMMERTS, W. E., *Armstrong Nurseries*, *Ontario*, *California*. Ethyl mercury iodide—an effective fungicide and nemacide. *Phytopathology*, 1940, v. 30, pp. 334–338. **672**

A product called DuBay 1155-HH made by Bayer-Semesan Company, Inc., and containing 5 per cent of ethyl mercury iodide as the toxic ingredient, was found to be a highly efficient soil disinfectant. It is applied at the rate of 1½ grammes per square foot of soil 4 to 7 days before seed is sown. More seedlings emerged and survived in treated soils, and growth was more vigorous than in either autoclaved soils or controls. Nematodes were completely eradicated from heavily infested soils.

1940. NIELSEN, L. W. Studies on the fungicidal properties of silver. *Phytopathology*, 1940, v. 30, p. 18. **673**

Silver iodide is only weakly fungicidal.

1940. WALLACE, E. R. Use of disinfectants in the hot water treatment of narcissus, 1936–38. *Agric. Inst. and Exp. Stat., Kirton, Boston, Lincs.*, Report on Bulb Experiments No. 7, 1940, pp. 43–56. **674**

Addition of iodine (1 oz. to 11 gallons of water containing 1½ oz. of potassium iodide) to the water improved the fungicidal effectiveness of the hot water treatment.

1941. ANSON, M. L., and W. M. STANLEY, *Rockefeller Institute*, *Princeton*, *New Jersey*. Some effects of iodine and other reagents on the structure and activity of tobacco mosaic virus. *J. Gen. Physiol.*, 1941, v. 24, pp. 679–690. **675**

Tobacco mosaic virus is inactivated by treatment with iodine solution or iodoacetamide under conditions which are described.

1941. ARK, P. A., *Division of Plant Pathology*, *University of California*. The use of iodine in the control of potato ring rot and scab. *Phytopathology*, 1941, v. 31, pp. 954–956. **676**

Iodine is a useful disinfectant for the cutting knife to reduce the spread of ring rot, and for *whole* seed tubers (1 minute immersion) to reduce the incidence of scab. An effective formula is 38 grammes of iodine and 76 grammes of potassium iodide in 1 pint of glycerine and 2 gallons of water. The dipping of *cut* seed pieces in a 0·5 per cent solution of iodine (with 1 per cent of potassium iodide) is injurious and is not effective against ring rot.

1941. ARK, P. A. Chemical eradication of crown gall on almond trees. *Phytopathology*, 1941, v. 31, pp. 956–957. **677**

The following formulae (amounts expressed in parts) gave very satisfactory results in eradicating crown gall (*Phytomonas tumefaciens*). Solution A: methyl alcohol 50; glacial acetic acid 25; glycerine 25; crystalline iodine 10. Solution B: methyl alcohol 100; glacial acetic acid 15; crystalline iodine 12. These are painted on the whole gall and surrounding area and are most effective when applied in summer.

1941. BLANK, LESTER M., *associate pathologist, Division of Cotton and Other Fiber Crops and Diseases, U.S. Bureau of Plant Industry*. Response of *Phymatotrichum omnivorum* to certain trace elements. *J. Agric. Research*, 1941, v. 62, pp. 129–159. **678**

As a preliminary to certain fundamental studies on the cotton root rot organism, *Phymatotrichum omnivorum*, experiments were made to find what trace elements are necessary for its optimum growth. Iodine was among those elements found non-essential for optimum growth under the conditions employed in these studies. The experiments were done in co-operation with the Texas Agricultural Experiment Station.

1941. BOYD, A. E. W., *botany department, Glasgow University*. Determination of death in the larvae of the potato root eelworm. *Nature*, London, 1941, v. 148, pp. 782–783. **679**

A solution of 0·025 gramme of iodine in 100 millilitres of 1 per cent aqueous potassium iodide is used as a stain to distinguish between living and dead eelworm larvae. The iodine penetrates and stains dead larvae yellow. Living larvae do not absorb the stain. Five drops of the solution are used in 2 millilitres of the larval suspension.

1941. KENDRICK, JAMES B., P. A. ARK and C. EMLEN SCOTT. Potato-ring-rot studies in California. *Phytopathology*, 1941, v. 31, p. 14. **680**

Dipping cut seed pieces in a 0·5 per cent solution of iodine (with 1 per cent of potassium iodide) is injurious and is not effective against ring rot caused by *Phytomonas sepedonica*.

1941. KÖHLER, ERICH, *laboratory for virus research, State Biological Institute for Agriculture and Forestry, Berlin*. Desinfektionsversuche an Rohsäften des Tabakmosaik- und des Kartoffel- X -Virus. [Disinfection experiments on the raw juices of the tobacco mosaic and potato X viruses.] *Zentralbl. Bakteriol.*, 2. *Abt.*, 1941, v. 103, pp. 325–334. **681**

It is briefly noted that erythrosin (an iodine-containing dyestuff) had no effect as a disinfectant, but no experimental details are given.

1941. SPEYER, E. R., and W. J. PARR. Root-knot eelworm (*Heterodera marioni* Cornu). *Exp. and Research Stat., Cheshunt, Herts.*, 27th Report, for 1941 (1942), pp. 60–61. **682**

Soil application of potassium iodide solutions, tested as a control measure for tomato eelworms, gave varying and inconclusive results.

1942. DYKSTRA, T. P., *Bureau of Plant Industry, U.S. Department of Agriculture, Washington, D.C.* Compilation of results in control of potato ring rot in 1941. *Amer. Potato J.*, 1942, v. 19, pp. 175–196. **683**

Iodine is an effective disinfectant for potato cutting knives to prevent the spread of ring rot.

1942. MEREDITH, CLIFFORD H., *Glenleigh Laboratory, Friends College, Highgate, Jamaica.* The effect of chemicals on *Fusarium oxysporum cubense* growing in the soil. *Phytopathology*, 1942, v. 32, pp. 182–184. **684**

Fusarium oxysporum cubense was killed by ethyl mercury iodide mixed with soil in a proportion of 0·0025 per cent. A mixture of 1 part soil, 1 part iodine and 2 parts water was also toxic.

1942. SPEYER, E. R. Animal pests. 1. Eelworms (*Nematoda*). *Exp. and Research Stat., Cheshunt, Herts.*, 28th Report, for 1942 (1943), pp. 48–50. **685**

A solution of one part of potassium iodide in 2400 of water applied at rates of 30 and 120 gallons per 100 square yards to soil infested with root-knot eelworm (*Heterodera marioni*) does not destroy the parasite. The effects on unspecified "soil-inhabiting eelworms" of immersion for varying periods of time in several strengths of potassium iodide are described.

1943. GLICK, DUDLEY PETERS, *Colorado Agricultural Experiment Station, Fort Collins.* The deterioration of disinfectants in agricultural use. *J. Bacteriol.*, 1943, v. 45, pp. 42–43. **686**

One gallon lots of 1 per cent iodine solution used for the continuous disinfection of rotary seed-potato cutting knives to control the spread of *Phytomonas sepedonica* failed to kill *Escherichia coli* after cutting eight 100 lb. sacks of potatoes.

1943. MEREDITH, CLIFFORD H., *Glenleigh Laboratory, Friends College, Highgate, Jamaica.* The effect of soil and chemical mixtures on the growth of *Fusarium oxysporum cubense*. *Phytopathology*, 1943, v. 33, pp. 398–400. **687**

The growth of the fungus is inhibited by iodine in concentrations of 1 : 100 and less.

1943. MEREDITH, CLIFFORD H. Mercury compounds applied to banana plants in the field. *Phytopathology*, 1943, v. 33, pp. 835–836. **688**

Ethyl mercury iodide inhibited the growth of *Fusarium oxysporum cubense* without damaging the banana plants.

1944. HORSFALL, JAMES G., and GEORGE A. ZENTMYER. Fungicidal action of reagents for amino acids, amines, aldehydes, and other reactive cell constituents. *Phytopathology*, 1944, v. 34, p. 1004. **689**

Potassium periodate is included among the fungistatic reagents mentioned.

1945. AGATOV, P., *Pedagogical Institute, Moscow.* Effect of iodine upon the activity of tobacco mosaic virus. *C.R. Acad. Sci.*, Moscow, 1945, v. 49, pp. 523–525. In English. **690**

Aqueous solution of iodine in potassium iodide completely inactivated the virus at hydrogen ion concentrations of 4·5 and 8·0, but had little effect at a hydrogen ion concentration of 5·5 to 6·0.

1946. SCHAAL, L. A., *pathologist, Bureau of Plant Industry, Soils and Agricultural Engineering, Agricultural Research Administration, U.S. Department of Agriculture, Washington, D.C.* Seed and soil treatment for the control of potato scab. *Amer. Potato J.*, 1946, v. 23, pp. 163–170. **691**

Potassium iodide treatment of potato scab infected soil before planting scab-free seed had no beneficial effect.

1948. REID, ROBERT D., *Department of Agriculture for Scotland.* Strawberry breeding at Auchincruive. *Scottish Agric.*, 1948, v. 27, pp. 218–223. **692**

On p. 222 it is reported that immersion of strawberry plants infested with bud eelworm (*Aphelenchoides fragariae*) in warm water containing iodine (1 : 20,000) for 30 minutes killed all the eelworms, but treated plants became re-infested a few months after planting in autoclaved soil.

1948. MCGOWAN, J. C., P. W. BRIAN and H. G. HEMMING, *Butterwick Research Laboratories, Imperial Chemical Industries Ltd.* The fungistatic activity of ethylenic and acetylenic compounds. 1. The effect of the affinity of the substituents for electrons upon the biological activity of ethylenic compounds. *Ann. Appl. Biol.*, 1948, v. 35, pp. 25–36. **693**

Preliminary investigations on 85 ethylenic compounds indicate that the highest fungistatic activity is shown by those compounds containing a strongly electron-attracting substituent group attached to one of the carbon atoms constituting the double bond. Tetraiodoethylene has high activity against *Fusarium graminearum* and *Penicillium digitatum* but this cannot be attributed solely to the withdrawal of electrons from the carbon atoms.

1949. MUIRHEAD, IRENE, *Butterwick Research Laboratories, Imperial Chemical Industries, Ltd.* The fungistatic activity of ethylenic and acetylenic compounds. 3. The fungistatic activity of tetraiodoethylene and related compounds. *Ann. Appl. Biol.*, 1949, v. 36, pp. 250–256. **694**

Examination of twenty-eight iodine compounds showed that several, especially tetraiodoethylene and diiodoacetylene, possessed high fungistatic activity against *Botrytis allii.*

SEED DISINFECTION
695–721

1923. GASSNER, GUSTAV, and ILSE ESDORN. Beiträge zur Frage der chemotherapeutischen Bewertung von Quecksilberverbindungen als Beizmittel gegen Weizensteinbrand. [The chemotherapeutic evaluation of mercury compounds in the treatment of seeds against bunt of wheat.] *Arb. biol. Reichsanst. Land- u. Forstwirtsch.*, 1923, v. 11, pp. 373–385. **695**

Methyl mercury iodide was found to be the most active compound tested as an inhibitor of the germination of bunt spores on wheat, but was discarded on the score of its highly poisonous character.

1926. VEREIN FÜR CHEMISCHE UND METALLURGISCHE PRODUKTION, *patentees.* Fungizides und bakterizides Mittel. [Fungicidal and bactericidal agent.] *German Patent No.* 438,241, Dec. 10, 1926. **696**

This patent claims that treatment of infected seeds with a 1 per cent solution of the condensation product from cinnamaldehyde and dimethylaminoquinaldine ethiodide, from dimethylaminobenzaldehyde and 2 :4 :6-trimethylpyridine ethiodide, or from glyoxal and ethoxyquinaldine ethiodide frees them from blight spores such as *Ustilago* and *Fusarium.*

1927. KLAGES, *Prof.* A., *Magdeburg.* Beiträge zur Giftwirkung der Quecksilberalkyle. [The poisonous action of alkylmercury compounds.] *Ztschr. angewandte Chem.*, 1927, v. 40, pp. 559–561. **697**

Methyl mercury iodide solution containing 0·0002 gramme of mercury per litre decreased the germination of barley smut spores to less than 15 per cent of the check. Ethyl mercury iodide gave exactly the same result. Isopropyl mercury iodide solution containing 0·0002 gramme of mercury per litre decreased the germination to less than 30 per cent of the check.

1927. SAYRE, J. D., and R. C. THOMAS, *Ohio Agricultural Experiment Station, Wooster.* New dust treatments for oats smuts. *Science*, 1927, v. 66, p. 398. **698**

Excellent results were obtained against oat smuts by the use of iodine vapour dust, made by mixing finely ground crystalline iodine with infusorial earth. The dust contained 5 per cent by weight of iodine.

1928. PERKINS, W. R., W. S. ANDERSON and W. W. WELBORNE, *Mississippi Agricultural Experiment Station, State College.* Report of the South Mississippi Branch Experiment Station for 1928. *Mississippi Agric. Exp. Stat.*, Bulletin No. 266, 1928, 38 pp. **699**

On pp. 24–25 the results are given of experiments to test the effect of treating cotton seed with different organic mercurials to control damping-off and cotton wilt. Substances named "Iodine Bentonite" and "Iodine Kieselguhr" were among those tested. The latter gave better results than any of the other ten treatments used.

1928. SAYRE, J. D., and R. C. THOMAS, *Ohio Agricultural Experiment Station, Wooster.* Formaldehyde and iodine dusts for the control of oats smut. *Bimonthly Bull. Ohio Agric. Exp. Stat.*, 1928, v. 13, pp. 19–21. **700**

Reports the successful control of smut on oats by the use of a dust treatment with iodine in fuller's earth.

1928. SAYRE, J. D., and R. C. THOMAS. New dust treatments for oat smuts. *Phytopathology*, 1928, v. 18, p. 139. **701**

See preceding entry.

1928. WALLACE, H. F., and J. L. COOLEY, Jr., *Mississippi Agricultural Experiment Station, State College.* Seed treatment for seed-borne diseases of cotton. *Mississippi Agric. Exp. Stat.*, Bulletin No. 262, 1928, pp. 16–17. **702**

In comparative tests with eight fungicides the largest crop yields were from seeds treated with iodine preparations.

1928. WISCONSIN AGRICULTURAL EXPERIMENT STATION. Dust fungicides effective for barley stripe and oat smut. *Wisconsin Agric. Exp. Stat.*, Bulletin No. 405 (Annual Report for 1927–28), 1929, p. 88. **703**

A short note that seed was given complete protection from barley stripe by treating it with potassium iodide before planting. Potassium iodide dusts also "gave excellent preliminary results in the treating of seed oats to control oat smut."

1929. BRENTZEL, W. E., *plant pathologist, North Dakota Agricultural Experiment Station, Fargo.* Wheat smut control. *North Dakota Agric. Exp. Stat.*, Bulletin No. 233 (Report for Biennum July 1927 to June 1929), 1930, pp. 97–98. **704**

Abavit B, an iodine-containing proprietary powder, was among the seed disinfectant preparations which completely prevented covered smut or bunt of wheat. Seed disinfection with Abavit B also produced good results in the control of root-rot, seedling blight, and loose smut of wheat.

1929. HORSFALL, JAMES G., *Cornell University, New York.* Dusting seed for oat smuts. *Phytopathology*, 1929, v. 19, pp. 173–175. **705**

Iodine dust was ineffective against oat smut.

1929. I. G. FARBENINDUSTRIE A.-G., *patentees, Frankfort-on-Main.* Mordant pour semences. [Seed disinfectant.] *French Patent No.* 654,674, April 9, 1929. **706**

Mixtures of organic compounds of mercury and salts of hydriodic acid are claimed as seed disinfectants.

1929. MEYER, LUDWIG, and FRITZ MEYER, *patentees, Mainz.* Dry disinfectant for seeds. *British Patent No.* 286,220, May 9, 1929. **707**

Disinfectants containing iodine are described.

1929. SAYRE, J. D., *Ohio Agricultural Experiment Station, Wooster.* Stinking smut of wheat. *Ohio Agric. Exp. Stat.*, Bulletin No. 446 (48th Annual Report for 1928–29), 1930, pp. 73–74. **708**

A very brief note that iodine gave better control of smut than formaldehyde dust or copper carbonate.

1929. WALLACE, H. F., and J. L. COOLEY, Jr., *Mississippi Agricultural Experiment Station, State College.* Seed treatment for seed-borne diseases of cotton. *Mississippi Agric. Exp. Stat.*, Bulletin No. 271, 1929, pp. 13–14. **709**

"Corona Merco" and "Iodine Bentonite" were the most effective of several seed disinfectants tested.

1930. KARNS, GEORGE M., *Mellon Institute of Industrial Research, Pittsburgh.* Effectiveness of iodine in the control of smut on oats. *Indust. Engin. Chem.*, 1930, v. 22, p. 864. Also in *Grain and Feed J. Consol.*, 1930, v. 65, p. 704. **710**

A preliminary report of trials demonstrating that a 10 per cent solution of iodine in carbon disulphide can be used effectively in the control of seed-borne smut.

1930. MARKS, *Sir* GEORGE CROYDON, *patentee, London.* Improvements in and relating to disinfecting seeds and the like. *British Patent No.* 330,548, May 29, 1930. **711**

Methyl mercuric iodide is among the substances for which claims are made.

1930. WESTON, W. A. R. DILLON, *M.A., School of Agriculture, Cambridge.* Ineffective nature of iodine dust as a fungicide against *Tilletia caries. Phytopathology*, 1930, v. 20, pp. 753–755. **712**

Samples of Little Joss wheat contaminated with bunt spores (*Tilletia caries*) were treated with infusorial earth dusts (containing 1½, 3, and 5 per cent of powdered iodine) applied at the rate of 2 oz. per bushel. The treatments were ineffective. The author concludes that iodine dust is of no use as a fungicide against bunt.

1931. CHEMISCHE FABRIK LUDWIG MEYER, *patentees, Mainz.* Saatgutbeize. [Seed dressing.] *German Patent No.* 521,235, March 21, 1931. **713**

Seed dressings containing iodine and iodine compounds are described.

1933. YOUNG, V. H., and C. K. MCCLELLAND, *Arkansas Agricultural Experiment Station, Fayetteville.* Control of oat smut. *Phytopathology*, 1933, v. 23, pp. 825–830. **714**

A 10 per cent solution of iodine in carbon disulphide applied at the rate of ½ oz. per bushel gave almost complete control of loose smut of oats in 1931 but was much less effective in 1932.

1937. LEUKEL, R. W., *Division of Cereal Crops and Diseases, U.S. Bureau of Plant Industry.* Studies on bunt, or stinking smut, of wheat and its control. *U.S. Department of Agriculture*, Technical Bulletin No. 582, 1937, 48 pp. **715**

A comprehensive account of experiments on bunt control carried out over 12 years at Arlington Experimental Farm, Virginia. Experience with five different iodine dusts is recorded. None of these reduced the percentage of bunt sufficiently to qualify as a bunt fungicide. In addition, the corrosive nature of iodine and its detrimental effect on germination "eliminate it from further consideration as a practical seed disinfectant." There is a useful bibliography of 52 references.

1940. BOLIDENS GRUVAKTIEBOLAG, *patentees, Joint Stock Company of Stockholm, Sweden.* Seed disinfectant. *British Patent No.* 522,396, June 17, 1940. **716**

A mixture of methyl mercury iodide and ethyl mercury chloride, diluted with a filler, is claimed as a fungicidal seed dressing, particularly against *Penicillium*.

1943. LEHMAN, S. G., *North Carolina State College of Agriculture and Engineering, Raleigh.* Vapor action of certain fungicidal materials prepared for dusting cotton seed. *Phytopathology*, 1943, v. 33, pp. 431–448. **717**

The vapour of ethyl mercury iodide is lethal to fungi which infest cotton seed.

1943. MOORE, W. D., H. REX THOMAS and EDWARD K. VAUGHAN, *Georgia Agricultural Experiment Station, Tifton.* Tomato seed treatments in relation to control of *Alternaria solani. Phytopathology*, 1943, v. 33, pp. 797–805. **718**

Treatment of seed with ethyl mercury iodide did not greatly reduce the incidence of the disease.

1943. Muskett, A. E., and J. Colhoun, *Plant Disease Division, Ministry of Agriculture, Queen's University of Belfast.* The prevention of seed-borne diseases of flax by seed disinfection. *Ann. Appl. Biol.*, 1943, v. 30, pp. 7–18. **719**

An alcoholic solution of iodine was among the numerous substances tested. It did not prove satisfactory.

1943. Ray, W. Winfield, *Oklahoma Agricultural Experiment Station, Stillwater.* The effect of cotton seed dusting on emergence of seedlings in soil infested with *Rhizoctonia. Phytopathology*, 1943, v. 33, pp. 51–55. **720**

Seed treated with ethyl mercury iodide gave a significantly higher emergence count than untreated seed.

1946. Taylor, Carlton F., and Joseph A. Rupert, *West Virginia Agricultural Experiment Station, Morgantown.* A study of vegetable seed protectants. *Phytopathology*, 1946, v. 36, pp. 726–749. **721**

Tests with silver iodide gave no special indication that this would be an effective agent in seed disinfection.

FRUIT PRESERVATION

722-745

1934. Tomkins, R. G., *Low Temperature Research Station, Cambridge.* Iodized wraps for the prevention of rotting of fruit. *J. Pomol.*, 1934, v. 12, pp. 311–320. **722**

The fungal rotting of grapes and tomatoes in storage was considerably reduced by wrapping or packing the fruit in paper impregnated with suitable amounts of iodine. Similar results were obtained with certain varieties of apples, plums and peaches.

1934. Tomkins, R. G. Treated wraps. *Department of Scientific and Industrial Research (Great Britain)*, Report of the Food Investigation Board for the year 1934 (1935), pp. 155–156. **723**

Mainly a summary of results of experiments reported in full elsewhere (see preceding entry).

1934. Tomkins, R. G. The absorption by grapes of iodine from iodized wraps. *Department of Scientific and Industrial Research (Great Britain)*, Report of the Food Investigation Board for the year 1934 (1935), pp. 156–158. **724**

Iodine is absorbed much more readily by the stalks than by the berries. Exposure to air for up to 10 days, does not result in any appreciable loss of absorbed iodine.

1935. Dreyer, D. J. The control of wastage in South African grapes by the use of iodized wraps. *Union of South Africa Department of Agriculture and Forestry*, Report of Low Temperature Research Laboratory for 1934–1935 (1936), pp. 140–154. **725**

Under commercial conditions iodized wrappers reduced wastage to some extent in every instance, and in most cases to about half the amount found in grapes wrapped in plain wrappers.

1935. Rattray, J. M. Grape wastage investigations. *Union of South Africa Department of Agriculture and Forestry*, Report of Low Temperature Research Laboratory for 1934–1935 (1936), pp. 121–140. **726**

Wrappers treated with a solution containing 1·5 per cent of iodine and 1 to 2 per cent of potassium iodide are the most effective in controlling wastage due to *Botrytis*.

1935. Tomkins, R. G. Wraps for the prevention of rotting of fruit. *Department of Scientific and Industrial Research (Great Britain)*, Report of the Food Investigation Board for the year 1935 (1936), pp. 129–131. **727**

It is considered that iodine is not the ideal substance with which to treat wrappers, since it is somewhat too volatile, stains packing material yellow and injures some varieties of fruit. Laboratory tests with a large number of substances revealed only one other than iodine (namely, diphenyl) which could possibly be used with some success.

1936. du Plessis, *Dr.* S. J., *department of plant pathology, University of Stellenbosch.* Studies on the wastage of export grapes with special reference to that caused by *Botrytis cinerea*, Pers. *Union of South Africa Department of Agriculture and Forestry*, Science Bulletin No. 151, 1936, 163 pp. **728**

After 7 days' cold storage, fruit which had been wrapped in paper treated with a 5 per cent solution of potassium iodide showed 67·8 per cent *Botrytis* infection as against 77·1 per cent in the control fruit.

1936. Nattrass, R. M., *Ph.D., D.I.C., plant pathologist.* Chemical treatment of fruits and wrappers. *Cyprus Department of Agriculture*, Annual Report for 1936 (1937), pp. 53–55. **729**

Little or no waste was found in fruit wrapped in iodized wrappers. The latter had no ill effect on the appearance or consistency of the fruit.

1936. Rattray, J. M. Grape wastage investigations. *Union of South Africa Department of Agriculture and Forestry*, Report of Low Temperature Research Laboratory for 1935–1936 (1937), pp. 167–187. **730**

Efficiency of iodized wrappers in reducing *Botrytis* wastage was increased when they were enclosed in non-porous "Crystalline" paper. Iodized crepe paper or cotton wool plugs inserted into the bunches and wrapped in the ordinary way reduced wastage to a large extent. Best results were obtained by using crepe paper plugs treated with 0·5 *N* alcoholic solution of iodine and potassium iodide and wrapping in "Crystalline" paper.

1936. Wardlaw, C. W., *Imperial College of Tropical Agriculture, Trinidad.* Iodine and the control of fungal wastage. *Trop. Agric.*, Trinidad, 1936, v. 13, p. 117. **731**

The use of iodized wrappers to prevent rotting of grapefruit, actually increased wastage. While the iodine destroyed superficial spores and hyphae, it increased the damage done by already established fungi through decreasing the resistance of the plant tissue.

1937. du Plessis, *Dr.* S. J., *department of plant pathology, University of Stellenbosch.* Control of

Botrytis rot of grapes. *Farming in South Africa*, 1937, v. 12, pp. 36–37. **732**

Wrappers soaked in a solution containing 1 per cent of iodine and 2 per cent of potassium iodide were found to be most effective in the control of *Botrytis*.

1937. RATTRAY, J. M. Grape wastage investigations, 1937. *Union of South Africa Department of Agriculture and Forestry*, Report of Low Temperature Research Laboratory for 1936–1937 (1938), pp. 75–91. **733**

None of the fungicides tested proved as effective as iodine against infection with *Botrytis cinerea*.

1937. REICHERT, I., *Ph.D.*, and F. LITTAUER, *Ph.D.*, *division of plant pathology, Agricultural Research Station, Rehovot, Palestine*. A new method of control of wastage in oranges. *Hadar*, 1937, v. 10, pp. 141–145. **734**

See entry **666**.

1937. SINGH, B. N., and G. P. JAKHANWAL, *Institute of Agricultural Research, Benares Hindu University*. The prevention of rots in tomatoes with especial reference to the mould's attack. *Proc. National Acad. Sci. India*, 1937, v. 7, pp. 39–44. **735**

Iodized wood shaving has a definite advantage over iodized paper wrap in the prevention of rot in tomatoes.

1937. WARDLAW, C. W., and E. R. LEONARD, *Imperial College of Tropical Agriculture, Trinidad*. Antiseptic and other treatments in the storage of Trinidad citrus fruits. *Trinidad Low Temperature Research Station*, Memoir No. 5, 1937, 27 pp. **736**

See entry **731**.

1938. DU PLESSIS, *Dr.* S. J., *department of plant pathology, University of Stellenbosch*. Further studies on the control of *Botrytis* rot in grapes. *Union of South Africa Department of Agriculture and Forestry*, Science Bulletin No. 166, 1938, 32 pp. **737**

Wrappers treated with a solution containing 1 per cent of iodine and 2 per cent of potassium iodide gave promising results.

1939. GERHARDT, FISK, *physiologist*, and A. LLOYD RYALL, *assistant pomologist, division of fruit and vegetable crops and diseases, U.S. Bureau of Plant Industry*. The storage of sweet cherries as influenced by carbon dioxide and volatile fungicides. *U.S. Department of Agriculture*, Technical Bulletin No. 631, 1939, 20 pp. **738**

Tests with various volatile chemicals used for impregnating fruit-packing materials showed that elementary iodine effectively checks *Penicillium* and *Rhizopus* rot but only when used in concentrations sufficient to produce some surface injury to the fruit. Fruit flavour is not impaired by the use of iodized wrappers.

1940. MARSHALL, ALBERT E., *patentee, New York*. Preservation of fruit. *United States Patent No.* 2,193,636, March 12, 1940. Assigned to Tolco, Incorporated, Toledo, Ohio. **739**

This patent covers the use of betaine iodide for treating air which comes in contact with fruit, the fruit surface itself, and the material in which fruit is wrapped.

1940. [TSERETELI, L. YA., and N. N. CHANTURIYA.] ЦЕРЕТЕЛИ, Л. Я., and Н. Н. ЧАНТУРИЯ, *Georgian Station for Plant Protection*. Препараты иода против грибов, вызывающих загнивание цитрусовых плодов. [Iodine preparations for use against fungi causing rotting in citrus fruits.] *Sovet. Subtropiki*, 1940, no. 11–12, pp. 31–33. **740**

The preparation "Iodin No. 1" prevented attack on citrus fruits by *Colletotrichum gloeosporioides*, *Alternaria citri*, *Penicillium italicum*, *P. digitatum*, *Phomopsis citri* and *Macrophoma* sp.

1944. WINGFOOT CORPORATION, *patentees, Akron, Ohio* Rubber hydrochloride film. *British Patent No.* 558,798, January 21, 1944. **741**

The invention covered is an iodinated film suitable for wrapping materials to be kept sterile. Free iodine is slowly liberated from the film.

1945. TOMKINS, R. G., *M.A.*, *Ph.D.*, *Low Temperature Research Station, Cambridge*. Impregnated wraps for fruit. *Food Manufacture*, 1945, v. 20, pp. 140–141. **742**

Fruit wraps impregnated with various substances, including iodine, are briefly discussed.

1947. MANLEY, H. *B.Sc*. The use of iodised fruit-wrappings. *Brit. Packer*, 1947, v. 9, no. 9, pp. 2–3; 15. **743**

A review, with the conclusion that iodized wrappings are the best available at present, giving a general reduction of at least 50 per cent in fruit wastage and often very much more than this.

1948. MANLEY, H., *B.Sc*. Fungicidal impregnants. *Chem. Prod. Chem. News*, 1948, v. 12, pp. 15–16. **744**

Use of iodized wrappers is discussed.

1948. MANLEY, H. Iodized fruit wraps. *Modern Packaging*, 1948, v. 21, no. 9, pp. 152–153; 204; 206; 208. **745**

A reprint of an earlier paper (see entry **743**).

WEED KILLERS 746-753

1933. HESSENLAND, MAX, FRITZ FROMM and LEO SAALMANN, *Technological Institute, Trade School, Königsberg*. Die Wirkung von Chlorat, Bromat und Jodat auf Pflanzenwuchs. [The effect of chlorate, bromate and iodate on plant growth.] *Angewandte Chem.*, 1933, v. 46, pp. 577–579. **746**

On account of its high stability, sodium iodate in aqueous solution was practically ineffective as a weed killer.

1933. [VLASYUK, *Prof.* P. A.] ВЛАСЮК, Проф. П. А., Новые приемы химизации в социалистическом земледелии. (Химическая стимуляция и каталитические удобрения.) [New methods of chemization in socialistic agriculture. (Chemical stimulation and catalytic fertilization.)] *Nauk. Zapiski Tsukr. Prom.*, 1933, v. 10, no. 28, pp. 113–131; English summary p. 132. **747**

See entry **360**.

1945. Andrews, F. W., *Agricultural Research Institute, Department of Agriculture and Forests, Sudan Government.* Water plants in the Gezira canals. A study of aquatic plants and their control in the canals of the Gezira cotton area (Anglo-Egyptian Sudan). *Ann. Appl. Biol.*, 1945, v. 32, pp. 1–14. **748**

A solution containing 1 part of mercuric chloro-iodide in 10,000 parts of water killed all the more important water plants immersed in it for a period of five days.

1945. Jones, Franklin D., *patentee, Upper Darby, Pa.* Methods and compositions for killing weeds. *United States Patent No.* 2,390,941, December 11, 1945. Assigned to American Chemical Paint Company, Ambler, Pa. **749**

Halogenated phenoxyacetic acids, including iodine derivatives such as 4-iodophenoxyacetic acid, are claimed as herbicides.

1946. Clements, Richard, *B.Sc., F.L.S.* Chemical stimulants for crops. Practical applications of growth-regulating substances. *Discovery*, 1946, v. 7, pp. 332–335. **750**

See entry **502**.

1946. Jones, Franklin D., *patentee, Llanerch, Pa.* Methods and compositions for killing weeds. *United States Patent No.* 2,394,916, February 12, 1946. Assigned to American Chemical Paint Company, Ambler, Pa. **751**

Covers the use of 2:3:5-triiodobenzoic acid and 4-iodophenylacetic acid (and their esters and salts) as weed killers.

1946. Swarbrick, T., *M.A., Ph.D.* Harnessing the hormone. The use of growth-regulating substances in gardens, fields and orchards. London: *Grower Publications Ltd.*, 1946, 52 pp. **752**

See entry **507**.

1947. Kraus, E. J., *department of botany, University of Chicago*, and J. W. Mitchell, *Bureau of Plant Industry, Soils and Agricultural Engineering, Beltsville, Maryland.* Growth-regulating substances as herbicides. *Botan. Gaz.*, 1947, v. 108, pp. 301–350. **753**

See entry **511**.

IODINE INSECTICIDES
754-818

1910. Maxwell-Lefroy, H., *M.A., F.E.S., F.Z.S., Imperial Entomologist, Pusa.* A new insecticide. *Agric. J. India*, 1910, v. 5, pp. 138–143. **754**

Iodoform is very toxic to caterpillars but useless as a field insecticide.

1913. Maxwell-Lefroy, H., *M.A., F.E.S., F.Z.S.*, and R. S. Finlow, *B.Sc., F.Z.S., Agricultural Research Institute, Pusa.* Inquiry into the insecticidal action of some mineral and other compounds on caterpillars. *Mem. Dep. Agric. India Entomol. Series*, 1913, v. 4, pp. 269–327. **755**

Iodoform showed varying toxicities when tested against several kinds of caterpillars and grasshoppers.

1915. Cooper, W. F., *B.A.*, and W. A. B. Walling, *Cooper Laboratory for Economic Research, Watford, Herts.* The effect of various chemicals on blowfly. *Ann. Appl. Biol.*, 1915, v. 2, pp. 166–182. **756**

Of the substances tested against blowfly larvae, powdered iodoform and iodine vapour were among the most effective.

1916. Holt, Joseph J. H., *M.B., Ch.B., D.P.H.* The cockroach: its destruction and dispersal. A comparison of insecticides and methods. *Lancet*, 1916, v. i, pp. 1136–1137. **757**

Crystalline iodoform kills the insects in 9 hours and iodine crystals in 13 hours. Both substances act on the respiratory system of the cockroach.

1917. Moore, William, *assistant professor of research in economic zoology, department of agriculture, University of Minnesota.* Toxicity of various benzene derivatives to insects. *J. Agric. Research*, 1917, v. 9, pp. 371–381. **758**

At 70° F, 0·00347 gramme of iodobenzene killed all the houseflies in a litre flask in 87 minutes. Lower concentrations took a correspondingly longer time.

1918. Lodge, Olive C. An examination of the sense-reactions of flies. *Bull. Entomol. Research*, 1918, v. 9, pp. 141–151. **759**

With regard to poisons, good results were obtained with sodium iodate, large numbers being killed when very small amounts were used.

1918. Moore, William, and Samuel A. Graham, *Minnesota Agricultural Experiment Station, St. Paul.* Toxicity of volatile organic compounds to insect eggs. *J. Agric. Research*, 1918, v. 12, pp. 579–587. **760**

When potato beetle eggs were dipped in iodobenzene and immediately removed, no hatching occurred.

1920. Tattersfield, F., and A. W. R. Roberts, *Rothamsted Experimental Station, Harpenden, Herts.* The influence of chemical constitution on the toxicity of organic compounds to wireworms. *J. Agric. Sci.*, 1920, v. 10, pp. 199–232. **761**

Experiments in air showed that iodobenzene was moderately toxic and iodoform non-toxic.

1923. Richardson, Charles H., *insect physiologist, Bureau of Entomology*, and C. R. Smith, *chemist, Bureau of Chemistry, U.S. Department of Agriculture, Washington, D.C.* Studies on contact insecticides. *U. S. Department of Agriculture*, Bulletin No. 1160, 1923, 15 pp. **762**

Ethyl pyridinium iodide as a spray against black aphides required a minimum concentration greater than 1 gramme per 100 millilitres to be toxic. The tolerance of dwarf nasturtium plants was between 0·8 and 1·0 gramme per 100 millilitres.

1925. Neifert, Ira E., F. C. Cook, R. C. Roark, W. H. Tonkin, *Bureau of Chemistry*, E. A. Back and R. T. Cotton, *Bureau of Entomology, U.S. Department of Agriculture, Washington, D.C.* Fumigation against grain weevils with various volatile organic compounds. *U.S. Department of Agriculture*, Bulletin No. 1313, 1925, 40 pp. **763**

As a fumigant against the flour, granary and rice weevils, 1-iodobutane (*n*-butyl iodide) gave 100 per cent kill after 24 hours with dosages of 8·26 and 7·90 lb. per 1000 cubic feet at 25° C and with 4·05 lb. at 24·5° C. Dosages of 2·21 lb. at 21·5 C and of 1·85 lb. at 4° C gave no kill.

1927. Parman, D. C., F. C. Bishopp, E. W. Laake, F. C. Cook and R. C. Roark. Chemotropic tests with the screwworm fly. *U.S. Department of Agriculture*, Departmental Bulletin No. 1472, 1927, 32 pp. **764**

Jars baited with 5 grammes of iodoform on beef liver attracted 6·8 per cent as many flies as check jars with untreated liver in a 5-day period. Iodoform was also a very good repellent when mixed with kaolin or liquid paraffin. It was not effective in preventing infestation, but no flies emerged from the iodoform-treated meat.

1927. Roark, R. C., D. C. Parman, F. C. Bishopp and E. W. Laake, *Bureau of Chemistry and Bureau of Entomology, U.S. Department of Agriculture, Washington, D.C.* Repellents for blowflies. *Indust. Engin. Chem.*, 1927, v. 19, pp. 942–943. **765**

The number of screwworm flies observed visiting fresh beef liver treated with undiluted iodoform was 76 as compared with 1116 visiting untreated fresh beef liver. When diluted iodoform was used, the ratio was 37 to 319.

1928. Parman, D. C., E. W. Laake, F. C. Bishopp and R. C. Roark. Tests of blowfly baits and repellents during 1926. *U.S. Department of Agriculture*, Technical Bulletin No. 80, 1928, 15 pp. **766**

Iodoform, a compound of low vapour pressure, had a somewhat smaller radius of effectiveness as a repellent to screwworm flies (*Cochliomyia macellaria* F.) than wood naphtha, a compound of fairly high vapour pressure. A jar baited with a powder consisting of 0·5 gramme of iodoform and 4·5 grammes of kaolin on beef liver was visited by only 12 per cent as many screwworm flies and 8 per cent as many greenbottle flies (*Lucilia* spp.) as a check jar baited with untreated liver.

1929. Lipp, J. William, *research laboratories, U.S. Bureau of Entomology, Moorestown, N.J.* Studies of substitutes for arsenate of lead as a soil insecticide. *J. Econ. Entomol.*, 1929, v. 22, pp. 600–601. **767**

Mercuric iodide tested at the rate of 1500 lb. per acre (168 grammes per square metre) was successful as a poison for the grubs of *Popillia japonica*.

1929. Roark, R. C., *Bureau of Chemistry and Soils*, and R. T. Cotton, *Bureau of Entomology, U.S. Department of Agriculture, Washington, D.C.* Tests of various aliphatic compounds as fumigants. *U.S. Department of Agriculture*, Technical Bulletin No. 162, 1929, 52 pp. **768**

Twelve iodine compounds were among the 309 substances tested against the rice weevil. Iodides are grouped with those substances showing the greatest toxicity. They are injurious to the germination of wheat and should be used with caution.

1930. Smith, C. R., *Bureau of Chemistry and Soils*, C. H. Richardson and H. H. Shepard, *Bureau of Entomology, U.S. Department of Agriculture, Washington, D.C.* Neonicotine and certain other derivatives of the dipyridyls as insecticides. *J. Econ. Entomol.*, 1930, v. 23, pp. 863–867. **769**

At a concentration of 0·5 gramme per 100 millilitres of water with 1 per cent of saponin, the two compounds, dimethyl 1:2′-bipyridinium iodide and dimethyl 3:3′-bipyridinium iodide, killed, respectively, 34 and 39 per cent of aphides after 24 hours. The tolerance of dwarf nasturtium plants was greater than this concentration.

1931. Laake, E. W., D. C. Parman, F. C. Bishopp and R. C. Roark. The chemotropic responses of the house fly, the green-bottle flies, and the black blowfly. *U.S. Department of Agriculture*, Technical Bulletin No. 270, 1931, 11 pp. **770**

The repellent action of iodoform against these flies was tested. 34·3 per cent fewer houseflies, 49·8 per cent fewer greenbottle flies, and 13·7 per cent fewer blowflies visited a jar treated with iodoform compared with the number of flies visiting an untreated check jar.

1934. Karns, George M., *patentee, Pittsburgh, Pa.* Insecticide and/or fungicide. *United States Patent No.* 1,964,518, June 26, 1934. Assigned to Iodine Educational Bureau, Inc., New York. **771**

Metallic iodides, mixed with substances such as sulphur which cause liberation of free iodine, are claimed as useful insecticides and fungicides.

1934. McGovran, Edward Rawson, *department of zoology and entomology, Iowa State College, Ames.* Physiological and toxicological studies on insects. *Iowa State Coll. J. Sci.*, 1934, v. 9, pp. 177–179. **772**

Iodine compounds at concentrations of 2 per cent or less in white oil were among the most toxic of the substances tested for toxicity to codling moth larvae.

1935. Ginsburg, Joseph M., *biochemist in entomology*, and Philip Granett, *research assistant, New Jersey Agricultural Experiment Station, New Brunswick.* Arsenical substitutes. 1. Chemicals tested as arsenical substitutes in 1934. *J. Econ. Entomol.*, 1935, v. 28, pp. 292–298. **773**

When tested as a dust on foliage against third instars of the silk moth, iodoxybenzoic acid did not kill any larvae in three days, and there was much feeding. The same negative result was obtained with 2:6-dimethylethylquinolinium iodide, but with this compound the amount of feeding was small.

1935. Pratt, F. S., A. F. Swain and D. N. Eldred. Study of auxiliary gases for increasing the toxicity of hydrocyanic gas. Part 2. Studies with citrus-infesting scale insects as indices of toxicity. *J. Econ. Entomol.*, 1935, v. 28, pp. 975–983. **774**

1-Iodobutane in concentrations of 0·05 and 0·25 per cent by weight in air showed no visible effect on second instars of the citricola scale and the black scale.

1936. Cupples, H. L., H. R. Yust and Julian Hiley, *Bureau of Entomology and Plant Quarantine*,

U.S. Department of Agriculture, Washington, D.C. Tests of possible substitutes for hydrocyanic acid in fumigation of California red scale. *J. Econ. Entomol.*, 1936, v. 29, pp. 611–618. **775**

Methyl iodide (iodomethane), methylene iodide (diiodomethane), ethyl iodide (iodoethane), *n*-propyliodide (1-iodopropane), and allyl iodide (3-iodopropene), showed slight or no toxicity to the California red scale when tested in conjunction with hydrocyanic acid.

1936. Fink, D. E., and D. L. Vivian, *Bureau of Entomology and Plant Quarantine, U.S. Department of Agriculture, Washington, D.C.* Toxicity of certain azo compounds to mosquito larvae. *J. Econ. Entomol.*, 1936, v. 29, p. 804. **776**

4-Iodoazobenzene was effective against mosquito larvae at a concentration of 1:10,000, and 4-(*p*-iodophenylazo)-*o*-cresol at a concentration of 2·5 parts per million.

1936. Ginsburg, Joseph M., and Chester J. Cavallito, *New Jersey Agricultural Experiment Station, New Brunswick*. Arsenical substitutes. 2. Some relationships between molecular structure and toxicity of organic compounds to the silkworm, *Bombyx mori*. *J. Econ. Entomol.*, 1936, v. 29, pp. 856–859. **777**

Tetraiodophthalic anhydride showed no toxicity to silkworm larvae.

1936. McGovran, E. R., *Bureau of Entomology and Plant Quarantine, U.S. Department of Agriculture, Washington, D.C.* Laboratory tests with impregnated oil as codling moth larvicides. *J. Econ. Entomol.*, 1936, v. 29, pp. 417–420. **778**

10 per cent by weight of *p*-diiodobenzene in refined petroleum oil gave between 25 and 40 per cent control of codling moth larvae entries in apples; 1 per cent by weight gave less than 25 per cent control of entries, 2 per cent by weight of 1-iodo-4-nitrobenzene gave between 41 and 48 per cent control of entries. 20 per cent by weight of 2-iodo-naphthalene gave between 25 and 40 per cent control. 1 per cent by weight of iodoform gave less than 25 per cent control.

1936. Smith, L. E., E. H. Siegler and F. Munger, *Bureau of Entomology and Plant Quarantine, U.S. Department of Agriculture, Washington, D.C.* Potential new insecticides. *J. Econ. Entomol.*, 1936, v. 29, p. 1027. **779**

1-Iodo-4-nitrobenzene showed high initial toxicity to codling moth larvae when tested under laboratory conditions by the apple-plug method.

1937. Guy, H. G., *University of Delaware Agricultural Experiment Station, Newark*. Investigation of organic compounds as insecticides. *Delaware Agric. Exp. Stat.*, Bulletin No. 206, 1937, 60 pp. **780**

Tetramethyl ammonium iodide, ethyltriphenyl phosphonium iodide, and methyltriphenyl phosphonium iodide, diluted to make 1:10, 1:20 and 1:30 dusts with talc, were tested for the control of Colorado potato beetle and Mexican bean beetle. Considerable success was achieved with the 1:10 dilutions but plant injury was in some cases severe. Sprays (1:50) of the two phosphonium iodides were also tested but control was less effective than with the dust.

1937. Pepper, J. H., *Montana Agricultural Experiment Station, Bozeman*. Breaking the dormancy in the sugar-beet webworm, *L. sticticalis* L., by means of chemicals. *J. Econ. Entomol.*, 1937, v. 30, p. 380. **781**

Ethyl iodide at a concentration of 0·001 millilitre per litre was not lethal to sugar beet webworms.

1937. Smith, Lloyd E., and Houston V. Claborn, *patentees, Washington, D.C.* Insecticide. *United States Patent No.* 2,100,493, November 30, 1937. **782**

Organic compounds of the general formula R(NO₂)(Iodine)(y), where R is a benzene nucleus, and y represents hydrogen, an alkyl group, iodine or a nitro group, are claimed as effective insecticides, which are relatively non-toxic to warm-blooded animals.

1937. Vivian, Donald L., and Herbert L. J. Haller, *patentees, Washington, D.C.* Insecticide. *United States Patent No.* 2,095,940, October 12, 1937. **783**

Arylazo compounds containing iodine, for example *p*-iodoazobenzene, are claimed as insecticides.

1938. Fink, D. E., L. E. Smith, D. L. Vivian and H. V. Claborn, *Bureau of Entomology and Plant Quarantine, U.S. Department of Agriculture, Washington, D.C.* Toxicity tests with synthetic organic compounds against culicine mosquito larvae. *U.S. Bureau of Entomology and Plant Quarantine*, Document No. E-425, 1938, 34 pp. **784**

Several iodine compounds were tested. Percentage mortalities after 16 hours were: 60·4 for *p*-iodophenyl thiocyanate at a concentration of 2·5 parts per million of water, 100 for *p*-iodoacetanilide at a concentration of 1:10,000 and 98 each for 1-chloro-4-iodobenzene and 1-iodo-2-nitrobenzene at a concentration of 1:25,000.

1938. Lindgren, D. L., *University of California Citrus Experiment Station, Riverside*. Methyl iodide as a fumigant. *J. Econ. Entomol.*, 1938, v. 31, p. 320. **785**

Results obtained against resistant and non-resistant red scales, confused flour beetles, lady beetles, and codling moth larvae indicate that methyl iodide has possibilities as a fumigant. At concentrations considerably above the lethal, methyl iodide was non-toxic to citrus seedlings.

1938. Smith, L. E., E. H. Siegler and F. Munger, *Bureau of Entomology and Plant Quarantine, U.S. Department of Agriculture, Washington, D.C.* Organic compounds highly toxic to codling moth larvae. *J. Econ. Entomol.*, 1938, v. 31, pp. 322–323. **786**

When 1-iodo-3-nitrobenzene and 1-iodo-4-nitrobenzene were tested against codling moth larvae by the apple-plug method, 83·3 and 100·0 per cent, respectively, of the plugs were free from worms.

1939. Siegler, E. H., F. Munger and L. E. Smith, *Bureau of Entomology and Plant Quarantine, U.S. Department of Agriculture, Washington, D.C.* Toxicity to the codling moth larva of derivatives of benzene containing halogen and nitro-groups. *J. Econ. Entomol.*, 1939, v. 32, pp. 129–131. **787**

Each of the following compounds, in a concentration

of 4 lb. per 100 gallons, was tested as a spray by the apple-plug method: iodobenzene, *o*-diiodobenzene, *m*-diiodobenzene, *p*-diiodobenzene, 1-iodo-2-nitrobenzene, 1-iodo-3-nitrobenzene, 1-iodo-4-nitrobenzene. The percentage of plugs free from worms varied from 100·0 with 1-iodo-4-nitrobenzene to 0·0 with iodobenzene.

1939. SIEGLER, E. H., F. MUNGER and L. E. SMITH. Toxicity of certain organic insecticides to codling moth larvae in laboratory tests. *U.S. Department of Agriculture*, Circular No. 523, 1939, 10 pp. **788**

Each of the following compounds, in a concentration of 4 lb. per 100 gallons, was tested as a spray by the apple-plug method: *p*-iodoaniline, 1-chloro-4-iodobenzene, 1-fluoro-4-iodobenzene, 2-iodobiphenyl, 4-iodobiphenyl, 4:4′-diiodobiphenyl, 2:4:6-triiodophenol. The percentage of plugs wormy varied from 93·0 with both 1-chloro-4-iodobenzene and 4-iodobiphenyl to 100·0 with 1-fluoro-4-iodobenzene.

1940. BRITTON, EDGAR C., GERALD H. COLEMAN and JOHN W. ZEMBA, *patentees*, *Midland*, *Michigan*. Insecticidal composition. *United States Patent No*. 2,212,536, August 27, 1940. Assigned to The Dow Chemical Company, Midland, Mich. **789**

Organic compounds containing iodine are claimed as insecticides.

1940. BUSHLAND, RAYMOND C., *Bureau of Entomology and Plant Quarantine*, *U.S. Department of Agriculture*, *Washington*, *D.C.* The toxicity of some organic compounds to young screwworms. *J. Econ. Entomol.*, 1940, v. 33, pp. 669–676. **790**

When several iodine compounds were tested against young screwworms by the jar method, in which the test material was mixed with ground beef, blood and water, the minimum lethal concentration per cent ranged from 0·03–0·05 for 1-iodo-3-nitrobenzene to 0·33–0·67 for ethylquinaldinium iodide.

1940. PETERS, *Dr*. G., *German Pest Control Company*, *Frankfort-on-Main*. Ein neues Schädlingsbekämpfungsmittel. [A new pest control agent.] *Chemikerzeitung*, 1940, v. 64, pp. 485–486. **791**

Iodoacetonitrile is highly toxic to insects.

1940. SMITH, LLOYD E., *patentee*, *Washington*, *D.C.* Insecticide. *United States Patent No*. 2,191,299, February 20, 1940. **792**

Assigned to Henry A. Wallace as Secretary of Agriculture of the United States of America and his successors in office. The invention relates to the use of iodoxybenzenes, and nitro-derivatives thereof, as insecticides which can be sprayed or dusted on foliage, and are non-toxic to warm-blooded animals.

1940. SMITH, LLOYD E., *patentee*. Insecticide. *United States Patent No*. 2,191,300, February 20, 1940. **793**

Assigned to Henry A. Wallace as Secretary of Agriculture of the United States of America and his successors in office. The invention relates to the use of iodosobenzenes, and nitro-derivatives thereof, as insecticides which can be sprayed or dusted on foliage, and are non-toxic to warm-blooded animals.

1940. SMITH, LLOYD E., *patentee*. Insecticide. *United States Patent No*. 2,191,301, February 20, 1940. **794**

Assigned to Henry A. Wallace as Secretary of Agriculture of the United States of America and his successors in office. The invention relates to the use of phenyliodochlorides, and nitro-derivatives thereof, as insecticides which can be sprayed or dusted on foliage, and are non-toxic to warm-blooded animals.

1941. HANSBERRY, ROY, *Ithaca*, and L. B. NORTON, *Geneva*, *New York*. Toxicity of several nicotine compounds to *Aphis rumicis*, L. *J. Econ. Entomol.*, 1941, v. 34, pp. 80–83. **795**

Dodecyl nicotinium iodide in a solution containing 0·05 per cent of actual nicotine and 10 per cent of ethyl alcohol gave a 7 per cent gross mortality of *Aphis rumicis*. Solutions containing 0·2 and 0·5 per cent of actual nicotine gave mortalities of 23 and 83 per cent, respectively. The corresponding percentage mortalities for didodecyl nicotinium diiodide in these same concentrations of actual nicotine were 8, 37 and 72, respectively.

1941. QUESTEL, D. D., S. I. GERTLER, L. E. SMITH and D. L. VIVIAN, *Bureau of Entomology and Plant Quarantine*, *U.S. Department of Agriculture*, *Washington*, *D.C.* Laboratory and field tests of toxicity of some organic compounds to the European corn borer. *U.S. Bureau of Entomology and Plant Quarantine*, Document No. E-557, 1941, 17 pp. **796**

Percentage mortalities of newly hatched larvae with 1-iodo-2-nitrobenzene, 1-iodo-4-nitrobenzene, iodosobenzene, 4:4′-diiodobiphenyl, 4-iodoazobenzene and 4:4′-diiodoazoxybenzene at a concentration of 4 lb. per 100 gallons of water were, respectively, 100·0, 100·0, 84·6, 17·4, 100·0 and 36·8.

1942. LEHMAN, RUSSELL S., *Bureau of Entomology and Plant Quarantine*, *U.S. Department of Agriculture*, *Washington*, *D.C.* Laboratory tests of organic fumigants for wireworms. *J. Econ. Entomol.*, 1942, v. 35, pp. 659–661. **797**

114 fumigants were tested, including various combinations of iodine. The highest toxicity was shown by allyl isothiocyanate with a median lethal concentration of 2·33 milligrammes per litre. Methyl iodide was the fifth most effective fumigant with a lethal concentration of 5·20 milligrammes and allyl iodide was sixth, with a lethal concentration of 5·54 milligrammes.

1942. SMITH, L. E., *Bureau of Entomology and Plant Quarantine*, *U.S. Department of Agriculture*, *Washington*, *D.C.* Synthetic organic compounds as potential insecticides. *Indust. Engin. Chem.*, 1942, v. 34, pp. 499–501. **798**

Attention is called to some of the synthetic organic compounds that have been tested by the U.S. Bureau of Entomology and Plant Quarantine and found to possess sufficient insecticidal value to warrant more extensive trial. The iodine compounds discussed are: ortho-, meta- and paranitrophenyl iodochlorides, iodosobenzene and iodoxybenzene and their mononitro-derivatives.

1943. BUSHLAND, R. C., and W. V. KING, *Bureau of Entomology and Plant Quarantine*, *U.S. Department of Agriculture*, *Washington*, *D.C.* Laboratory tests with organic compounds as larvicides for *Culex quinquefasciatus* Say. *U.S. Bureau of Entomology and Plant Quarantine*, Document No. E-585, 1943, 15 pp. **799**

Several iodine compounds were tested. Average mortalities after 16 hours ranged from 5 per cent for *p*-iodosonitrobenzene at a concentration of 100 parts per million to 98 per cent for *p*-thiocyanoiodobenzene at 2 parts per million.

1944. MARTIN, H., and R. L. WAIN. The qualitative examination of insecticidal properties. Progress report, 1944. *Agric. and Hort. Research Stat., Long Ashton, Bristol*, Annual Report, 1944, pp. 121–140. **800**

When tested as contact insecticides against woodlice and cabbage moth larvae, 1-trichloro-2:2-*bis* (*p*-iodophenyl)-ethane was less effective than DDT and 1-dichloro-2:2-*bis* (*p*-iodophenyl)-ethylene showed negligible toxicity.

1944. SWINGLE, M. C., A. M. PHILLIPS and J. B. GAHAN, *Bureau of Entomology and Plant Quarantine, U.S. Department of Agriculture, Washington, D.C.* Preliminary tests of synthetic organic compounds as insecticides. Part 1. *U.S. Bureau of Entomology and Plant Quarantine*, Document No. E-621, 1944, 134 pp. **801**

Of 883 compounds tested under laboratory conditions against one or more of 20 species of insects, 3 iodine compounds, namely *p*-bromoiodobenzene, *p*-chloroiodobenzene and *o*-nitroiodobenzene, were among the twenty-five most toxic compounds. Varying activity was shown by 3:5-diiodosalicylic acid, *o*- and *p*-iodoaniline, *p*-iodoazobenzene, *p*-iodo-N-dimethylaniline, β-iodonaphthalene, 2-iodo-1-nitronaphthalene, *o*-iodosonitrobenzene, iodoxybenzene, *m*-iodonitrobenzene, *p*-nitroiodosobenzene acetate, *o*- and *m*-nitrophenyliodochloride and 2:4:6-triiodophenol.

1945. BHATTACHARYYA, JYOTIRMOY, *department of applied chemistry, University College of Science, Calcutta*. Halogenated organic insecticides. Part 1. *Ann. Biochem. Exp. Med.*, Calcutta, 1945, v. 5, pp. 127–130. **802**

1-Trichloro-2:2-*bis* (*p*-iodophenyl)-ethane in kerosene solution has a toxic effect on mosquito larvae but is not as effective as DDT.

1945. BOWEN, C. V., and H. L. HALLER, *Bureau of Entomology and Plant Quarantine, U.S. Department of Agriculture, Washington, D.C.* Insecticidal action of organic halogen compounds. A comparison of selected literature references. *U.S. Bureau of Entomology and Plant Quarantine*, Document No. E-678, 1945, 14 pp. **803**

The compounds discussed include various aliphatic and aromatic iodine derivatives.

1945. SWINGLE, M. C., J. B. GAHAN and A. M. PHILLIPS, *Bureau of Entomology and Plant Quarantine, U.S. Department of Agriculture, Washington, D.C.* Preliminary tests of synthetic organic compounds as insecticides. Part 2. *U.S. Bureau of Entomology and Plant Quarantine*, Document No. E-634, 1945, 23 pp. **804**

o-Iodoacetanilide was found to be toxic to certain species of insects.

1945. WOLCOTT, GEORGE N., *entomologist, Agricultural Experiment Station, Rio Piedras, Puerto Rico*. How to make wood unpalatable to the West Indian dry-wood termite, *Cryptotermes brevis* Walker. *Caribbean Forester*, 1945, v. 6, pp. 245–256. **805**

Mahogany was eaten by the termite in preference to wood impregnated with 0·2 per cent of cuprous iodide, 0·5 per cent of mercuric iodide or 0·2 per cent of cadmium iodide.

1946. FISHER, E. H., A. J. RIKER and T. C. ALLEN, *department of economic entomology and plant pathology, University of Wisconsin*. Bud, blossom, and pod drop of canning string beans reduced by plant hormones. *Phytopathology*, 1946, v. 36, pp. 504–523. **806**

As measured by crop yield inconclusive results were obtained by the use as insecticides of dusts containing 40, 80 and 160 parts of 2:3:5-triiodobenzoic acid per million of inert material.

1946. ODUM, EUGENE P., and W. T. SUMERFORD, *department of zoology and school of pharmacy, University of Georgia*. Comparative toxicity of DDT and four analogues to goldfish, gambusia, and culex larvae. *Science*, 1946, v. 104, pp. 480–482. **807**

1-Trichloro-2:2-*bis* (*p*-iodophenyl)-ethane is somewhat less toxic than DDT. It is pointed out, however, that molecule for molecule this analogue has to be rated the more toxic.

1946. OETTINGEN, W. F. VON, and N. E. SHARPLESS, *National Institute of Health, U.S. Public Health Service, Bethesda, Md.* The toxicity and toxic manifestations of 2, 2-*bis*-(*p*-chlorophenyl)-1, 1, 1-trichloroethane (DDT) as influenced by chemical changes in the molecule. *J. Pharmacol. Exp. Ther.*, 1946, v. 88, pp. 400–413. **808**

Toxicity of DDT is only slightly attenuated by replacing the ring-substituted chlorine by iodine.

1946. SCHNEIDER, M., and I. FANKUCHEN, *department of chemistry, Polytechnic Institute of Brooklyn, New York*. X-ray study of some DDT analogs. *J. Amer. Chem. Soc.*, 1946, v. 68, pp. 2669–2670. **809**

Some of the analogues studied contain iodine.

1947. DAVIS, HAROLD S., *patentee, Greenwich, Connecticut*. Halogen-substituted acrylonitriles as insecticides. *United States Patent No.* 2,433,742, December 30, 1947. Assigned to American Cyanamid Company, New York. **810**

Several of the acrylonitrile derivatives claimed contain iodine.

1947. FREAR, D. E. H., and E. J. SEIFERLE, *Pennsylvania State College, State College*. Chemical structure and insecticidal efficiency. *J. Econ. Entomol.*, 1947, v. 40, pp. 736–741. **811**

Results from the literature and private communications are tabulated. The following were the percentage positive toxicities in organic compounds containing the groupings named: iodoxy 95·8, iodoso 93·1, monoiodo 80·2, diiodo 53·8, triiodo 50·0. Inorganic iodides showed a positive toxicity of 75·0 per cent.

1947. JAIN, B. C., B. H. IYER and P. C. GUHA, *department of pure and applied chemistry, Indian Institute of Science, Bangalore*. Studies in sulphones. Part 3. Synthesis of new contact insecticides. *J. Indian Chem. Soc.*, 1947, v. 24, pp. 220–222. **812**

Syntheses of *p*-chlorophenylchloromethylsulphone, the active principle of the German insecticide "Leuseto neu" and five of its analogues, including *p*-iodophenylchloromethylsulphone, are described.

1947. PROVERBS, M. D., and FRANK O. MORRISON, *department of entomology, Macdonald College, McGill University, Quebec Province*. The relative insecticidal activities of DDT and related organic molecules. *Canad. J. Research* [D], 1947, v. 25, pp. 12–44. **813**

By the use of the impregnated paper technique no mortality was observed in adult *Drosophila melanogaster* following exposures to 1-trichloro-2:2-*bis* (*p*-iodophenyl)-ethane in doses as high as 500 milligrammes per 10 millilitres of alcohol.

1947. SUMERFORD, W. T., *College of Pharmacy, University of Georgia*. Chlorosulfonic acid in the synthesis of DDT and its *p*-halogen analogues. *J. Amer. Pharm. Assoc., Sci. Ed.*, 1947, v. 36, pp. 127–128. **814**

Synthesis of 1-trichloro-2:2-*bis*(*p*-iodophenyl)-ethane is described and a brief report on its biological activity is given.

1948. FERGUSON, J., and H. PIRIE, *alkali and general chemicals division, Imperial Chemical Industries Ltd.* The toxicity of vapours to the grain weevil. *Ann. Appl. Biol.*, 1948, v. 35, pp. 532–550. **815**

Toxic effects of alkyl iodides are demonstrated.

1948. LINDUSKA, J. P., F. A. MORTON and W. C. MCDUFFIE, *Bureau of Entomology and Plant Quarantine, U.S. Department of Agriculture, Washington, D.C.* Tests of materials for the control of chiggers on the ground. *J. Econ. Entomol.*, 1948, v. 41, pp. 43–47. **816**

Iodine (33 per cent in talc) was applied as a dust to the ground at the rate of 100 lb. per acre. There was an 85 per cent reduction of mites (*Trombicula* spp.) after the first day, but the apparent control was not maintained beyond the second day.

1948. LORD, K. A., *Rothamsted Experimental Station, Harpenden, Herts.* The contact toxicity of a number of D.D.T. analogues and of four isomers of benzene hexachloride to *Macrosiphoniella sanborni* and *Oryzaephilus surinamensis*. *Ann. Appl. Biol.*, 1948, v. 35, pp. 505–526. **817**

Analogues included 1-trichloro-2:2-*bis*(*p*-iodophenyl)-ethane and 1-tribromo-2:2-*bis*(*p*-iodophenyl)-ethane. Neither substance was superior to DDT when tested as a contact insecticide against the chrysanthemum aphis and the saw-toothed grain beetle by a direct spraying technique.

1949. LORD, K. A., *Rothamsted Experimental Station, Harpenden, Herts.* The effect of insecticides on the respiration of *Oryzaephilus surinamensis:* an attempt to compare the speeds of action of a number of D.D.T. analogues. *Ann. Appl. Biol.*, 1949, v. 36, pp. 113–138. **818**

Application of toxic concentrations of 1-trichloro-2:2-*bis*(*p*-iodophenyl)-ethane as a dust decreased slightly the oxygen uptake of the saw-toothed grain beetle.

AUTHOR AND SUBJECT INDEXES

AND

KEY TO ABBREVIATED TITLES OF PERIODICALS

AUTHOR INDEX

According to entry numbers

Åberg, B., 416, 579
Ader, F., 10
Adler, E., 620, 621
Agatov, P., 690
Agostini, A., 469
Aitken, H. A. A., 82, 253
Albano, S. F., 295
Albaum, H. G., 494
Albert, R., 64
Aldous, J. G., 631
Allard, R. W., 503
Allary, E., 35
Allen, T. C., 806
Alm, F., 618
Alschinger, A., 203
Amadori, L., 318, 324
Amlinsky, I. E., 482
Andersen, A., 346
Anderson, T., 28
Anderson, W. S., 699
Andouard, P., 451
Andrews, F. M., 362
Andrews, F. W., 748
Anitescu, K., 104
Annales de Chimie et de Physique, 184
Anson, M. L., 675
Aoki, S., 78
Arata, M., 480
Arenz, B., 455
Ark, P. A., 676, 677, 680
Arnon, D. I., 381
Aso, K., 283, 285, 530
Atkins, W. R. G., 524
Audidier, L., 441, 451
Averkiev, N. D., 59, 72
Avery, Jr., G. S., 546

Babichev, I. A., 533
Babiy, J., 210
Back, E. A., 763
Baeyens, J., 453, 459
Bailhache, G., 294
Balch, D. M., 47
Balls, A. K., 536
Baranowski, T., 622
Barinova, S. A., 636
Barron, E. S. G., 578
Bawden, R. F., 501
Bear, F. E., 325
Beaumont, A. B., 259, 361
Bégué, H., 650
Berger, J., 546
Bergold, M., 231
Bernhauer, K., 635
Bertram, P., 9, 264
Bertrand, G., 596
Besser, W., 333
Bhattacharyya, J., 802
Biederbeck, A., 425
Bilger, F., 614
Bishopp, F. C., 764–766, 770
Bjerresø, G., 103
Black, W. A. P., 119–121
Blagoveschensky, A. V., 597
Blair, A. W., 293
Blanchard, K. C., 616
Blank, L. M., 678
Blengini, D., 272
Blom, I. J. B., 225
Boas, F., 590
Boas, I. H., 65
Bobko, E. V., 382
Bodnár, J., 538
Bolidens Gruvaktiebolag, 716
Bolomey, P., 624, 625
Bombay Province. Department of Industries, 102
Bond, L., 516
Bonet, M., 26
Bonner, Jr., W. D., 517, 518
Borodina, O. J., 541
Bosher, J. E., 661
Bourcet, P., 206, 208
Bowen, C. V., 649, 803
Boyd, A. E. W., 679
Boyd, F. T., 503
Brain, E. D., 483, 484
Brandt, K., 627
Branham, S. E., 591
Brasher, E. P., 263
Braun, H., 525
Braun, J., 427
Brenchley, W. E., 13, 303, 376, 409, 410, 414, 457, 655
Brentzel, W. E., 704
Brian, P. W., 693
Brichta, H., 426
Briones, N., 38
Brioux, C., 442, 445, 451
British Sugar Beet Review, 448
Britton, E. C., 789
Brocq-Rousseu, —, 632
Brown, H. D., 266
Brown, R., 528
Bruevich, S. V., 80
Budington, R. A., 461, 463
Buen, V. de, 73
Burd, J. S., 53
Bushland, R. C., 790, 799
Butkevich, V. S., 636
Butler, M. R., 75

Caldwell, J., 479, 534
Calfee, R. K., 379, 449
Cameron, A. T., 51, 54, 211
Cappelletti, C., 638
Carlson, W. E., 560
Carrisson, G., 569
Casaseca, J. L., 200, 202
Castan, R., 491
Cavallito, C. J., 777
Cavill, G. W. K., 646
Cayrol, P., 606
Chaix, P., 576
Chang, C. S., 92
Chanturiya, N. N., 740
Chatin, G. A., 190–192, 201
Chemical and Engineering News, 515
Chemin, E., 133, 138, 139, 153
Chen, S.-M., 408
Chester, K. S., 647
Chilean Nitrate Educational Bureau, Inc., 17, 18
Chodat, F., 569
Chouard, P., 472, 476
Claborn, H. V., 782, 784
Claus, G., 593
Clements, R., 502
Clifton, C. E., 628
Closs, K., 76, 158, 165
Coleman, G. H., 789
Colhoun, J., 719
Collado, E. G., 68
Commoner, B., 494, 495
Conner, W. H., 252
Cook, F. C., 763, 764
Cooley, Jr., J. L., 702, 709
Cooper, W. F., 756
Corrie, F. E., 19
Costa, T., 304
Cotte, G., 477
Cotton, M., 345
Cotton, R. T., 763, 768
Coupin, H., 277, 279
Courth, H., 245
Courtois, B., 21
Cox, G. H., 253
Croce, P. E., 66

Cruellas, J., 93
Cuniasse, L., 44
Cupples, H. L., 775
Curtin, T. P., 644
Czibulka, F., 7, 10

Dafert, O., 426
Dangeard, P., 71, 140–146, 154, 159–161, 166, 169
Davis, E. E., 473
Davis, H. S., 810
Davy, H., 22
de Buen, V. *See* Buen, V. de
Deckterioff, A., 453
de Grazia, S. *See* Grazia, S. de
Demolon, A., 451
Demoussy, E., 276
Denny, F. E., 319, 334, 391
Densch, A., 436
Deramond, J., 451
Desmoires, A., 60
de Waard, J. *See* Waard, J. de
Dickie, G., 185
Dietz, C., 266, 267
Dillon, T., 155
Dircks, —, 273
Dixit, S. C., 74
Dixon, M., 615
Doerell, E. G., 335, 336
Doherty, W., 63
Donovan, W., 77
Dopter, P., 555
Dorfman, A., 574
Dreyer, D. J., 725
Ducrue, H., 240
Dunn, M. S., 485
Dupasquier, A., 25
du Plessis, S. J., 728, 732, 737
Dykstra, T. P., 683

Eddelbüttel, H., 3, 430
Egnér, H., 421
Egypt. Union des Agriculteurs, 323
Ehling, L., 431
Ehrenfeld, M., 478
Ehrenfest, E., 603, 607
Eisenmenger, W. S., 262, 265, 268
Ekdahl, I., 417
Eldred, D. N., 774
Elleder, H., 432
Engels, O., 326, 339, 368, 383, 433
Ennis, Jr., W. B., 503
Eschle, —, 123
Esdorn, I., 695
Espil, L., 570
Eto, T., 129
Euler, H. von, 620
Ezekiel, W. N., 667

Fabris, U., 81
Fankuchen, I., 809
Favorski, M. V., 392
Fedorov, M. V., 562
Fehling, H. von, 193
Feilitzen, H. von, 421
Feldmann, G., 182
Feldmann, J., 182
Fellenberg, T. von, 213, 215, 310, 311, 327
Ferguson, J., 815
Ferretti, C., 552
Fester, G. A., 93
Field, Jr., J., 565, 566
Field, S. M., 565, 566
Fink, D. E., 776, 784
Finkle, R. D., 574
Finlow, R. S., 755
Fischer, G., 226
Fisher, E. H., 806
Fisher, G. B., 85, 171
Florentin, P., 478
Florschütz, P. A., 519
Fones, W., 513
France. Institut des Recherches Agronomiques, 443
Franklin, M. T., 669
Frear, D. E. H., 651, 652, 811
Free, E. E., 299
Freundler, P., 110–116, 147, 148
Frey-Wyssling, A., 369
Friedemann, T. E., 578
Fromageot, C., 576
Fromm, F., 746
Fudge, J. F., 667
Fyfe, A., 183

Gahan, J. B., 801, 804
Gain, E., 632
Galston, A. W., 510
Garola, J., 447
Gartman, A. N., 80
Gassner, G., 695
Gaultier de Claubry, H., 23
Gaus, W., 340
Gautier, A., 207
Gautier, F., 39
Gerhard, H., 98
Gerhardt, F., 738
Gerlach, M., 437
Gertler, S. I., 796
Giesecke, F., 454
Gilbert, F. A., 20
Ginsburg, J. M., 773, 777
Gleisberg, J., 659
Glick, D. P., 686
Glimm, E., 219
Goeppert, H. R., 271
Golenkin, M., 122
Goodwin, W., 657
Gordon, A., 314
Graham, S. A., 760
Granett, P., 773
Grant, W. M., 630
Grazia, S. de, 419, 420
Great Britain. Medical Research Council, 4
Greaves, J. D., 588
Greaves, J. E., 553, 556, 588
Greenfield, S. S., 398, 404
Griessbach, R., 340
Grosse, —, 24
Günther, E., 436
Günther, G., 620, 621
Guha, P. C., 812
Gum, R., 341
Guy, H. G., 780

Haag, E., 624, 625
Haas, A. R. C., 328
Hageman, R. H., 405, 407
Halasa, S., 219
Halden, W., 614
Hale, W. S., 536
Haller, H. L., 803
Haller, H. L. J., 783
Hansberry, R., 795
Harries, R., 352
Hartt, C. E., 545
Haselhoff, E., 428, 438
Hastings, R. J., 661
Havas, L. J., 479, 490
Hawaii Agricultural Experiment Station, 88
Heckel, E., 274
Hemming, H. G., 693
Hendrick, J., 55, 56
Hercus, C. E., 82, 233, 253
Hessenland, M., 746
Heymann, J. A., 214
Hiley, J., 775
Hiltner, E., 231, 238
Hitchcock, A. E., 496–498
Hoagland, D. R., 126
Hock, A., 7
Hodge, E. S., 405
Holland, E. B., 262, 361
Hollrung, —, 290
Holt, J. J. H., 757
Hong, W. L., 475
Hoogerheide, J. C., 608
Horsfall, J. G., 689, 705
How, G. K., 70
Howard, F. H., 493
Hudig, J., 16
Hykes, O. V., 471

I.G. Farbenindustrie A.-G., 706
Irving, Jr., G. W., 512, 515
Ishikawa, M., 563
Itallie, L. van, 37, 57
Itano, A., 83, 84, 554
Iterson, C. van, 312

Iverson, V. E., 670
Iyer, B. H., 812

Jacobson, L., 415
Jacques, A. G., 179, 181
Jain, B. C., 812
Jakhanwal, G. P., 735
Johnson, E. M., 637, 639
Jones, F. D., 749, 751
Joret, G., 451
Justus, J., 209

Kahlenberg, L., 526
Kaho, H., 355, 531
Karnahl, H., 551
Karns, G. M., 259, 710, 771
Kasparova, S. A., 384
Katalimov, M. V., 371
Kay, H. D., 156
Kelly, F. C., 241
Kelly, H. C., 670
Kendrick, J. B., 680
Kentucky Agricultural Experiment Station, 220, 370, 377
Khalizev, A. A., 356, 371
King, W. V., 799
Kinsey, V. E., 630
Kissel, F., 10
Klages, A., 697
Klein, G., 234
Klein, W., 660
Kluyver, A. J., 608
Knight, E. C., 637, 639
Knop, W., 273
Knudsen, H., 49
Köhler, E., 681
Köhler, R., 239, 244, 250, 251
Kohl, F., 7, 10
Kohn, H. I., 532
Kollo, C., 104
Komarovski, A. S., 85
Kooijmans, J., 592
Korentsvit, A., 178
Koser, S. A., 574
Kossowicz, A., 581
Kotsovsky, D., 492
Kou, F. C., 95
Kraus, E. J., 511
Krause, M., 64
Krengel, W., 357
Krüger, E., 671
Krumey, F., 612
Kryukova, N., 540
Kucinski, K. J., 265, 268
Kushima, B., 564
Kylin, H., 127, 128, 149, 157, 162, 163, 167

Laake, E. W., 764-766, 770
Lafon, A. J., 313
Lami, R., 164
Lammerts, W. E., 672
Lanshina, M. N., 364
Lapicque, L., 109
Lászlo, D., 583
Laurent, Y., 110–112, 116
Legendre, R., 133
Lehman, B., 362
Lehman, R. S., 797
Lehman, S. G., 717
Lehr, J. J., 16
Leitch, I., 1, 4, 5
Lelièvre, J., 116, 117
Leon, C., 40, 41
Leonard, E. R., 736
Leroux, D., 12, 394, 399, 406, 558, 559
Leukel, R. W., 715
Lewis, J. C., 400, 401, 561
Lieben, F., 583
Lindemuth, J. R., 50
Lindgren, D. L., 785
Linduska, J. P., 816
Lipman, C. B., 314
Lipman, J. G., 293
Lipp, J. W., 767
Lipski, V. I., 79
Littauer, F., 666
Lizandr, A. A., 509
Lo, T.-Y., 408
Lodeman, E. G., 654
Lodge, O. C., 759
Loew, O., 282, 286, 300, 305–307, 320
Loew, W., 581
Lord, K. A., 817, 818
Losana, L., 66
Lunde, G., 97, 158, 165
Lundsgaard, E., 600, 601, 604
Lustig, B., 488

Macadam, S., 198
McCallan, S. E. A., 648
McClelland, C. K., 714
McClendon, J. F., 86, 99
McClintock, L., 493
MacDougal, D. T., 291, 296
McDuffie, W. C., 816
Macfarlane, M. G., 602
McGovran, E. R., 772, 778
McGowan, J. C., 693
McHargue, J. S., 221, 224, 228, 269, 379, 405, 407, 439, 449
Machlis, S., 616
Mack, W. B., 263
McLean, H. C., 293
McMurtrey, Jr., J. E., 385
Madras Fisheries Department, 94
Malhotra, R. C., 254, 347
Manceau, P., 477
Mandillon, G., 570
Mangenot, G., 135, 150, 151
Manley, H., 743–745
Marchand, E., 30, 194
Marck, W. von der, 188
Marks, G. C., 711
Marshall, A. E., 739
Marsson, T., 27
Martens, P., 42, 43
Martin, H., 800
Maschmann, E., 571
Massart, L., 629
Masuda, E., 170, 174, 175, 177
Matlin, D. R., 547, 548
Matsuura, A., 554
Maurer, E., 240
Maxwell-Lefroy, H., 754, 755
Mayer-Pitsch, E., 614
Mazé, P., 297, 302
Mazé-Launay, A., 33
Meiklejohn, J., 534
Ménager, Y., 110–112, 116, 117
Menon, A. S., 229
Meredith, C. H., 684, 687, 688
Merz, A. R., 52
Messiner-Klebermass, L., 605
Meyer, A. H., 348
Meyer, C., 477, 481
Meyer, F., 589, 707
Meyer, K., 567, 568
Meyer, L., 707, 713
Meyrac, V., 195
Michaelis, M., 572
Michlin, D. M., 541
Mitchell, J. H., 255
Mitchell, J. W., 511, 512, 515
Miyama, K., 58
Molisch, H., 67
Moore, P. W., 298
Moore, W., 758, 760
Moore, W. D., 718
Moreau, F., 640
Moreau, *Mme*. F., 640
Morrison, F. O., 813
Morton, F. A., 816
Muckenhirn, R. J., 378
Müller, —, 186
Müller, D., 633
Münter, F., 337, 338
Muirhead, I., 694
Munger, F., 779, 786–788
Murray, M. A., 522
Muskett, A. E., 719

Nadler, G., 204
Nadson, G. A., 315
Narasimham, M., 100
Nattrass, R. M., 729
Nehring, K., 353
Neifert, I. E., 763
Newman, M. S., 513
Newton, W., 661
Nicol, H., 486
Nielsen, L. W., 673

Niethammer, A., 464, 465, 470
Niklas, H., 7, 10
Nishida, K., 174, 175
Nishikawa, T., 78
Noortgaete, C. van den, 629
Norman, A. G., 508
Norton, L. B., 795

Ødelien, M., 270
Odum, E. P., 807
Oettingen, W. F. von, 808
Okuda, Y., 129
Ollivier, G., 136
Opotski, V. F., 89, 171
Oregon Agricultural Experiment Station, 386, 435
Orr, J. B., 1, 4, 5, 241
Osterhout, W. J. V., 180, 181
Ostern, P., 622
Oswald, A., 125
Overstreet, R., 415
Owen, I. L., 293
Owen, O., 505, 656

Pal, S. N., 100
Parga Pondal, I., 69
Parker, E. G., 50
Parman, D. C., 764–766, 770
Parr, W. J., 682
Pearce, A. A., 641
Pellieux, J., 33
Pelphrey, J. G., 224, 439
Pennsylvania Agricultural Experiment Station, 577
Pepper, J. H., 781
Perkins, W. R., 699
Personne, J., 196
Pestemer, M., 614
Peters, G., 791
Pfeiffer, G., 245
Phillips, A. M., 801, 804
Phillips, J. N., 646
Picado T., C., 349, 411
Pickett, M. J., 628
Piettre, L., 529
Pirie, H., 815
Platt, M. E., 609, 610
Poate, H. R. G., 662
Pogrebinska, S., 89
Pontailler, S., 412
Powers, W. L., 387, 393, 400, 401, 557
Prasad, S., 389
Pratt, F. S., 774
Prokoshev, S. M., 533
Proverbs, M. D., 813
Pulver, R., 626

Questel, D. D., 796
Quillard, C., 313

Rabinowitch, E., 535
Rabuteau, —, 275
Rademacher, B., 663
Rafaïlesco, M., 308
Rahm, —, 422
Raleigh, W. P., 664
Rapkine, L., 617
Rasmussen, H. B., 103
Rathje, W., 454
Rattray, J. M., 726, 730, 733
Raucourt, M., 650
Ray, W. W., 720
Read, B. E., 70
Rebello, S., 462
Reed, H. S., 328
Reichert, I., 666
Reid, R. D., 692
Reilly, D., 644
Reith, J. F., 246, 247
Remington, R. E., 222
Remizov, S. A., 356
Remy, T., 429
Renoll, M., 513
Richardson, C. H., 762, 769
Richter, A. A., 402
Rietsema, I., 456
Rigg, G. B., 105
Righini, G., 187
Riker, A. J., 806
Rivet, —, 653
Rivière, G., 294
Roark, R. C., 763–766, 768, 770
Roberts, A. W. R., 761
Roberts, K. C., 233
Roodenburg, J. W. M., 520
Roy, W. R., 224, 439
Runnström, J., 618, 627
Rupert, J. A., 721
Ryall, A. L., 738

Saalmann, L., 746
Salmon, E. S., 657
Saunders, F., 574
Sauvageau, C., 130–132, 134, 137, 152
Sayre, J. D., 698, 700, 701, 708
Scaglia, G., 466, 468
Schaal, L. A., 691
Schäffner, A., 612
Scharrer, K., 2, 6, 14, 235-237, 260, 331, 350, 351, 450, 452, 586, 587, 593, 594
Schmalfuss, K., 454, 460
Schmidt, —, 311
Schmidt, E. W., 354, 372
Schmidt, O., 663
Schmidt, W., 353
Schmitz, E., 342
Schneider, M., 809
Schöne, A., 329
Scholz, W., 363
Schott, O., 34
Schroeder, E. F., 609, 610
Schropp, W., 240, 260, 350, 351, 450, 452, 455
Schulz, H., 580
Schulz, J., 611
Schwaibold, J., 216, 235, 260
Schwartz, W., 586, 587, 594
Schwarz, H., 227
Scott, C. E., 680
Scurti, F., 108
Seale-Hayne Agricultural College, 668
Seiferle, E. J., 811
Seifert, R., 101
Sellei, J., 474
Sergeev, L. V., 223
Servat, F., 43
Sharpless, N. E., 808
Shcherbakov, A. P., 373, 374, 388
Shepard, H. H., 769
Sherman, G. D., 407
Shkatelov, V., 61
Shkolnik, M. Ya., 358
Siegler, E. H., 779, 786–788
Simpson, B. W., 217, 256
Singh, B. N., 389, 735
Sinotô, Y., 395
Sirot, A., 451
Skopintsev, B. A., 87
Slanina, F., 635
Smith, C. R., 762, 769
Smith, L. E., 779, 782, 784, 786–788, 792–794, 796, 798
Smythe, C. V., 613, 623
Snyder, W. E., 523
Söderbaum, H. G., 301
Sorokina, T. A., 597
South Carolina Agricultural Experiment Station, 248
Speyer, E. R., 682, 685
Stanford, E. C. C., 29, 31, 32, 36
Stanley, W. M., 675
Stanton, E. N., 334
Steinberg, R. A., 645
Steiner, R., 665
Steinfatt, K., 436
Steppuhn, O., 582
Stiles, W., 15
Stoklasa, J., 249, 257, 309, 321, 322, 330, 343, 423, 424, 550
Strobel, A., 232, 236, 237, 331
Ströbele, F., 344
Stuart, G. L., 241
Stuart, W., 292
Sturm, A., 611
Sukhov, K. S., 364
Sumerford, W. T., 807, 814
Suneson, S., 168
Sutoh, H., 396
Suzuki, K., 78
Suzuki, S., 281, 283, 285
Swain, A. F., 774
Swanson, C. P., 503, 508

Swarbrick, T., 506, 507
Swingle, M. C., 801, 804
Synerholm, M. E., 500

Takahashi, T., 107
Tang, P.-S., 91, 92, 95, 96
Tang, T. H., 95
Tankó, B., 538
Tattersfield, F., 761
Taubenhaus, J. J., 667
Taylor C. F., 721
Terszakoweć, J., 622
Teske, H., 261
Thatcher, R. W., 8
Thiel, H., 230
Thimann, K. V., 495, 517, 518
Thom, C. C., 643
Thomas, H. R., 718
Thomas, R. C., 698, 700, 701
Thompson, H. E., 508
Thomson, H. M. S., 253
Tomkins, R. G., 722–724, 727, 742
Tonkin, W. H., 763
Toryu, Y., 172
Traxler, R., 526
Trofimov, A. V., 80, 173, 176
Tseng, C. K., 96
Tsereteli, L. Ya., 740
Tserling V. V. 403 (*See also under* Zerling, V. V.)
Tumanov, I. I., 509
Tunmann, —, 45
Turner, J. S., 537, 619
Turrentine, J. W., 48
Tyulpina, A. F., 85, 89, 171

Uchiyama S. 288, 289
Ungerer, E., 316
United States. Bureau of Agricultural and Industrial Chemistry, 514
Utkin-Ljubowzoff, L., 582

Van Derlinden L., 418
Vasileva, N. G., 402
Vaughan, E. K., 718
Vedrinski, A. I., 118
Vegesack, R. von, 380
Verein für Chemische und Metallurgische Produktion, 696
Verner, R. R., 397
Verona, O., 552
Verzár, F., 626
Vincent, J. M., 646
Vivian, D. L., 776, 783, 784, 796
Vlasyuk, P. A., 359, 360
Voelcker, A., 189
Voelcker, J. A., 278, 280, 284, 287
Vogel, F., 365
Vyvere, E. van de, 197

Waard, J. de, 519, 520
Wache, R., 258
Wachtel, H., 488
Wain, R. L., 800
Walker, R. D., 521
Walker, T. K., 637, 639
Wallace, E. R., 674
Wallace, H. F., 702, 709
Walling, W. A. B., 756
Wardlaw, C. W., 731, 736
Ware, W. M., 657
Warington, K., 413
Wasicky, R., 11
Weber, A. P., 487, 596, 598
Weber, H. J., 366
Weber, U., 98
Wei, W.-T., 106
Weigelt, —, 273
Weis, E., 124
Weiske, F., 440
Weiss, J., 535
Welborne, W. W., 699
Wellman, R. H., 648
Wendt, G. von, 346
Werba, K., 317
Weston, W. A. R. D., 712

Whang, P.-C., 91
White, C. J., 46
White, P. R., 390
Whiting, A. G., 522
Wiebull, M., 62
Wijnberg, A., 312
Winckler, F. L., 199
Wingfoot Corporation, 741
Winterstein, E., 212
Wisconsin Agricultural Experiment Station, 703
Wolcott, G. N., 805
Wolf, J., 539
Wolfe, W. C., 512
Wood, J. W., 512, 515
Woodward, G. E., 609, 610
Wrangell, M. von, 218, 332
Wright, H. D., 573, 575
Wynd, F. L., 367

Yamamoto, A., 634
Young, D. W., 449
Young, R. S., 375
Young, V. H., 714
Yuasa, A., 395
Yun, I. S., 475
Yust, H. R., 775

Zande, J. van der, 57
Zeller, H., 584, 585
Zemba, J. W., 789
Zenger, H., 205
Zentmyer, G. A., 689
Zerling, V. V., 382 (*See also under* Tserling, V. V.)
Zielstorff, W., 353
Zimmerman, P. W., 496–500
Zinova, E. S., 90
Zobell, C. E., 588
Žolkevič, A. J., 315
Zollikofer, C., 489
Zuckerkandl, F., 605

SUBJECT INDEX

According to entry numbers

Abavit B, seed disinfectant, 704
Achlya, effect of iodine, 640
Acremonium, resistance to iodine, 632
Acrylonitriles, iodine-containing, as insecticides, 810
Actinomyces, effect of iodine, 552
Adiantum, iodine content, 187
Agar, iodine content, 83, 84
Agaves, iodine content, 184
Alaria, iodine content, 33, 52, 80, 105
Alaska, seaweeds, iodine content, 105
Aldehyde mutase, activity, effect of iodoacetic acid, 541
Alfalfa, effect of iodine compounds, 386, 393, 509
Algae, freshwater, effect of iodine, 375
freshwater, iodine content, 207
marine. *See* Seaweeds
Alkyl iodides, toxicity to grain weevils, 815
Allium bulbs, effect of thyroid and thyroxine, 461, 473, 478
Allyl iodide, insecticide, 775, 797
Almond trees, crown gall on, eradication, 677
Alternaria, effect of iodine, 718, 740
Ammonification, in soil, effect of iodine, 293, 552
Ammonium iodide, effect on wheat, 277
Anabaina, iodine content, 195
Antilles, plants, iodine content, 201
Antithamnion, iodine content, 127
Aphides, iodine compounds toxic to, 762, 769, 795, 817
Apples, iodine absorption by, 526
preservation, use of iodine, 722, 723
Apricot trees, effect of iodine injections, 314
Arenaria, iodine content, 183
Armeria, iodine content, 189
Arthrothamnus, iodine content, 58, 107
Arylazo compounds, as insecticides, 783
Ascophyllum, iodine content, 80, 103, 120
Ascorbic acid, content of plants, effect of iodine, 405, 408
Asparagopsis, iodine content, 74, 130, 131
Asparagus, effect of iodine, 381
Aspergillus, diiodohydroxybenzoate fungistatic against, 646
effect of iodine, 581, 643, 645
effect of iodoacetic acid, 634-637, 639
enzymes from, effect of iodoacetic acid, 633
iodide oxidation by, 641
Asplenium, iodine content, 187
Asters, effect of thyroxine, 472
Astilbe, effect of ethyl iodide, 292
Australia, seaweeds, iodine content, 46, 63, 65
Azotobacter, effect of iodine, 553, 554, 556, 561, 562

Bacillus, growth and metabolism, effect of iodoacetic acid, 570, 571
physiological activities, effect of iodine, 554
Bacteria, growth and metabolism, effect of iodine compounds, 563-579, 581, 590
iodine content, 207
soil. *See* Soil microflora
Bactericides, iodine compounds as, 649, 670, 676, 677, 680, 683, 686
Bananas, iodine content, 200
Barilla, iodine content, 184
iodine production from, 183
Barley, effect of Chilean nitrate of soda, 420, 426, 460
effect of iodine compounds, 278, 280, 284, 287, 289, 303, 342, 350, 351, 440, 501, 515
iodine enrichment by manuring, 236
Barley roots, radio-active iodine absorption by, 415
Barley seedlings, effect of iodoform, 392
Barley smut, effect of iodine compounds, 697
Barley stripe, control by iodine, 703
Basil seeds, germination, effect of iodine, 318
Beans, effect of iodine compounds, 301, 318, 332, 341, 342, 346, 365, 402, 475, 512, 515, 522
iodine absorption by, 524
iodine enrichment by manuring, 263
Beets. *See also* Sugar beet
effect of Chilean nitrate of soda, 427, 433, 454, 455
effect of iodine, 310, 311, 349, 364, 365, 412, 438
iodine absorption by, 262
iodine content, 212, 230
Beggiatoa, iodine content, 207
Betaine iodide, for fruit preservation, 739
Blowflies, repellents for, 764-766, 770
Blowfly larvae, iodine compounds toxic to, 756
Bonnemaisonia, iodine content, 128, 130, 162
liberation of free iodine by, 122, 164
Botrytis, effect of iodine compounds, 694
Botrytis infection, in fruit, control, 726, 728, 730, 732, 733, 737
Bromoiodobenzene, insecticide, 801
Brucella, growth, effect of iodine, 574
Buckwheat, effect of Chilean nitrate of soda, 451
effect of iodine, 273, 345, 348, 376, 377, 388, 451
Bud development, effect of iodine compounds, 502, 523
Bulbs, use of iodine in treatment of, 662, 668, 674
Bunt. *See* Wheat bunt
Butyl iodide, insecticide, 763, 774

Cabbage, effect of Chilean nitrate of soda, 436
effect of iodine, 349, 355, 365
effect of thyroid extract, 468
iodine enrichment by manuring, 268
Cabbage moth larvae, iodine compounds toxic to, 800

Cadmium iodide, effect on cabbage, 355
insecticide, 805
Cakile, iodine content, 197
Calcium iodide, effect on plants, 279, 341
Canada, seaweeds, iodine content, 75
Cardamine seeds, effect of thyroid preparations, 488
Carrageen, iodine content, 24, 37
Carrots, effect of Chilean nitrate of soda, 436, 447
effect of iodine, 327, 341, 359, 360, 365, 436
iodine absorption by, 526
iodine content, 212
iodine enrichment by manuring, 245, 254, 262
Caterpillars, iodoform toxic to, 754, 755
Cauliflower, effect of iodine, 365, 366
Celery, effect of iodine, 341, 365
iodine content, 212, 230
Ceramium, iodine content, 104, 127
Cereals. *See also* Maize; Wheat, etc.
iodine content, 219
Chara, iodine content, 198
Chenopodiaceae, iodine absorption, 206, 208
Cherries, preservation, use of iodine, 738
Chicory, effect of iodine, 384
Chiggers, iodine for control of, 816
Chile, seaweeds, iodine content, 38-43
Chilean nitrate of soda, effect on iodine content of plants, 233, 253, 439, 441, 449, 451, 455, 456, 460
effect on plants, 336, 337, 344, 419-460, 660
China, seaweeds, iodine content, 70, 91, 92, 95, 96, 106
Chlorella, effect of iodine compounds, 398, 404, 532
Chlorides, antagonism to iodine toxicity in maize, 401
Chlorodiiodobenzoic acid, effect on tomatoes, 500
Chloroiodobenzene, insecticide, 784, 788, 801
Chlorophyceae, iodine content, 60, 207
Chlorophyll, assimilation in seaweeds, relation to iodine, 111
development, promotion by iodine, 393
oxidation, effect of iodine, 535
relation to iodine content of plants, 207, 222
Chondrus, iodine content, 24, 37
Chorda, iodine content, 23
Chrysanthemum, effect of thyroxine, 472
Chrysanthemum aphis, iodine compounds toxic to, 817
Citrus fruits, preservation, 666, 731, 736, 740
Cladophora, effect of iodine and of thyroid preparations, 482
Cladosporium, effect of iodine, 552
Clover, effect of iodine, 278, 393
iodine content, 221
iodine content, effect of Chilean nitrate of soda, 439
Coal, iodine content, 258
Cochayuyo, iodine content, 38-43
Cockroaches, destruction by iodine, 757
Codium, iodine content, 69
Codling moth larvae, iodine compounds toxic to, 772, 778, 779, 785-788
Colletotrichum, effect of iodine, 656, 740
Colorado beetle, iodine compounds toxic to, 760, 780
Colza, effect of iodine, 276
Convolvulus, germination, effect of iodine, 318
iodine content, 197
Corchorus, effect of iodine, 295
Corn borer, iodine compounds toxic to, 796
Cotton root rot, effect of iodine, 667, 678
Cottonseed, disinfection, 699, 702, 709, 717, 720
Cress, effect of iodine compounds, 273, 275, 341, 477, 481, 491
Crown gall, eradication from almond trees, 677
Cryptotermes, iodine compounds toxic to, 805
Cucumber, effect of iodine, 332, 365, 376
iodine absorption by, 526
Cuprous iodide, insecticide, 805
Cyanodon, iodine content, 229
Cyanophyceae, iodine content, 207
Cynoglossum, iodine content, 197
Cyperaceae, iodine content, 197
Cystophora, iodine content, 82
Cystoseira, iodine content, 61, 104

Daffodils, eelworm in, destruction, 662
Dalmatia, plants, iodine content, 203
DDT analogues, iodine-containing, as insecticides, 800, 802, 807-809, 813, 814, 817, 818
Dehydrogenases, iodoacetic acid and, 615, 620, 621
Delesseraceae, iodine content, 54
Denitrification, effect of iodine, 551, 552
Desmarestia, iodine content, 80
Diatomaceae, iodine content, 76
Didodecyl nicotinium iodide, insecticide, 795
Diiodoacetylene, fungicide, 694
Diiodoazoxybenzene, insecticide, 796
Diiodobenzene, insecticide, 778, 787
Diiodobiphenyl, insecticide, 788, 796
Diiodo compounds, insecticidal efficiency, 811
Diiodohydroxybenzoate, fungistatic activity, 646
Diiodophenoxyacetic acid, plant hormone, 513
Diiodosalicylic acid, insecticide, 801
Dimethylaminoquinaldine ethiodide, condensation product from, fungicide, 696
Dimethyl bipyridinium iodide, insecticide, 769
Dimethylethylquinolinium iodide, insecticide, 773
Diplodia, iodine for control of, 666
Dodecyl nicotinium iodide, insecticide, 795
Drosophila, iodine compounds toxic to, 813
Dunes, plants, iodine content, 197
Durvillea, iodine content, 38-43, 82

Ecklonia, iodine content, 46, 58, 63, 65, 107, 129, 170, 174, 177
Eelworms. *See also* Nematodes
control by iodine, 662, 668, 669, 682, 685, 692
Eelworm larvae, determination of death in, 679
Egregia, iodine content, 53
Eisenia, iodine content, 78, 107
Endive, effect of Chilean nitrate of soda, 456
effect of iodine, 365
Enhaulis, iodine content, 94
Enteromorpha, iodine content, 100, 104
Enzyme action, effect of iodoacetic acid, 533, 536, 541, 546, 568, 600, 602, 605, 612, 613, 615, 618, 620, 621, 624, 625, 633

Equisetum, iodine content, 198
Eryngium, iodine content, 197
Erythrosin, as disinfectant, 681
Ethoxyquinaldine ethiodide, condensation product from, fungicide, 696
Ethyl iodide, effect on plant growth, 292, 319, 334, 391
effect on seed germination, 275
insecticide, 775, 781,
Ethyl mercury iodide, effect on *Fusarium*, 684, 688
seed disinfectant, 717, 718, 720
Ethyl pyridinium iodide, toxic to aphis, 762
Ethylquinaldinium iodide, insecticide, 790
Ethyltriphenyl phosphonium iodide, insecticide, 780
Eucheuma, iodine content, 92

Falkenbergia, form of iodine in, 138, 149
presence of free iodine in, 130, 133, 134, 136, 137, 149, 152
Feijoa, fruit, iodine content, 223
Ferns, aquatic, effect of thyroid extract, 469
iodine content, 183
Flax, effect of iodine compounds, 358, 371, 373, 374, 509
Flax seed, disinfection, 719
Flies, iodine compounds toxic to, 758, 759, 764-766, 770
Florideae, iodine content, 60, 127, 130-134, 139, 207
Flour beetles, methyl iodide toxic to, 785
Fluoroiodobenzene, insecticide, 788
Forage crops, iodine content, 224
France, decrees relating to use of iodides, 650
seaweeds, iodine content, 35, 60, 71
Fruits, iodine absorption by, 526
Fruit preservation, use of iodine, 722-745
Fucus, form of iodine in, 123-125
iodine content, 22, 23, 25-31, 33, 35, 37, 44, 49, 52, 54-56, 60, 62, 74, 98, 101, 103, 121, 183
liberation of free iodine by, 143, 145
Fungi. *See also* Aspergillus; Penicillium, etc.
effect of iodates, 579
growth and metabolism, effect of iodine compounds, 581, 590, 632-646
iodine content, 212
Fungicides, iodine compounds as, 647-649, 652-654, 656, 657, 659, 660, 664-668, 671-674, 676, 678, 684, 687-689, 691, 692, 694-745, 771
Furcellaria, iodine content, 62
Fusarium, effect of iodine compounds, 552, 668, 684, 687, 688, 693

Gambusia, iodine compounds toxic to, 807
Garlic, iodine content, 206
Gelidium, iodine content, 83, 91, 185
Geranium, effect of iodine, 299
Germany, seaweeds, iodine content, 64, 98
Germination. *See* Seed germination
Gigartina, iodine content, 77
Goldfish, toxicity of iodine-containing DDT analogues, 807
Gracilaria, iodine content, 68, 74, 78
Grapes, effect of Chilean nitrate of soda, 451
iodine absorption by, 526
preservation, use of iodine, 722-726, 728, 737
Grapefruit, preservation, use of iodine, 731, 736
Grasses. *See also* Pasture grasses; Forage crops, etc.
iodine content, 197
Grasshoppers, iodoform toxic to, 755
Greenbottle flies, iodine compounds toxic to, 766, 770
Growth regulating substances, iodine compounds as, 493-523

Hai-pai-t'sai, iodine content, 70
Halicystis, accumulation of iodine by, 181
Halidrys, iodine content, 23, 33, 62
Halymenia, iodine content, 74
Hawaii, seaweeds, iodine content, 88
Hay, composition, effect of Chilean nitrate of soda, 441
Heterodera, use of iodine compounds against, 663, 669, 682, 685
Himanthalia, iodine content, 64
Hippophaë, iodine content, 197
Hops, effect of iodine compounds, 336, 521
use of iodized fertilizer, 418
Hop downy mildew, effect of iodine vapour, 657
Horse beans, effect of iodine, 342, 402
Houseflies, iodine compounds toxic to, 758, 770
Hyacinths, effect of thyroid preparations, 462, 466, 468
Hydriodic acid, effect on seed germination, 271
Hydroponics, use of iodine in, 547, 548
Hyssop, iodine content, 261

Iceland moss, iodine content, 261
India, grasses, iodine content, 229
seaweeds, iodine content, 74, 94, 100, 102
Insecticides, use of iodine compounds, 360, 649, 651, 691, 754-818
Iodide oxidase, in *Aspergillus*, 641
in seaweeds, 157, 159, 163
"Iodine Bentonite", seed disinfectant, 699, 709
Iodine chloride, effect on wheat, 389
Iodine dust, fungicide, 698, 700, 701, 703, 705, 712, 715
Iodine green, use against *Heterodera*, 663
"Iodine Kieselguhr", seed disinfectant, 699
Iodine vapour, absorption through leaves of mustard, 431
fungicidal action, 657
toxic to blowfly larvae, 756
Iodized chalk, effect on tomatoes, 660
Iodized cottonwool, for fruit preservation, 730
Iodized wood shaving, for fruit preservation, 735
Iodized wrappers, for fruit preservation, 722-733, 735-739, 741-745
Iodoacetamide, effect on plant growth, 493
effect on tobacco mosaic virus, 675
effect on yeast, 623
inhibition of photosynthesis by, 532
Iodoacetanilide, insecticide, 784, 804
Iodoacetic acid, effect on *Aspergillus*, 634-637, 639
effect on enzyme action, 533, 536, 538, 541, 546, 568, 600, 602, 605, 612, 613, 615, 618, 620, 621, 624, 625, 633
effect on growth and metabolism of bacteria, 565-567, 569-573, 575, 576, 578

effect on nitrogen fixation by *Azotobacter*, 562
effect on plant growth, 494, 495, 502, 517
effect on synthesis of sucrose in plants, 540, 545
effect on tissue respiration, 534, 537, 539
effect on yeasts, 600-631
inhibition of photosynthesis by, 532
Iodoacetonitrile, insecticide, 791
Iodoaniline, insecticide, 788, 801
Iodoazobenzene, insecticide, 776, 783, 796, 801
Iodobenzene, insecticide, 758, 760, 761, 787
Iodobiphenyl, insecticide, 788
Iodochlorophenoxyacetic acid, plant hormone, 508, 513
Iodo-N-dimethylaniline, insecticide, 801
Iodoform, effect on barley seedlings, 392
insecticide, 754-757, 761, 764-766, 770, 778
Iodohydroxyquinoline sulphonic acid, protective agent for plants, 665
Iodonaphthalene, insecticide, 778, 801
Iodonitrobenzene, insecticide, 778, 779, 784, 786, 787, 790, 796, 801
Iodonitrobenzoic acid, effect on plant growth, 512, 514, 515
Iodonitronaphthalene, insecticide, 801
Iodophenoxyacetic acid, weed killer, 749
Iodophenylacetic acid, weed killer, 751
Iodophenylazocresol, insecticide, 776
Iodophenylchloromethylsulphone, insecticide, 812
Iodophenyl thiocyanate, insecticide, 784
Iodopropionic acid, effect on yeast, 604
Iodosobenzenes, as insecticides, 793, 796, 798
Iodoso compounds, insecticidal efficiency, 811
Iodosonitrobenzene, insecticide, 799, 801
Iodoxybenzenes, as insecticides, 792, 798, 801
Iodoxybenzoic acid, insecticide, 773
Iodoxy compounds, insecticidal efficiency, 811
Iridaea, iodine content, 53
Iris, iodine content, 198
Irish moss, iodine content, 24, 37

Japan, seaweeds, iodine content, 58, 78, 86, 107
Juncaceae, iodine content, 197
Juncus, effect of iodine, 396
Jungermannia, iodine content, 188, 196

Kale, iodine content, 230
Kelp. *See* Seaweed
Kjellmaniella, iodine content, 58
Kohl-rabi, effect of iodine, 365

Lady beetles, methyl iodide toxic to, 785
Laminaria, distribution of iodine in, 151, 165
form of iodine in, 123, 158, 165, 172, 174, 175
growth and reproduction, effect of iodine, 352
iodine content, 23, 28, 29, 31, 33, 35, 45, 49, 51, 53-56, 58, 60, 62, 64, 69, 70, 73, 75, 76, 80, 96, 97, 103, 110-117, 119
liberation of free iodine by, 142-145, 147, 148, 154-156, 158, 161, 163, 166-169, 182
Larvicides. *See* Insecticides
Laurencia, iodine content, 68
Lentils, effect of thyroxine, 481
Lettuce, effect of Chilean nitrate of soda, 451, 456
effect of iodine, 346, 365, 366, 376, 378, 381, 393, 413, 435, 451
iodine content, 212
iodine enrichment by manuring, 233, 262, 266-268
Libya, seaweeds, iodine content, 66
Lichens, iodine content, 183
Lilac, effect of ethyl iodide, 334
effect of thyroid extract, 465
Liliaceae, iodine absorption, 206, 208
Lily of the valley, effect of ethyl iodide, 292
Limonium, iodine content, 197
Lithium iodide, effect on cereals, 287
Liverwort, iodine content, 188, 196
Lobelia, colour improved by iodine, 346
Lupins, effect of iodine, 380
Macrocystis, iodine content, 47, 50, 52, 53, 93, 105
Macrophoma, effect of iodine, 740
Macrosiphoniella, iodine compounds toxic to, 817
Macrosporium, effect of iodine, 552
Magnesium iodide, effect on wheat, 279
Maize, effect of Chilean nitrate of soda, 442, 451, 460
effect of iodine compounds, 273, 297, 302, 342, 347, 370, 393, 401, 451, 512
iodine content, 200
iodine enrichment by manuring, 232, 269
Malt, iodine content, 219
Manganese, oxidation in soil, effect of iodine, 407
Manganese iodide, effect on cereals, 284, 287
Mangolds. *See also* Beets
effect of iodine, 359, 360, 365, 380
Marrows, effect of iodine, 359, 360
Mediterranean coast, iodine content of plants, 201
Mentha, iodine content, 198
Menyanthes, iodine content, 198
Mercuric chloro-iodide, weed killer, 748
Mercuric iodide, insecticide, 767, 805
Methylene iodide, insecticide, 775
Methyl iodide insecticide, 775, 785, 797
Methyl mercury iodide, seed disinfectant, 711, 716
Methyltriphenyl phosphonium iodide, insecticide, 780
Mexican bean beetle, iodine compounds toxic to, 780
Millet, effect of iodine, 289
Mites, iodine for control of, 816
Mosquito larvae, iodine compounds toxic to, 776, 784, 799, 802, 807
Moulds. *See* Fungi
Mung bean sprouts, effect of iodine, 408
Mushrooms, iodine content, 183
Mustard, effect of Chilean nitrate of soda, 426, 442, 451
effect of iodine, 303, 315, 341, 371, 451
effect of thyroid extract, 468
iodine vapour absorption through leaves, 431
Myosotis, iodine content, 198

Narcissus bulbs, effect of thyroid preparations, 463
hot water treatment, use of iodine, 668, 674
Nasturtium, germination, effect of iodine, 318
iodine tolerance, 762, 769
Nematodes. *See also* Eelworms
use of iodine compounds against, 661, 663, 672
Nereocystis, iodine content, 47, 50, 52, 53, 105
Netherlands, seaweeds, iodine content, 57
New Zealand, pastures, iodine content, 217
seaweeds, iodine content, 77
Nitrogen cycle, effect of iodine, 549-562
Nitroiodosobenzene acetate, insecticide, 801
Nitrophenyliodochlorides, as insecticides, 794, 798, 801
Norway, seaweeds, iodine content, 49
Nostoc, iodine content, 70

Oats, effect of Chilean nitrate of soda, 424, 460
effect of iodine compounds, 282, 283, 286, 301, 342, 350, 351, 371, 428, 438, 440, 512
effect of thyroidin, 480
iodine enrichment by manuring, 231, 236
Oat seedlings, effect of iodoacetamide, 493
effect of iodoacetate, 494, 495, 517
Oat smut, effect of iodine compounds, 698, 700, 701, 703, 705, 710, 714
Oedogonium, effect of iodine and of thyroid preparations, 482
Oidium, use of manures containing iodine against, 653
Onions, effect of iodine, 378
iodine absorption by, 262
Oranges, wastage, iodine for control of, 666
Orange trees, effect of iodine, 328
Orchard grass hay, iodine content, 224
Oryzaephilus, iodine compounds toxic to, 817, 818
Oscillaria, iodine content, 195

Pacific coast, seaweeds, iodine content, 47, 48, 50, 53, 78, 82
Padina, iodine content, 100
Pasture grasses, effect of Chilean nitrate of soda, 441 451
effect of iodine, 353
iodine content, 217, 225, 229
iodine enrichment by manuring, 231, 236, 253, 255, 260, 441
Peaches, iodine absorption by, 526
preservation, use of iodine, 722, 723
Pear trees, effect of iodine injections, 314
Peas, effect of iodine compounds, 281, 282, 346, 356, 394, 399, 406, 509, 516
iodine enrichment by manuring, 236
Pelagophycus, iodine content, 47, 53
Pelargonium, effect of iodine, 299
Pelvetia, iodine content, 121
Penicillium, effect of iodine compounds, 552, 581, 638, 644, 693, 716, 738, 740
Peppermint, iodine manuring experiments, 261
Perilla, effect of triiodobenzoic acid, 509
Periodic table, position in, relation to function in plant nutrition, 8
Phaeophyceae, iodine content, 60, 157, 163
Phenoxy compounds, iodine-containing, as plant hormones, 496, 508, 513
Phenyliodochlorides, as insecticides, 794, 798
Philippines, seaweeds, iodine content, 68
Phomopsis, effect of iodine, 740
Photosynthesis, effect of iodine compounds, 398, 402, 404, 532
Phragmites, iodine content, 198
Phyllophora, iodine content, 59, 72, 79, 85, 89, 171, 178
Phymatotrichum, growth, effect of iodine, 678
Phytomonas, effect of iodine, 670, 676, 677, 680, 683, 686
Phytophthora. *See* Potato blight
Plants, atmospheric iodine and, 214, 218, 246, 431
freshwater, iodine content, 190-192, 194-196, 205, 207, 213, 227
growth and metabolism, effect of Chilean nitrate, 419-460
growth and metabolism, effect of iodine compounds, 271-418
growth and metabolism, effect of thyroxine and thyroid preparations, 461-492
iodine content, 183-230, 261
iodine content, effect of Chilean nitrate, 439, 441, 449, 455, 456, 460
iodine content, effect of iodine manuring, 231-270, 332, 340, 341, 343, 365, 431, 449
Plant cells, effect of iodine, 362, 395
iodine content, 209, 210
Plant hormones, iodine compounds as, 493-523
Plant juices, liberation of iodine from iodide by, 530
Plant ovaries, effect of iodine injections, 291, 296
Plant plasma, coagulating action of iodide, 531
Plantago, iodine content, 183, 197
Plums, iodine absorption by, 526
preservation, use of iodine, 722, 723
Pollen germination, effect of iodine, 382, 403
effect of thyroid preparations, 470
Polysiphonia, iodine content, 100, 132
Pondweed, iodine content, 204
Popillia grubs, mercuric iodide toxic to, 767
Poplar twigs, effect of thyroxine, 485
Porphyra, iodine content, 75, 91
Potamogeton, iodine content, 198
Potassium periodate, effect on plant growth, 261, 350, 351
fungistatic reagent, 689
Potatoes, effect of Chilean nitrate of soda, 451
effect of iodine compounds, 319, 366, 438, 440, 451, 503
iodine content, 206, 212
iodine enrichment by manuring, 270
Potato blight, effect of iodine, 657, 671
Potato leaves, effect of ethyl iodide, 391
Potato ring rot, control by iodine, 670, 676, 680, 683, 686
Potato root eelworm, determination of death in larvae, 679
Potato scab, control by iodine, 370, 676, 691
Potato seeds, disinfection, 647, 664, 670, 686
Potato X virus, effect of iodine compounds, 681
Propyl iodide, insecticide, 775

Protease activity, effect of iodoacetic acid, 533, 536
Psamma, effect of iodine, 273
Pseudoperonospora, effect of iodine vapour, 657

Radioactive iodine, absorption by barley roots, 415
 use in plant growth studies, 512, 514, 515
Radishes, effect of Chilean nitrate of soda, 451
 effect of iodine, 274, 282, 283, 286, 298, 349, 365, 451
 iodine content, 230
 iodine enrichment by manuring, 245
Ranunculus, iodine content, 198
Rape, effect of iodine, 341
Rhizoctonia, iodine for control of, 664
Rhizopus, effect of iodine, 552, 738
Rhodomela, iodine content, 29
Rhodophyceae, form of iodine in, 157
Rhodotorula, effect of iodine, 596, 598
Rhodymeniaceae, iodine content, 54
Rhubarb, effect of iodine, 346
Rice, effect of iodine, 285, 286
Ripening, of tomatoes, effect of Chilean nitrate of soda, 451
 of vegetables, effect of iodine, 366
"Roméritos", iodine content, 184
Root growth, effect of iodine, 417
Rose hips, iodine content, 230
Rumania, seaweeds, iodine content, 104
Russia, iodine production, statistics, 72
 seaweeds, iodine content, 59, 61, 72, 79, 80, 85, 87, 89, 90, 118, 176, 178
Rye, effect of Chilean nitrate of soda, 419, 420, 454, 460
 effect of iodine, 350, 351
 iodine absorption by, 239
 iodine enrichment by manuring, 258
Ryegrass, iodine enrichment by manuring, 231

"Sabila", iodine content, 184
Saccorhiza, iodine content, 33, 119
Salicornia, iodine content, 197
Salsola, iodine content, 183, 197
Sand-oats, effect of iodine, 273
Sargassum, iodine content, 68, 70, 74, 92, 94, 95, 129
Sarsaparilla roots, iodine content, 199
Savoys, effect of iodine, 365
Scale insects, iodine compounds toxic to, 774, 775, 785
Sclerotinia infection, effect of iodine, 384
Scotland, seaweeds, iodine content, 28, 36, 119-121
Screwworm flies, iodine compounds toxic to, 764-766, 790
Scrophularia, ovaries, effect of iodine, 291, 296
Seapinks, iodine content, 189
Seaweeds, accumulation of iodine by, 181
 discovery of iodine in, 21
 distribution of iodine in, 135, 150, 151, 165, 176
 form of iodine in, 82, 123-126, 129, 135, 153, 157, 162, 165, 170-175, 177, 178
 iodide-oxidases in, 157, 159, 163
 iodine content, 21-107, 202
 iodine content, effect of age, 60, 110, 128
 iodine content, relation to reproductive development, 108
 iodine content, seasonal variations, 60, 108-121
 liberation of free iodine by, 122, 127, 139-146, 148, 149, 154-156, 158-161, 163, 164, 166-169, 182
 manurial value, 28, 653
 penetration of iodide into, 179, 180
 presence of free iodine in, 130-139, 149, 152
Seeds, iodine absorption by, 524, 525, 528, 529
Seed disinfection, use of iodine compounds, 647, 695-721
Seed germination, effect of iodine compounds, 261, 271, 274, 275, 284, 303, 308, 315, 318, 324, 342, 343, 347, 350, 351, 372, 501, 768
 effect of thyroid preparations, 464, 474, 481, 488
Sesame, effect of iodine, 288
Setaria, iodine content, 229
Sewage sludge, as iodine fertilizer, 250, 251
Silkworm larvae, iodine compounds toxic to, 773, 777
Silver iodide, fungicide, 673, 721
Smut. *See* Oat smut
Soda hispanica, iodine production from, 183
Sodium iodate, toxic to flies, 759
 weed killer, 746
Sodium nitrate, synthetic and Chilean, comparison, 421-429, 431-438, 442, 443, 445, 447, 450-456, 459, 460
Sodium periodate, effect on plants, 342, 351, 440
Soil microflora, effect of iodine, 321, 330, 393, 549-562
Soil sterilization, use of iodine compounds, 303, 655, 672, 692, 767
Solanaceae, iodine absorption, 206, 208
Somaliland, seaweeds, iodine content, 81
South Africa, grasses, iodine content, 225
Soya beans, effect of thyroidin, 492
 effect of triiodobenzoic acid, 510
 germination, effect of iodine, 318
Spain, seaweeds, iodine content, 26, 34, 69, 73
Spermothamnion, iodine content, 127, 128
Sphaerococcus, iodine content, 23
Spiderwort, effect of iodine, 362
Spinach, effect of Chilean nitrate of soda, 451
 effect of iodine, 288, 346, 361, 365, 440, 451
 iodine enrichment by manuring, 231, 236, 262
Spirogyra, effect of iodine, 552
Sponges, iodine content, 183
Stachylidium, resistance to iodide, 638
Staphylococci, growth and metabolism, effect of iodoacetic acid, 569, 570, 574
Statice, iodine content, 197
Strawberries, eelworms in, control by iodine, 692
 effect of iodine, 346
Streptococci, growth and metabolism, effect of iodine, 574, 575
String beans, effect of triiodobenzoic acid, 806
Sugar beet. *See also* Beets
 effect of Chilean nitrate of soda, 423, 424, 432, 433, 448, 451-455, 459
 effect of iodine, 290, 304, 309, 312, 313, 316, 317, 322, 323, 337, 338, 340, 343, 354, 359, 360, 372, 380, 440, 451
 iodine content, 193
 iodine enrichment by manuring, 232, 235, 236, 340, 343
Sugar beet webworms, ethyl iodide toxicity, 781

Sugar cane, effect of iodine, 349
Sunflower, effect of triiodobenzoic acid, 509
oil formation, stimulation with iodine, 397
Sweden, seaweeds, iodine content, 62

Termites, iodine compounds toxic to, 805
Tetraiodoethylene, fungicide, 693, 694
Tetraiodophthalic anhydride, insecticide, 777
Tetramethyl ammonium iodide, insecticide, 780
Thermal waters, iodine content of plants growing in, 195
Thiocyanoiodobenzene, insecticide, 799
Thyroid extract, effect on yeast, 589
Thyroid preparations, effect on plants, 461-492
Thyroxine, effect on plant growth, 471-473, 475, 477, 481, 485, 489, 491
effect on yeasts, 598
Timothy, effect of iodine, 375
Tissue respiration, effect of iodoacetic acid, 534, 537, 539
Tobacco, effect of iodine, 377
iodine content, 201, 202, 216
Tobacco mosaic virus, effect of iodine compounds, 675, 681, 690
Tomatoes, effect of Chilean nitrate of soda, 451, 456
effect of iodine compounds, 303, 318, 365-367, 376, 377, 379, 390, 405, 451, 498, 500, 505, 520, 521
iodine absorption by, 526
iodine enrichment by manuring, 254, 267
preservation, use of iodine, 722, 723, 735
Tomato diseases, use of iodine compounds, 656, 659, 660, 682, 718
Tradescantia, effect of iodine, 362
Trailliella, form of iodine in, 153, 157, 162
Trees, ash, iodine content, 194
Triiodobenzoic acid, insecticide, 806
plant hormone, 497-499, 501-507, 509-511, 516, 518-523
weed killer, 502, 507, 511, 751
Triiodo compounds, insecticidal efficiency, 811
Triiodophenol, insecticide, 788, 801
Trimethylpyridine ethiodide, condensation product from, fungicide, 696
Trombicula, iodine for control of, 816
Turbinaria, iodine content, 94, 129
Turnips, effect of Chilean nitrate of soda, 426, 447
effect of iodine, 361
effect of thyroid extract, 468
iodine enrichment by manuring, 232, 233, 259, 263
Tylenchus, use of iodine compounds against, 661

Ultraviolet irradiation, effect on liberation of iodine in seaweeds, 164
Ulva, iodine content, 22, 95, 100
Umbelliferae, iodine absorption, 206, 208
Undaria, iodine content, 96

Valerian, iodine manuring experiments, 261
Valonia, accumulation of iodine by, 179-181
Vegetables. *See also* Carrots; Radishes, etc.
iodine content, 206, 226, 230, 370
iodine enrichment by manuring, 240, 263, 370
Viricides, iodine compounds as, 675, 681, 690

Watercress, iodine content, 186, 190, 197, 200, 204, 220, 227, 230
Wax beans, iodine enrichment by manuring, 263
Weed killers, use of iodine compounds, 360, 502, 507, 511, 746-753
Weevils, iodine compounds toxic to, 763, 768, 815
Wheat, effect of Chilean nitrate of soda, 420, 460
effect of iodine compounds, 277-280, 284, 287, 294, 342, 350, 351, 389, 416, 417, 509, 768
effect of thyroid extract, 474
iodine absorption by, 525, 528, 529
Wheat diseases, effect of iodine compounds, 695, 704, 708, 712, 715
Wheat straw, iodine content, 224
Wireworms, iodine compounds toxic to, 761, 797
Woodlice, iodine compounds toxic to, 800

Yeasts, effect of inorganic iodine, 554, 574, 580-599
effect of iodoacetic acid, 600-631

Zostera, iodine content, 29, 57, 66, 76, 103, 197

ALPHABETICAL KEY TO ABBREVIATED TITLES OF PERIODICALS

The arrangement is alphabetical according to the first word, or part of a word, of each abbreviated title. The titles of periodicals and places of their publication are those current at the time the papers cited in the bibliography were published.

Acta Phytochim. Acta Phytochimica. *Tokyo.*

Actes Soc. Sci. Chili. Actes de la Société Scientifique du Chili. *Santiago.*

Agric. and Hort. Research Stat., Long Ashton, Bristol. Agricultural and Horticultural Research Station, Long Ashton, Bristol.

Agric. Inst. and Exp. Stat., Kirton, Boston, Lincs. Agricultural Institute and Experimental Station, Kirton, Boston, Lincs.

Agric. J. India. Agricultural Journal of India. *Calcutta.*

Amer. Fertil. American Fertilizer. *Philadelphia.*

Amer. J. Botany. American Journal of Botany. *Lancaster, Pa.*

Amer. J. Pharm. American Journal of Pharmacy. *Philadelphia.*

Amer. Potato J. American Potato Journal. *New Brunswick, N.J.*

Amer. Soc. Brewing Chem. Proc. American Society of Brewing Chemists, Proceedings. *Sawyer, Wis.*

Amtsbl. Landwirtschaftskammer Regierungsbez. Kassel. Amtsblatt der Landwirtschaftskammer für den Regierungs-Bezirk Kassel. *Kassel, Germany.*

Angewandte Botanik. *Berlin.*

Angewandte Chem. Angewandte Chemie. *Berlin.*

Ann. Agron., Paris. Annales Agronomiques. *Paris.*

Ann. Appl. Biol. Annals of Applied Biology. *Cambridge.*

Ann. Biochem. Exp. Med., Calcutta. Annals of Biochemistry and Experimental Medicine. *Calcutta.*

Ann. Botany. Annals of Botany. *London.*

Ann. Chem. Pharm. Annalen der Chemie und Pharmacie. *Heidelberg.*

Ann. Chim. Annales de Chimie. *Paris.*

Ann. Chim. Anal. Annales de Chimie Analytique. *Paris.*

Ann. Chim. Appl. Annali di Chimica Applicata. *Rome.*

Ann. Chim. Phys. Annales de Chimie et de Physique. *Paris.*

Ann. Ferment. Annales des Fermentations. *Paris.*

Ann. Inst. Pasteur. Annales de l'Institut Pasteur. *Paris.*

Ann. Missouri Botan. Garden. Annals of Missouri Botanical Garden. *St Louis, Mo.*

Ann. Phys. Annalen der Physik. *Leipzig.*

Ann. Physiol. Physicochim. Biol. Annales de Physiologie et de Physicochimie Biologique. *Paris.*

Ann. Sci. Nat. Botan. Biol. Vég. Annales des Sciences Naturelles. Botanique et Biologie Végétale. *Paris.*

Ann. Soc. Méd.-Chirurg. Bruges. Annales de la Société Médico-Chirurgicale de Bruges. *Bruges.*

Arb. biol. Reichsanst. Land- u. Forstwirtsch. Arbeiten aus der biologischen Reichsanstalt für Land- und Forstwirtschaft. *Berlin.*

Arch. Math. Naturvidenskab. Archiv for Mathematik og Naturvidenskab. *Oslo.*

Arch. Mikrobiol. Archiv für Mikrobiologie. *Berlin.*

Arch. path. Anat. Archiv für pathologische Anatomie und Physiologie und für klinische Medizin. *Berlin.*

Arch. Pharm., Berlin. Archiv der Pharmazie. *Berlin.*

Arch. Pharm., Halle. Archiv der Pharmacie. *Halle.*

Arch. Pharm., Hanover. Archiv der Pharmacie. *Hanover.*

Arch. Sci. Phys. Nat. Archives des Sciences Physiques et Naturelles. *Geneva.*

Arch. Soc. Biol. Montevideo. Archivos de la Sociedad de Biología de Montevideo. *Montevideo.*

Arizona Agric. Exp. Stat. Arizona Agricultural Experiment Station, Tucson.

Ark. Botanik. Arkiv för Botanik. *Stockholm.*

Ark. Kemi Mineral. Geol. Arkiv för Kemi, Mineralogi och Geologi. *Stockholm.*

Arkansas Agric. Exp. Stat. Arkansas Agricultural Experiment Station, Fayetteville.

Atti Soc. Toscana Sci. Nat. Pisa, Memorie. Atti della Società Toscana di Scienze Naturali residente in Pisa. Memorie. *Pisa.*

Atti Soc. Toscana Sci. Nat. Pisa, Processi Verbali. Atti della Società Toscana di Scienze Naturali residente in Pisa. Processi Verbali. *Pisa.*

Australian Garden Lover. *Melbourne.*

Beihefte botan. Zentralbl. Beihefte zum botanischen Zentralblatt. *Kassel, Germany.*

Beitr. Pflanzenzucht. Beiträge zur Pflanzenzucht. *Berlin.*

Ber. deutschen botan. Ges. Bericht der deutschen botanischen Gesellschaft. *Berlin.*

Ber. deutschen pharm. Ges. Berichte der deutschen pharmazeutischen Gesellschaft. *Berlin.*

Ber. Ōhara Inst. landwirtsch. Forsch. Kurashiki. Berichte des Ōhara Instituts für landwirtschaftliche Forschungen in Kurashiki. *Kurashiki, Japan.*

Ber. Verhandl. königl. sächsischen Ges. Wissensch. Leipzig. Berichte über die Verhandlungen der königlich sächsischen Gesellschaft der Wissenschaften zu Leipzig. *Leipzig.*

Beretning 7e Kongr. Nord. Jordbrugsforsk. Forenings. Beretning om Nordiske Jordbrugsforskeres Forenings Syvende Kongres, Oslo. *Copenhagen.*

Biedermanns Zentralbl., Abt. A. Biedermanns Zentralblatt für Agrikulturchemie und rationellen Landwirtschaftsbetrieb. Abteilung A. Allgemeiner und referierender Teil. *Leipzig.*

Biedermanns Zentralbl., Abt. B. Biedermanns Zentralblatt für Agrikulturchemie und rationellen Landwirtschaftsbetrieb. Abteilung B. Tierernährung. Zeitschrift für die gesamte Futterungslehre und Futtermittelkunde. *Leipzig.*

Bimonthly Bull. Ohio Agric. Exp. Stat. Bimonthly Bulletin. Ohio Agricultural Experiment Station. *Wooster.*

Biochem. J. Biochemical Journal. *London.*

Biochem. Ztschr. Biochemische Zeitschrift. *Berlin.*

Biokhimiya. Biokhimiya [Биохимия]. *Moscow* and *Leningrad.*

Biol. Bull. Biological Bulletin of the Marine Biological Laboratory, Woods Hole, Massachusetts. *Woods Hole.*

Biol. Rev. Biological Reviews of the Cambridge Philosophical Society. *Cambridge.*

Biol. Zentralbl. Biologisches Zentralblatt. *Leipzig.*

Biologe. Der Biologe. *Munich* and *Berlin.*

Bodenk. Pflanzenernähr. Bodenkunde und Pflanzenernährung. *Berlin.*

Botan. Gaz. Botanical Gazette. *Chicago.*

Botan. Mag., Tokyo. Botanical Magazine. *Tokyo.*

Botan. Notiser. Botaniska Notiser. *Lund.*

Botan. Rev. Botanical Review. *Lancaster, Pa., New York.*

Botan. Zhurnal SSSR. Botanicheski Zhurnal SSSR [Ботанический Журнал СССР]. *Leningrad* and *Moscow.*

Botaniste. Le Botaniste. *Paris.*

Brit. Packer. British Packer. *London.*

Brit. Sugar Beet Rev. British Sugar Beet Review. *London.*

Bull. Agric. Chem. Soc. Japan. Bulletin of the Agricultural Chemical Society of Japan. *Tokyo.*

Bull. Assoc. Amicale Anciens Élèves Inst. Nat. Agron. Bulletin Mensuel de l'Association Amicale des Anciens Élèves de l'Institut National Agronomique (Ingénieurs Agronomes). *Paris.*

Bull. Biol. Méd. Exp. URSS. Bulletin de Biologie et de Médecine Expérimentale de l'URSS. *Moscow.*

Bull. College Agric. Tokyo Imp. Univ. Bulletin of the College of Agriculture, Tokyo Imperial University. *Tokyo.*

Bull. Entomol. Research. Bulletin of Entomological Research. *London.*

Bull. Histol. Appl. Physiol. Path. Techn. Microsc. Bulletin d'Histologie Appliquée à la Physiologie et à la Pathologie et de Technique Microscopique. *Paris.*

Bull. Imp. Central Agric. Exp. Stat. Japan. Bulletin of the Imperial Central Agricultural Experiment Station, Japan. *Tokyo.*

Bull. Mém. Soc. Méd. Chirurg. Bordeaux. Bulletins et Mémoires de la Société de Médecine et de Chirurgie de Bordeaux. *Paris* and *Bordeaux.*

Bull. Soc. Botan. France. Bulletin. Société Botanique de France. *Paris.*

Bull. Soc. Chim. Biol. Bulletin de la Société de Chimie Biologique. *Paris.*

Bull. Soc. Chim. France. Bulletin de la Société Chimique de France. *Paris.*

Bull. Soc. Chim. Paris. Bulletin de la Société Chimique de Paris. *Paris.*

Bull. Soc. Hist. Nat. Afrique du Nord. Bulletin de la Société d'Histoire Naturelle de l'Afrique du Nord. *Algiers.*

Bull. Soc. Imp. Nat. Moscou. Bulletin de la Société Impériale des Naturalistes de Moscou. *Moscow.*

Bull. Soc. Linn. Lyon. Bulletin Mensuel de la Société Linnéenne de Lyon. *Lyons.*

Bull. Stat. Biol. Arcachon. Bulletin de la Station Biologique d'Arcachon. *Bordeaux.*

Bull. Torrey Botan. Club. Bulletin of the Torrey Botanical Club. *New York.*

Bull. Union Agric. Égypte. Bulletin de l'Union des Agriculteurs d'Égypte. *Cairo.*

C.R. Acad. Agric. France. Comptes Rendus Hebdomadaires des Séances de l'Académie d'Agriculture de France. *Paris.*

C.R. Acad. Sci., Moscow. Comptes Rendus de l'Académie des Sciences de l'URSS. *Moscow.*

C.R. Acad. Sci., Paris. Comptes Rendus Hebdomadaires des Séances de l'Académie des Sciences. *Paris.*

C.R. 4e Congr. Internat. Techn. Chim. Indust. Agric., Brussels. Comptes Rendus, 4e Congrès International Technique et Chimique des Industries Agricoles. *Brussels.*

C.R. 5e Congr. Internat. Techn. Chim. Indust. Agric., Scheveningen. Comptes Rendus, 5e Congrès International Technique et Chimique des Industries Agricoles. *Scheveningen.*

C.R. Soc. Biol., Paris. Comptes Rendus Hebdomadaires des Séances et Mémoires de la Société de Biologie et de ses Filiales. *Paris.*

California Agric. Exp. Stat. California Agricultural Experiment Station, Berkeley.

California Fish and Game. *Sacramento, Calif.*

Canad. J. Research. Canadian Journal of Research. *Ottawa.*

Canad. J. Research [D]. Canadian Journal of Research. Section D. Zoological Sciences. *Ottawa.*

Caribbean Forester. *Rio Piedras, Puerto Rico.*

Cereal Chem. Cereal Chemistry. *St Paul, Minn., Lancaster, Pa.*

Chem. Abstr. Chemical Abstracts. *Columbus, Ohio.*

Chem. Age, London. Chemical Age. *London.*

Chem. Engin. Chemical Engineer. *Philadelphia, Chicago, New York.*

Chem. Engin. Mining Rev. Chemical Engineering and Mining Review. *Melbourne.*

Chem. Engin. News. Chemical and Engineering News. *Easton, Pa.*

Chem. Gaz. Chemical Gazette, or, Journal of Practical Chemistry. *London.*
Chem. News. Chemical News and Journal of Physical Science. *London.*
Chem. Prod. Chem. News. Chemical Products and The Chemical News. *London.*
Chemikerzeitung. Die Chemiker-Zeitung. *Cöthen* (*Köthen*), *Germany.*
Chem.-pharm. Centralbl. Chemisch-pharmaceutisches Centralblatt. *Leipzig.*
Chinese J. Physiol. Chinese Journal of Physiology. *Peiping.*
Contrib. Boyce Thompson Inst. Plant Research. Contributions from Boyce Thompson Institute for Plant Research, Inc. *New York.*
Cornell Univ. Agric. Exp. Stat. Cornell University Agricultural Experiment Station, Ithaca, N.Y.
Current Sci. Current Science. *Bangalore, India.*
Dansk Tidsskr. Farm. Dansk Tidsskrift for Farmaci. *Copenhagen.*
Delaware Agric. Exp. Stat. Delaware Agricultural Experiment Station, Newark.
Deutsche Apotheker-Ztg. Deutsche Apotheker-Zeitung. *Berlin.*
Deutsche landwirtsch. Presse. Deutsche landwirtschaftliche Presse. *Berlin.*
Deutsche Zuckerindust. Die Deutsche Zuckerindustrie. *Berlin.*
Dingler's polytechn. J. Dingler's polytechnisches Journal. *Augsburg.*
Discovery. *London.*
Dokladi Akad. Nauk SSSR. Dokladi Akademi Nauk SSSR [Доклады Академии Наук СССР]. *Leningrad.*
Edinburgh New Phil. J. Edinburgh New Philosophical Journal. *Edinburgh.*
Edinburgh Phil. J. Edinburgh Philosophical Journal. *Edinburgh.*
Endokrinologie. Endokrinologie. Zentralblatt für das Gebiet der inneren Sekretion und Konstitutionsforschung. *Leipzig.*
Enzymologia. Enzymologia. Acta Biocatalytica. *The Hague.*
Ergebn. Agrikulturchem. Ergebnisse der Agrikulturchemie. *Berlin.*
Ergebn. Physiol. Ergebnisse der Physiologie. *Wiesbaden, Munich.*
Exp. and Research Stat., Cheshunt, Herts. Experimental and Research Station, Cheshunt, Herts.
Farming in South Africa. *Pretoria.*
Florida Agric. Exp. Stat. Florida Agricultural Experiment Station, Gainesville.
Food Manufacture. *London.*
Food Research. *Champaign, Ill.*
Fortschr. Landwirtsch. Fortschritte der Landwirtschaft. *Vienna.*
Gartenbauwissenschaft. Die Gartenbauwissenschaft. *Berlin.*
Gartenflora. *Berlin.*
Gaz. Méd. Paris. Gazette Médicale de Paris. *Paris.*
Gazz. Chim. Ital. La Gazzetta Chimica Italiana. *Rome.*
Georgia Agric. Exp. Stat. Georgia Agricultural Experiment Station, Experiment.
Golden Sea Research Inst. China. Golden Sea Research Institute of Chemical Industry. *Szechwan, China.*
Gos. Hidrol. Inst. Issled. Morei SSSR. Gosudarstvenni Hidrologicheski Institut, Issledovaniya Morei SSSR [Государственный Гидрологический Институт, Исследования Морей СССР]. *Leningrad.*
Grain and Feed J. Consol. Grain and Feed Journals Consolidated. *Chicago.*
Gynécologie. *Paris.*
Hadar. *Tel-Aviv, Palestine.*
Hawaii Agric. Exp. Stat. Hawaii Agricultural Experiment Station, Honolulu.
Hawaiian Planters' Rec. Hawaiian Planters' Record. *Honolulu.*
Heil- u. Gewürzpflanzen. Heil- und Gewürzpflanzen. *Munich.*
Indian J. Agric. Sci. Indian Journal of Agricultural Science. *Delhi.*
Indust. Engin. Chem. Industrial and Engineering Chemistry. *Easton, Pa.*
Internat. Rev. Agric. 1. Monthly Bull. Agric. Sci. Pract. International Review of Agriculture. 1. Monthly Bulletin of Agricultural Science and Practice. *Rome.*
Iodine Facts. *London.*
Iowa State Coll. J. Sci. Iowa State College Journal of Science. *Ames, Iowa.*
Izvestiya Akad. Nauk SSSR, 7 Ser., Otdelenie Mat. Estestv. Nauk. Izvestiya Akademi Nauk SSSR. 7 Seriya. Otdelenie Matematicheskikh i Estestvennikh Nauk [Известия Академии Наук СССР. 7 Серия. Отделение Математических и Естественных Наук]. *Moscow.*
Izvestiya Akad. Nauk SSSR, Otdelenie Mat. Estestv. Nauk, Ser. Biol. Izvestiya Akademi Nauk SSSR. Otdelenie Matematicheskikh i Estestvennikh Nauk. Seriya Biologicheskaya [Известия Академии Наук СССР. Отделение Математических и Естественных Наук. Серия Биологическая]. *Moscow.*
J. Agric. Chem. Soc. Japan. Journal of the Agricultural Chemical Society of Japan [Nippon Nogeikagaku Kaisi]. *Tokyo.*
J. Agric. Research. Journal of Agricultural Research. *Washington, D.C.*
J. Agric. Sci. Journal of Agricultural Science. *Cambridge.*
J. Amer. Chem. Soc. Journal of the American Chemical Society. *Easton, Pa.*
J. Amer. Pharm. Assoc., Sci. Ed. Journal of the American Pharmaceutical Association. Scientific Edition. *Washington, D.C.*
J. Amer. Soc. Agron. Journal of the American Society of Agronomy. *Geneva, N.Y.*
J. Assoc. Official Agric. Chem. Journal of the Association of Official Agricultural Chemists. *Washington, D.C.*
J. Bacteriol. Journal of Bacteriology. *Baltimore, Md.*
J. Biol. Chem. Journal of Biological Chemistry. *Baltimore, Md.*
J. Board Agric., London. Journal of the Board of Agriculture. *London.*
J. Cell. Comp. Physiol. Journal of Cellular and Comparative Physiology. *Philadelphia.*
J. Chem. Indust., Japan. Journal of Chemical Industry [Kōgyō-Kwagaku Zasshi]. *Tokyo.*
J. Chim. Méd. Journal de Chimie Médicale, de Pharmacie et de Toxicologie. *Paris.*

J. Chim. Phys. Journal de Chimie Physique. *Paris.*
J. Chosen Med. Assoc. Journal of the Chosen Medical Association. *Chosen, Japan.*
J. College Agric. Univ. Tokyo. Journal of the College of Agriculture, Imperial University of Tokyo. *Tokyo.*
J. Dep. Agric. Victoria. Journal of the Department of Agriculture of Victoria, Australia. *Melbourne.*
J. Econ. Entomol. Journal of Economic Entomology. *Geneva, N.Y., Menasha, Wis.*
J. Franklin Inst. Journal of the Franklin Institute. *Lancaster* and *Philadelphia, Pa.*
J. Gen. Physiol. Journal of General Physiology. *New York.*
J. Helminthol. Journal of Helminthology. *St Albans, Herts.*
J. Hyg., Cambridge. Journal of Hygiene. *Cambridge.*
J. Indian Chem. Soc. Journal of the Indian Chemical Society. *Calcutta.*
J. Indust. Engin. Chem. Journal of Industrial and Engineering Chemistry. *Easton, Pa.*
J. Infect. Dis. Journal of Infectious Diseases. *Chicago.*
J. Inst. Brewing. Journal of the Institute of Brewing. *Cambridge.*
J. Landwirtsch. Journal für Landwirtschaft. *Berlin.*
J. Path. Bacteriol. Journal of Pathology and Bacteriology. *London.*
J. Pharm. Chim., Paris. Journal de Pharmacie et de Chimie. *Paris.*
J. Pharm., Paris. Journal de Pharmacie et des Sciences Accessoires. *Paris.*
J. Pharm. Soc. Japan. Journal of the Pharmaceutical Society of Japan. *Tokyo.*
J. Pharmacol. Exp. Ther. Journal of Pharmacology and Experimental Therapeutics. *Baltimore, Md.*
J. Pomol. Journal of Pomology and Horticultural Science. *London.*
J. prakt. Chem. Journal für praktische Chemie. *Leipzig.*
J. Proc. Roy. Soc. New South Wales. Journal and Proceedings of the Royal Society of New South Wales. *Sydney.*
J. Roy. Agric. Soc. England. Journal of the Royal Agricultural Society of England. *London.*
J. Soc. Arts. Journal of the Society of Arts. *London.*
J. Soc. Chem. Indust., London. Journal of the Society of Chemical Industry. *London.*
J. Soc. Nationale Hort. France. Journal de la Société Nationale d'Horticulture de France. *Paris.*
Jahrb. wissensch. Botanik. Jahrbücher für wissenschaftliche Botanik. *Berlin* and *Leipzig.*
Jap. Ztschr. Mikrobiol. Path. Japanische Zeitschrift für Mikrobiologie und Pathologie [Nippon Biseibutsugaku Byorigaku Zasshi]. *Kyoto, Japan.*
Johns Hopkins Univ. Circular. Johns Hopkins University Circular. *Baltimore, Md.*
Kentucky Agric. Exp. Stat. Kentucky Agricultural Experiment Station, Lexington.
Khimizatsiya Sotsialist. Zemledel. Khimizatsiya Sotsialisticheskovo Zemledeliya [Химизация Социалистического Земледелия]. *Selkhozgiz* and *Ogiz, U.S.S.R.*
Koninkl. Nederlandsche Akad. Wetensch. Proc. Koninklijke Nederlandsche Akademie van Wetenschappen, Proceedings. *Amsterdam.*
Kungl. Lantbruks-Högskolans Ann. Kungliga Lantbruks-Högskolans Annaler. *Uppsala.*
Kunstdünger u. Leim. Kunstdünger und Leim. *Berlin.*
Lancet. *London.*
Landbouwkundig Tijdschr. Landbouwkundig Tijdschrift. *Wageningen, Netherlands.*
Landwirtsch. Blätter, Speyer. Landwirtschaftliche Blätter. *Speyer-on-Rhine, Germany.*
Landwirtsch. Fachpresse Tschechoslowakei. Landwirtschaftliche Fachpresse für die Tschechoslowakei. *Prague.*
Landwirtsch. Jahrb. Landwirtschaftliche Jahrbücher. *Berlin.*
Lingnan Sci. J. Lingnan Science Journal. *Canton.*
Manufacturing Chem. Manufacturing Chemist. *London.*
Massachusetts Agric. Exp. Stat. Massachusetts Agricultural Experiment Station, Amherst.
Meddel. Centralanst. Försöksv. Jordbruks. Meddelande från Centralanstalten för Försöksvasendet på Jordbruksområdet. *Stockholm.*
Mem. Dep. Agric. India Entomol. Series. Memoirs of the Department of Agriculture in India. Entomological Series. *Pusa.*
Metallbörse. Die Metallbörse. *Berlin.*
Mikrobiologiya. Mikrobiologiya [Микробиология]. *Leningrad* and *Moscow.*
Mississippi Agric. Exp. Stat. Mississippi Agricultural Experiment Station, State College.
Mitt. Geb. Lebensmitteluntersuch. Hyg. Mitteilungen aus dem Gebiete der Lebensmitteluntersuchung und Hygiene. *Berne.*
Mitt. Lab. preuss. geol. Landesanst. Mitteilungen aus den Laboratorien der preussischen geologischen Landesanstalt. *Berlin.*
Modern Packaging. *New York.*
Monatsh. Chem. Monatshefte für Chemie und verwandte Teile anderer Wissenschaften. *Leipzig* and *Vienna.*
Montana Agric. Exp. Stat. Montana Agricultural Experiment Station, Bozeman.
Münchener med. Wochenschr. Münchener medizinische Wochenschrift. *Munich.*
Nature, London. Nature. *London.*
Naturwissenschaften. Die Naturwissenschaften. *Berlin.*
Natuurwetensch Tijdschr. Natuurwetenschappelijk Tijdschrift. *Ghent.*
Nauk. Zapiski Tsukr. Prom. Naukovi Zapiski z Tsukrovoï Promislovosti [Наукові Записки з Цукрової Промисловости]. *Kiev.*
New Jersey Agric. Exp. Stat. New Jersey Agricultural Experiment Station, New Brunswick.
New Phytol. New Phytologist. *Cambridge.*
New Zealand J. Agric. New Zealand Journal of Agriculture. *Wellington.*
North Dakota Agric. Exp. Stat. North Dakota Agricultural Experiment Station, Fargo.
Notizen Geb. Natur- und Heilk. Notizen aus dem Gebiete der Natur- und Heilkunde. *Weimar.*

Nuovo Giorn. Botan. Ital. Nuovo Giornale Botanico Italiano. *Florence.*

Obst- u. Gemüsebau. Der Obst- und Gemüsebau. *Berlin.*

Österreich. botan. Ztschr. Oesterreichische botanische Zeitschrift. *Vienna.*

Österreich. Chemikerztg. Österreichische Chemikerzeitung und Zeitschrift für Nahrungsmitteluntersuchung, Hygiene und Warenkunde. *Vienna.*

Ohio Agric. Exp. Stat. Ohio Agricultural Experiment Station, Wooster.

Onderstepoort J. Vet. Sci. Onderstepoort Journal of Veterinary Science and Animal Industry. *Onderstepoort, S. Africa.*

Oregon Agric. Exp. Stat. Oregon Agricultural Experiment Station, Corvallis.

Pennsylvania Agric. Exp. Stat. Pennsylvania Agricultural Experiment Station, State College.

Pflügers Arch. ges. Physiol. Pflügers Archiv für die gesamte Physiologie des Menschen und der Tiere. *Bonn.*

Pharm. Centralbl. Pharmaceutisches Central-Blatt. *Leipzig.*

Pharm. Weekblad Nederland. Pharmaceutisch Weekblad voor Nederland. *Amsterdam.*

Pharm. Zentralhalle. Pharmazeutische Zentralhalle für Deutschland. *Leipzig* and *Dresden.*

Phil. Trans. Roy. Soc. Philosophical Transactions of the Royal Society of London. *London.*

Philippine Agric. Philippine Agriculturist. *Los Baños.*

Philippine Agric. Forester. Philippine Agriculturalist and Forester. *Los Baños.*

Phytopath. Ztschr. Phytopathologische Zeitschrift. *Berlin.*

Phytopathology. *Lancaster, Pa.*

Plant and Soil. *The Hague.*

Plant Physiol. Plant Physiology. *Lancaster, Pa.*

Planta. Planta. Archiv für wissenschaftliche Botanik. *Berlin.*

Potasse, Mulhouse. La Potasse. *Mulhouse.*

Prakt. Blätter Pflanzenbau. Praktische Blätter für Pflanzenbau und Pflanzenschutz. *Stuttgart, Munich.*

Proc. Imp. Acad. Japan. Proceedings of the Imperial Academy (of Japan). *Tokyo.*

Proc. Inst. Food Technologists. Proceedings of the Institute of Food Technologists. *Champaign, Ill.*

Proc. 3rd Internat. Congr. Microbiol. Proceedings of the 3rd International Congress of Microbiology. *New York.*

Proc. National Acad. Sci. India. Proceedings of the National Academy of Sciences, India. *Allahabad.*

Proc. National Acad. Sci., Washington. Proceedings of the National Academy of Sciences of the United States of America. *Washington, D.C.*

Proc. Roy. Soc. [A]. Proceedings of the Royal Society. Series A. Mathematical and Physical Sciences. *London.*

Proc. Soc. Exp. Biol. Med. Proceedings of the Society for Experimental Biology and Medicine. *New York.*

Proc. Trans. Roy. Soc. Canada. Proceedings and Transactions of the Royal Society of Canada. *Ottawa.*

Prometheus. Prometheus. Illustrierte Wochenschrift über die Fortschritte in Gewerbe, Industrie und Wissenschaft. *Leipzig.*

Protoplasma. *Leipzig.*

Quart. J. Med. Quarterly Journal of Medicine. *Oxford.*

R. K. Boeren- en Tuindersstand. De Roomsch Katholieke Boeren- en Tuindersstand. *Den Bosch, Netherlands.*

Rapport Inst. Recherches Agron., Paris. Rapport sur le Fonctionnement de l'Institut des Recherches Agronomiques. *Paris.*

Reale Ist. Lombardo Sci. Lettere Rendiconti. Reale Istituto Lombardo di Scienze e Lettere, Rendiconti. *Milan.*

Recherches Fertilisation Stat. Agron., Douai. Recherches sur la Fertilisation effectuées par les Stations Agronomiques. *Douai, France.*

Report Brit. Assoc. Report of the British Association for the Advancement of Science. *London.*

Rev. Fac. Quím. Indust. Agríc. Univ. Santa Fé. Revista de la Facultad de Química Industrial y Agrícola (Universidad Nacional del Litoral, Santa Fé, Argentina). *Santa Fé.*

Rev. Gén. Botan. Revue Générale de Botanique. *Paris.*

Rev. Ingen. Indust. Revista de Ingenieria Industrial. *Madrid.*

Rev. Inst. Defensa Café Costa Rica. Revista del Instituto de Defensa del Café de Costa Rica. *San José.*

Rhein. Monatsschr. Obst-, Garten- u. Gemüsebau. Rheinische Monatsschrift für Obst-, Garten- und Gemüsebau. *Bonn.*

Riv. Ital. Essenze Profumi. Rivista Italiana delle Essenze, dei Profumi e delle Piante officinali. *Milan.*

Schmidt's Jahrb. in- u. ausländ. ges. Med. Schmidt's Jahrbücher der in- und ausländischen gesammten Medicin. *Leipzig.*

Sci. Proc. Roy. Dublin Soc. Scientific Proceedings of the Royal Dublin Society. *Dublin.*

Sci. Rep. Tôhoku Imp. Univ. Science Reports of the Tôhoku Imperial University. *Sendai, Japan.*

Science. *New York, Baltimore, Md., Lancaster, Pa.*

Scientia, Bologna. Scientia. *Bologna.*

Scottish Agric. Scottish Agriculture. The Journal of the Department of Agriculture for Scotland. *Edinburgh.*

Scottish J. Agric. Scottish Journal of Agriculture. *Edinburgh.*

Scritti Biol. Scritti Biologici Raccolti da Luigi Castaldi. *Siena, Italy.*

Skand. Arch. Physiol. Skandinavisches Archiv für Physiologie. *Berlin.*

Soil Sci. Soil Science. *Baltimore, Md.*

Soil Sci. Soc. Amer. Proc. Soil Science Society of America, Proceedings. *Morgantown, W. Va.*

South Carolina Agric. Exp. Stat. South Carolina Agricultural Experiment Station, Clemson.

South East. Nat. Antiquary. South Eastern Naturalist and Antiquary. *London.*

South. Med. J. Southern Medical Journal. *Birmingham, Ala.*

Sovet. Subtropiki. Sovetskie Subtropiki [Советские Субтропики]. *Moscow.*

Staz. Sper. Agrarie Ital. Le Stazioni Sperimentali Agrarie Italiane. *Modena.*

Süddeutsche Apotheker-Ztg. Süddeutsche Apotheker-Zeitung. *Stuttgart.*

Sugar Beet. *Philadelphia.*

Suomen Kemistilehti [B]. Suomen Kemistilehti. Part B. *Helsinki.*

Svensk Kem. Tidskr. Svensk Kemisk Tidskrift. *Stockholm.*

Texas Agric. Exp. Stat. Texas Agricultural Experiment Station, College Station.

Tijdschr. Algem. Techn. Vereenig. Beetwortelsuikerfabr. Tijdschrift der Algemene Technische Vereeniging van Beetwortelsuikerfabrikanten en Raffinadeurs. *Amsterdam.*

Trans. Botan. Soc. Edinburgh. Transactions of the Botanical Society of Edinburgh. *Edinburgh.*

Trans. Faraday Soc. Transactions of the Faraday Society. *London.*

Trans. Highland Agric. Soc. Scot. Transactions of the Highland and Agricultural Society of Scotland. *Edinburgh.*

Trop. Agric., Trinidad. Tropical Agriculture. Journal of the Imperial College of Agriculture. *St. Augustine, Trinidad.*

Trudi Arkhangelskovo Vodoroslevovo Nauch.-Issled. Inst. Trudi Arkhangelskovo Vodoroslevovo Nauchno - Issledovatelskovo Instituta [Труды Архангельского Водорослевого Научно-Исследовательского Института]. *Archangel.*

Trudi Gos. Okeanogr. Inst. Trudi Gosudarstvennovo Okeanograficheskovo Instituta [Труды Государственного Океанографического Института]. *Moscow.*

Trudi Priklad. Botan. Genetike i Selektsi. Trudi po Prikladnoi Botanike, Genetike i Selektsi [Труды по Прикладной Ботанике, Генетике и Селекции]. *Leningrad.*

U.S. Bureau of Entomology and Plant Quarantine. Bureau of Entomology and Plant Quarantine, United States Department of Agriculture, Washington, D.C.

Ukrainski Khem. Zhurnal. Ukrainski Khemichni Zhurnal [Український Хемічний Журнал]. *Kharkov.*

Umschau. Die Umschau. *Frankfort-on-Main.*

Vermont Agric. Exp. Stat. Vermont Agricultural Experiment Station, Burlington.

Water en Gas. *The Hague.*

Wisconsin Agric. Exp. Stat. Wisconsin Agricultural Experiment Station, Madison.

Wissensch Arch. Landwirtsch., Abt. A. Wissenschaftliches Archiv für Landwirtschaft. Abteilung A. Pflanzenbau (*later* Archiv für Pflanzenbau). *Berlin.*

Wochenschr. Brauerei. Wochenschrift für Brauerei. *Berlin.*

Zentralbl. Bakteriol., 2. Abt. Zentralblatt für Bakteriologie, Parasitenkunde und Infektionskrankheiten. 2. Abteilung. Allgemeine, landwirtschaftliche, technische, Nahrungsmittel-Bakteriologie und Mykologie, usw. *Jena.*

Zhurnal Priklad. Khim. Zhurnal Prikladnoi Khimii [Журнал Прикладной Химии]. *Moscow* and *Leningrad.*

Zhurnal Russkovo Fis.-Khim. Obshchestva. Zhurnal Russkovo Fisiko-Khimicheskovo Obshchestva [Журнал Русского Физико-Химического Общества]. *Moscow* and *Leningrad.*

Ztschr. allgem. österreich. Apotheker-Vereines. Zeitschrift des allgemeinen österreichischen Apotheker-Vereines. *Vienna.*

Ztschr. anal. Chem. Zeitschrift für analytische Chemie. *Wiesbaden, Munich.*

Ztschr. angewandte Chem. Zeitschrift für angewandte Chemie. *Leipzig, Berlin.*

Ztschr. Botanik. Zeitschrift für Botanik. *Jena.*

Ztschr. Ernähr. Zeitschrift für Ernährung. *Leipzig.*

Ztschr. Gärungsphysiol. Zeitschrift für Gärungsphysiologie allgemeine landwirtschaftliche und technische Mykologie. *Berlin.*

Ztschr. Pflanzenernähr. Düng. Zeitschrift für Pflanzenernährung, Düngung und Bodenkunde. *Berlin.*

Ztschr. Pflanzenernähr. Düng. [A]. Zeitschrift für Pflanzenernährung und Düngung (*later* Zeitschrift für Pflanzenernährung, Düngung und Bodenkunde). A. Wissenschaftlicher Teil. *Berlin.*

Ztschr. Pflanzenernähr. Düng. [B]. Zeitschrift für Pflanzenernährung und Düngung (*later* Zeitschrift für Pflanzenernährung, Düngung und Bodenkunde). B. Wirtschaftlich-Praktischer Teil. *Berlin.*

Ztschr. phys. chem. Unterricht. Zeitschrift für den physikalischen und chemischen Unterricht. *Berlin.*

Ztschr. physiol. Chem. Hoppe-Seyler's Zeitschrift für physiologische Chemie. *Strassburg, Berlin.*

Ztschr. Vereins deutschen Zuckerindust. Zeitschrift des Vereins der deutschen Zucker-Industrie. *Berlin.*

Ztschr. Wirtschaftsgr. Zuckerindust. Zeitschrift der Wirtschaftsgruppe Zuckerindustrie. *Berlin.*

Ztschr. Zuckerindust. Čechoslovakischen Republik. Zeitschrift für Zuckerindustrie der Čechoslovakischen Republik. *Prague.*